THE AUTHOR

VINCENT EDWARD SMITH, PH.D., is the
well-known editor of *The New Scho-*

Philosophical Physics

Philosophical Physics

by

Vincent Edward Smith *1915 -*

Harper & Brothers, Publishers New York

To Virginia, for being what she is

Contents

Preface

The philosophical science of nature, aware that it is not just critical in aim but enriched by its own original insights into matter's make-up, finds it very hard today to reach its readers.

On the one hand, there are those who are totally unschooled in modern physics, and for them the philosophy of nature must be carved down to the bones of a few generalities that truly seem a skeleton in the living world of experimental flesh. There are others whom modern physics has dosed with a mass of technical data apparently at variance with the great teachings of great minds in the past; such readers would often insist that philosophy stands or falls in their laboratories and that, if it stands at all, it must certainly brave their stubborn experimental fact. Between these two extremes are those who have a smattering of both modern physics and genuine philosophy, and their degrees of knowledge in both fields differ from group to group and from person to person.

To many of these appetites and interests on the part of the modern reader, these pages hope to appeal. This is a highly technical age, and one of the crucial problems which it urges is the value of modern methods in the study of our world. It is an age when physics and philosophy are no longer calling each other names; they are not even speaking to each other. It is an age when educators and psychologists, statesmen, and even journalists, are pleading for integration. If a truly inquiring mind is to integrate itself, neither worshiping modern physics as a god nor dismissing it as an evil, it must certainly confront experimental reality with philosophical realism somewhere in its career.

This book is directed in general toward the lay reader, who has at least an introduction to philosophy but who has not yet graduated to metaphysics. The author has also kept in mind that in the age of experiment the reader will bring to the book an interest in modern physics and some slight knowledge of both its general direction and its major conclusions regarding matter.

For lower division students, or in short courses, or in the case of the ordinary layman unversed in modern physics, the book cannot be covered in full. Part One is slanted at this group. It spreads out the broad principles of the philosophical science of nature, with a minimum of reference to experimental technicality. Part Two covers the same ground as Part One at a more advanced level and ranges into a discussion of subjects not compressible into the elementary sections. Part Two is inclined toward readers with a moderate background in physics and a nimbler knowledge of philosophy than the readers envisioned by Part One. Part Two is designed especially for those who feel that there is a cleavage between modern experimental fact and genuine philosophical principle. It has been necessary to dip a little deeply into the problems of both fields to show that this apparent conflict is only a paper war.

The selection and organization of topics in each Part were dictated by practical matters, such as the length of Part One, which is geared for quick coverage, and the wish to reserve adequate spatial facilities for such items as place and time where the storm of modern ideas has broken with unusual thunder. In the discussions of Part Two not paralleled in Part One there is ample elementary material, especially at the beginnings of chapters, to be read hastily by anyone who wishes. Part Two might lend itself to study groups.

Despite the stunted character of Part One, it is complete to the extent that it covers the four-ply causality in nature, with a chapter on the ever timely subject of infinity.

This book outlines the philosophical science of nature, and in the proper sense, only what pertains to motion is at home inside it. However, to meet objections and also at times to round out a given discussion by steering it to the level where it is properly settled, the author has not hesitated to cross academic barriers, especially into mathematics which is in the second order of abstraction and into the metaphysics of knowledge which is in the third.

Throughout the whole discussion, it should be clear that there is no quarrel with modern physics in its proper place but only when modern physics transgresses on the territory of philosophy and becomes what is called scientism. To reject physics, in its place, would be nonsense. To take a stand against physics would be to spurn not only the great advantages which the experimental methods have brought in the way of mechanical convenience but also to repudiate a vast field of data which the philosopher can interpret for the enrichment of his own aims to know the *what* and the *why* of things.

Because the book is for beginners, the usual academic aspect has been minimized, and references are supplied only where opinions cited are not too well known from standard works or where the opinions have some other weight, unusually critical. The readers envisioned throughout this venture will not be so interested in details as in the broader works listed at the ends of the chapters.

The author is profoundly indebted to his wife, not only for her careful and critical reading of the material but for her warm and deep and abiding inspiration.

He wishes to thank Dr. Pierre Conway, of Providence College, and Professor Yves R. Simon, of the University of Chicago, for their expert and helpful criticisms of the manuscript. Naturally, they do not subscribe to all the ideas in this book, but they are greatly responsible for supplementing and clarifying much of the ensuing development. There is a debt also to the author's former students who lighted up truths through their questions and discussions.

V. E. S.

March, 1950

PART ONE

1

The Science of Mobile Being

THIS STUDY EXPLORES THE MOTIONS OF MATTER

What is matter made of, what moves it, and why does it move as it does? In answering these questions, philosophical physics is born.

The mysteries of matter have always tormented the spirit of man, and from the earliest of times, he has attempted to crack open the secrets with the tools of his philosophy. Sometimes he has decided that matter is only a mosaic of atoms, a magical interplay of number, or an indeterminate stuff kneaded into present form by agencies beyond itself. Amazed at the apparent fertility of things, he has at other times judged matter to be only motion, some philosophers declaring this rhythm to be only that of a machine, others clinging to a principle of life and even of spirit in the bosom of what we usually call inanimate nature. Still other thinkers have identified the universe with God, or described God in such a way that matter becomes only an illusion, with no existence at all.

The twentieth century is by no means an exception to this general interest in the factors making matter what it is and charging it with the force of its operations. Perhaps at no time has the concern about such things been as heated and as hardy as it is now. The tales brought back by modern physics from its expeditions into the make-up of matter have shaken the convictions of western man that his older intellectual approach was scientific and safe. The atom has become an everyday word, even a political personality. The taming of matter has been so striking in the

3

laboratory that the method of modern physics has been invited to turn its tremendous power on nearly every other phase of human endeavor. The science of the age has made this the Age of Science, and men are asking their physics to be a spokesman on the material world, without bothering too much to learn its origin, its authority, and its ultimate destination. In a day when the so-called scientific method for solving problems has become almost a goal, if not the badge, for being educated or enlightened, it becomes of the utmost importance to scan again through the recesses of matter to check what man has learned about the universe and how modern physics squares with that experience of matter that it apparently sets out to explain for men.

This is a highly useful study. It is important to reflect upon the material universe at any time, but today there is the added question of appreciating the self-styled scientific picture of the world which has won the plaudits of modern man and confiscated his philosophy. The decisions on the nature of matter and on the present-day physics which studies it are not mere classroom exercises. According to the answers, man can appreciate the world in which he lives, evaluate his modern physics, orient his intellectual life, assess the values that are at large in today's civilization, reconsider the ends of education, think, judge, and act in that realism which all rational creatures struggle to develop. The suicide or survival of society depends greatly on the verdict put by modern man upon his "sciences" which own such moral and physical power in today's world.

Does modern experiment yield the ultimate science humanly possible about the universe? Is measurement the only way of knowing matter? Does the spirit of Galileo and Newton, of Einstein and Planck, form the only intellectual turnpike that can speed man onward in his questions of the universe, its nature, its origins, its destinies, and its laws? Truly philosophical scientists reject so narrow a stand. To them indeed the title of science belonged centuries before the modern method of experiment usurped it, and if science is certain and causal knowledge, this philosophical depth of inquiry into nature still enjoys a loftier scientific eminence than the more modern disciplines.

In an original sense, the word *physics* meant the philosophy of nature, a scientific or causal study of mobile being. It can still be termed philosophical physics. Likewise, with no apologies at all, it can still be defined as the science of nature.

To alight upon an appropriate name for modern physics is embarrassing. And new words should be coined only after those in ordinary usage are unable to express the ideas in question. Modern physics might, of course, be called empirical physics, but philosophy, originating in experience, can also claim to be empirical. Another suggestion, and a fitting one indeed, would be experimental physics; for the primary and principal aspect of modern physics is experiment. The mathematical and theoretical aspects of such physics register experimental results, but the most important aim of theory is to suggest, organize, and especially to predict experiment. The whole superstructure of physical theories is thus subordinated to experimental tests, and so experimental physics would be a felicitous phrase to mark off the physics, so prominent today, from the older philosophical physics whose aim was knowledge and whose origin was not experiment but experience. However, the name "experimental physics" does not fully accent physical theory. Oftentimes, theoretical physics is clashed against experimental physics as almost coördinate parts of the same study.

More forceful and more complete is Jacques Maritain's expression *empiriological*. To term modern physics empiriological physics does justice to its experimental character (*empeiria*) as well as to its theory (its *logos*). Philosophical physics can thus be contrasted with empiriological physics, without the danger of ambiguity in the word *empirical* and without the weakness of the term *experimental*.

A defense of this choice of words will have to await later chapters. Maritain clashes empiriological with ontological knowledge, and there will be something of this same contrast, though not exactly in Maritain's sense, when the empiriological method is examined in Chapter 5. Here it might suffice simply to mention that *empiriological physics* is a generic term taken to mean what is usually termed modern physics, the physics of Galileo and Newton, of Einstein and Planck, of Bohr and Heisenberg and Schroedinger. Empiriological method will mean in these pages the so-called "scientific method," whether applied in physics or in biology and chemistry and the other modern disciplines. Such a method, the method of modern physics which is usually taken as the best example of so-called "scientific method," begins in experiment, elaborates a theory, and returns to the experimental world to apply the theory in new contexts. Empiriological physics thus includes theory and experiment, the mathematical techniques of modern physics together with its physical, experimental interference with reality in the laboratory. The word is new or at least not generally used, but the physics for which it stands is so crowded across the modern mind that it needs no introduction. Writers often say "physics and philosophy," as though they were two separate and well-defined fields. The approach of these pages holds that there is a physics which is philosophical and thus unites the terms *physics* and *philosophy* which are customarily contrasted. A new name must be found for non-philosophical physics. The suggested substitute is *empiriological*.

The immense territory of philosophical physics is often dismembered into two sectors—the study of the lifeless which Wolff called cosmology, and psychology, which is the study of the living. Despite the convenience of brevity, the term *cosmology* is vague and vaporous. Though still rather young, it has already descended to mean a synthesis of the empiriological disciplines, with the empiriological method itself mixing the mortar.

Besides that, the study of the lifeless and the study of the living are not just coördinate branches of the same science. The philosophical science of nature studies mobile being. Something ought to be said in it first of all about motion in general, and then the various motions of the world ought to be classified. Two of

the six species of motion—generation, corruption, local movement, alteration, augmentation, and diminution—turn out to involve life, which leads into a discussion of the soul and all that it
entails. This means then that psychology, the tract on the soul, is
a late arrival in the philosophical science of nature, making its
appearance after a study of mobile being in general has been
elaborated. If motion in general were not studied ahead of the six
species, there would be a useless repetition since every study of
the particular types of movement would involve elaborating anew
the philosophy of mobile being in general. It is better to have one
overall treatment of motion first, moving then from the general
to particular, from the common principles of motion to the various species.

Such is the plan of the pages that follow, beginning with
Chapter 2. Philosophical physics may be defined as the science,
elaborated by reason alone, of the material, causes, and principles
of mobile being (*ens mobile*), in what makes it mobile being.
Unfortunately, in the study of the species of motion after the
common issues have been settled, the study of life and of souls
must be omitted because it would lead too far astray. There will
be a general discussion of mobile being and then a study of those
species of motion which are not those of life but are found only
at the level of the inorganic. But before this house can be built,
certain preliminary blueprints must be examined.

INTELLECTUAL INSIGHT IS USED

A character like Hamlet can be appreciated only when the audience, just as the actor, projects itself into the lines and action of
the play to become another Hamlet in its own right. T. S. Eliot
says that it takes a poet to appreciate poetry. Rousseau wanted to
define experimental physics by teaching it. The foregoing definition of philosophical physics can be best illuminated when the
reader becomes a philosophical physicist himself. This task can
be made easier by inspecting the way in which the various forms

of knowledge are divided and the place, within the hierarchy, proportioned to the study of nature.

The broadest division of the whole of human knowledge is arranged according to the threefold division of abstraction.

Abstraction in general is the operation of the mind disengaging the essence of a sensible thing from that which is non-essential or only incidental in its make-up.

Suppose that a student is dealing with a bookseller, paying off a just debt. From such a transaction in which two patches of color called arms are moving about and two cavities called mouths are emitting noises, the idea of justice is formed by an observer; yet nowhere does the concept of justice become visible or tangible, measurable or picturable, weighed or timed. There are men, books, and money. There is an exchange of energy in the physical process. But the idea of justice has been abstracted from these things, none of which either in their parts or in their sum constitutes justice. The idea of justice has been abstracted from what is not justice but matter seen and heard. The same exchange of energy could be achieved in different circumstances, where it would yield a totally different idea, perhaps that of a holdup.

A modern analysis of the above situation, springing immediately from John Stuart Mill and reaching its peak in the contemporary emphasis on statistics in learned study, would hold that the general notion of justice is the mere name for a collection of instances. A vast number of just acts are counted—in the courts, in social life, in stores, in factories, in homes, and elsewhere—and summing up the cases is supposed, on sensist premises, to yield the idea of justice as a name for the collection. But there is a similarity detected (abstracted) in the instances examined; otherwise, we would not know how to collect them into one class. An abstraction is thus made not after but before the collection of instances that sensism proposes as a substitute. Individual cases of justice are abstracted as such before they can be part of the sum that is to replace abstraction. Abstraction cannot be denied in the conclusion of an argument that must use its work as a premise. Hence, the notion of justice is truly the fruit of abstraction and of insight into essences; it does not contain reference to material things—like individual men, money, and books. It is immaterial and dimensionless.

In the picture of *a* triangle drawn on a blackboard, the mathematician studies *the* triangle. Studying the properties of his three lines, he must think away the representation which can be seen, and attend only to what is represented, which is invisible. Since lines have length but no thickness, to represent the triangle as it is involves rubbing the drawing out. To see the lines, they must have thickness, but to study them the thickness must be thought away. The whole achievement is another example of abstraction. The mathematician does not study *a* triangle that he has drawn but *the* triangle that he has abstracted. True enough, he uses the pictured triangle as a support for his imagination, but from it he abstracts general relations of a different order from the drawing which he sees. In a similar way, justice is in a different order from matter, from the two men in the store who are to the abstracter of justice what a drawing is to the abstracter of the triangle.

These two examples are homely ones. Abstraction is perhaps even more striking in the domain of empiriological physics which, according to many of its admirers, has banished the intellect into exile. The surest proof that the mind is not a captive of space and time is that it represents these two realities and thus surmounts them.

Far from a concrete thing that shocks our senses into action, space is almost a pure relation. It is extension, evacuated of content by the abstracting mind, purged of all quality, free of all motion, homogeneous, enlargeable without end. Equipped with the notion of space, the mind is not localized like an atom, a leaf, a cow; it can range anywhere in the universe and find itself at home. Even newly discovered entities, because they are in space, are not complete strangers to their finders.

Transcendence of time is another of man's feats, and this can easily be illustrated by our reference to the future. Staring out toward a world that is not yet real, the mind can get ahead of the clock by witnessing in a general way what is only possible. Outstripping sense knowledge which is always tied to the here and now, the idea can be formed of the future, in Bergson's words, as an infinity of possibility.

The representation of time and space is an index that the intellect operates outside of both. In fact empiriological physics is becoming more and more abstract, and it is truly a paradox that the greater the abstraction the stronger runs the current in modern philosophy to deny that abstraction exists.

THE ORDER OF ABSTRACTION IS PHYSICAL

There are three orders of abstraction, three high-water marks of the mind in rising from the concrete individuals in the sense world to their principles and their causes.

The first order is that of so-called physical abstraction, and the mind is said here to leave aside individual sensible matter but not common sensible matter. Take the case of a fifty-cent piece. Such a coin is made of silver, but if a study is to be made of the silver, an abstraction must be made from the fact that it is an individual piece of silver, *this* silver. As *this* silver, it could not be made the object for study since every individual is unique, ineffable, incapable therefore of being related in a universal statement. And without the universal, science would not only perish; it could never even be born.

This silver occupies this space at this time; it is these atoms which are of this age—in this thermodynamical state. No, the study of silver requires that the *this*-ness which all cases of silver own in nature be disregarded. The individuality of the silver in the half dollar cannot be scientifically considered, and yet the silver is not without its reference to matter. If the *this*-ness of the silver were not thought away, there would be no science; if the matter were completely thought away, there would be no silver. The answer to the problem is that individual sensible matter is left aside in the first order of abstraction, but what, for want of a better term, is called common sensible matter remains. The silver is no longer considered as *this,* but it is still considered as silver, hence as something material, invested with sensible properties.

In the second order of abstraction, the common sensible matter is relinquished, but not the quantity. This order is that of mathematical abstraction. In the piece of silver, the mind can detect the meaning of half, of fifty, of circle, of solidity as a tri-dimensional status. But there is no intrinsic reference to physical matter.

Quantity is not matter but matter's attribute. Even if the two are tightly intertwined in nature, quantity can be mentally lifted from its qualitative home. $\sqrt{2}$ has never been rationalized, and $\sqrt{-1}$ is an imaginary number. Neither of these two quantities represents an entity that man can put his finger on or even represent with his imagination. Both numbers, however, are intelligible. They have been abstracted from matter, the locus of qualitative, sensible, moving reality.

It was said that in the first order of abstraction the mind considers sensible matter. In this so-called physical abstraction, the subject of study exists in matter and is thought of as existing in matter. In the second and mathematical order, the subject of study exists in matter but is not thought of as existing in matter. Intelligence considers it apart from matter, and so quantified being might be called intelligible matter—matter that is above change and sense content and is considered as an affair of parts. Fifty, circle, solidity, and other such mathematical entities abstracted from the coin can be applied to any other metal and any other matter. Silver implies a kind of matter, but fifty does not, since it applies to all kinds. Silver implies certain qualities; circularity does not, since its line of circumference has no thickness and is only intelligible matter. Silver refers to the senses in the discovery of its weight, color, and heat; half is something above sensation and can apply to the data of sight as well as of hearing, to touch as well as to taste and smell; it implies only parts without saying what the parts are.

In the second order of abstraction, the subject is matter because it has parts. But it is not sensible. It is only intelligible, because it does not have the resources to appeal to the senses—there is no thickness to a line, no color to a number, no sound to an angle, no taste to a square root, no smell to a logarithm. Intelligible matter is a fortunate term to characterize quantified being.

The third order of abstraction is that of metaphysics. Here the mind thinks away the individual matter, the common matter, and even the intelligible matter or quantity. Being is studied in so far as it is being, without quality and without quantity as these two realities occur in the physical and mathematical zones. To say that the silver is a being is to abstract from its matter and its quantity; for both the silver and the circle, both matter and the number fifty are beings. Being is that which is, the deepest and most universal characteristic of a reality. And it is not just a characteristic. It is a synonym for the reality itself.

In the first order of abstraction, it is said that silver is a being of sensible matter; in the second it is said that silver is a being of intelligible matter; in the third, it is said that silver is a being or, what is the same thing, that silver is.

Everything that is, is a being. Being's opposite is nothingness. When it is said of the silver that it is, without regarding its character as silver or as quantity, the very depths of the silver's reality have been touched. Further than saying *the silver is* it is impossible to go in the direction of its ultimates. For beyond being lies nothing; beyond the *is* there is only the *is not*. Hence being is truly ultimate.

At the lower echelons of abstraction, various kinds or determinations of being are considered—sensible being in the first order and quantified being in the second. But when being as such is attained and studied, no determinations occur in it. For these determinations would also be beings, already included in the thing that they determine. It is obvious then that being is not only an ultimate beyond which there is nothing but a universal in the highest sense, such that no instance of reality can lie outside it.

In the first order of abstraction, the things studied exist in matter and are thought of as existing in matter. In the second order, the subject exists in matter but is not thought of as existing in matter. In the third order, what is studied neither exists in matter nor is thought of as existing in matter. Being is deeper and higher and wider than matter because it applies to all things, and a thing need not be material, sensibly or intelligibly, in order to exist, in order to be.[1]

PHILOSOPHICAL PHYSICS DOES NOT AIM CHIEFLY AT QUANTITY

Knowledge is divided according to the three orders of abstraction. To the first order belongs philosophical physics. Empiriological physics, at least for the origin, testing, and use of ideas, makes contact with this first order. In the second order is mathematics, while metaphysics is at the core of the third order. What is important for present purposes is that philosophical and empiriological physics are fellow citizens in the first order of abstraction, at least when modern physics comes home from its journeys into mathematics to test the ideas brought back and to gather new ones for fresh theoretical elaboration.

The first difference between philosophical and empiriological physics is a matter of method. The one seeks causes and principles; the other aims chiefly to measure. The one takes its rise from full experience; the other uses experiment, considering only portions of experience and controlling what it considers. These two differences must be more fully explained, the first in the present section and the second in the next.

---

[1] For beginner's purposes, the foregoing exposition is satisfactory enough because it is general. But it would be a mistake to think that the three orders of abstraction are symmetrical like three steps in a stairway. There is a much greater heterogeneity among the three orders than is sometimes emphasized, since the first involves a total abstraction, the second a formal abstraction, and metaphysics a special type which Thomas Aquinas calls *separatio*. Cf. *In Boethii de Trinitate*, q. 5, a. 3, ed. P. Wyser (Fribourg, 1948), pp. 40–41; cf. also L. Geiger, "Abstraction et séparation d'après Saint Thomas in de Trinitate, q. 5, a. 3," *Revue des sciences philosophiques et théologiques*, XXXI (1947), pp. 3–40.

The empiriological approach does not keep the difference between the first and second orders of abstraction as clear-cut as the philosophical scientist; the reason for this will have to await later chapters to be more clearly stated. The empiriological spirit attempts to wed the two orders, more or less looking to the first for material (*material object*) and to the second for the way in which the material is studied (*formal object*). The philosophical science of nature, realizing that something is lost when we advert only to the quantity of things, insists that the first order of abstraction yields a richness and a meaning that the second cannot handle. Only when we study things on their own levels do we study them as they are. A realism insists that the first order of abstraction be more fully patrolled before climbing to the second, and that sensible, mobile matter be examined on its own terms if a truly inductive approach to experience is to be won.

In general then, empiriological and philosophical physics have the same material object, mobile being, but each takes a different slant on it, each has a different interest in it, each has a different formal object. The philosopher takes mobile being as mobile; the empiriologist explores it as quantified. This distinction can suffice as a first approximation, at least until Chapter 5 can attend in more precise form to the nature of the empiriological method.

But philosophy is not a statement of how things ought to be. It is primarily a statement of what things are. The plain fact is that in the present-day study of matter the distinction between the first and second orders of abstraction has been blurred, and philosophy must take account of the results to see where they lead. Has empiriological physics raised motion up to quantity, or has it drawn quantity down to motion? A positive answer to the first question is the theme of one philosophy of the empiriological method called logicalism and popularized by Bertrand Russell, while a *yes* to the second question opens the way to another philosophy of the empiriological method now current in America, the naturalism of John Dewey.

The implications of the two rival schools cannot be developed here without a complex and needless digression. But in general, it may be said that there is a strong bias in modern thought to reduce empiriological physics to a mathematical exercise. Such a view was ushered in by Descartes who identified quantity with the very substance of material things and thus made it legal for mathematics, the science of quantity, to pose as the science of matter. Empiriological physics has retained its Cartesian heirloom. It has become so enamored of its mathematical tools that it tends to neglect the real estate of the world on which they work. Sir James Jeans echoed rather than created a modern cry when he held that mathematics can tell us all there is to tell about reality and that God is the Great Mathematician.

According to logicalism or more precisely logical empiricism, which proposes to install mathematical logic on the throne from which metaphysics once presided over the sciences, any statement that cannot be cloaked in a mathematical formula is a meaningless verbalism. Empiriological physicists caution against the use of picturable constructs like the billiard-ball atom models of the last century. For Sir Arthur Eddington empiriological physics is a science of pointer readings, and Tobias Dantzig says the same thing in characterizing empiriological disciplines as the reading and obeying of instruments.

The brute success of empiriological physics with its mathematical techniques has seemed to justify the scrapping of Kant's idea that behind the quantity resides an unknown x, the noumenon. The empiriological physicist has been able to dispense in practice with the being behind the quantity, the thing that has inertia, the substance that supports the properties. And not only has the typical modern scholar persuaded himself that a science of nature, distinct from empiriology, is outmoded, but that metaphysics, the science of being, has been overthrown also.

Quantity of course is duly studied in philosophical physics, but it is studied only in the light of motion which is the primary and principal interest in the first order of abstraction. To begin baldly and blankly with quantity is to tend toward the second order of abstraction and to invite an *a priori* philosophy of nature that does not study matter on its own terms and as it is. As in the case of Plato, who insisted so much on the mathematical, to make quantity the core of philosophical physics is to view the world as merely phenomena; a truly inductive philosophy is replaced by descending upon the world from the high heaven of an innate metaphysics rather than having one's feet on the solid earth of experience from the very start.

The philosophical science of nature does not study *ens quantum* or quantity, as its chief stock in trade, and it does not start out with it. Indeed, it is incorrect to say that its object is corporeal substance. The fact that changeable or mobile being is a body must be established in this science rather than assumed. The starting point for philosophical physics is this changing or mobile being itself. Moreover, it does not strictly encumber the philosophical physicist to define and defend the reality of this changing being. This is the concern of the metaphysics of knowledge which defends the first principles of the lesser sciences.

PHILOSOPHICAL PHYSICS IS BASED ON EXPERIENCE

The philosophical science of nature studies not quantity but mobile being, and whatever conclusions it reaches must be drawn from motion and what motion implies. This distinction between the empiriological approach which measures quantity and the philosophical approach which studies motion is a crucial one. But there is another and more important aspect to the method of empiriological physics which makes it different from mathematics. It is experimental.

Experience and experiment, although etymologically related, are by no means the same thing. Experience is preëxperimental. It is a qualitative, warm, and deeply moving contact with reality, involving the whole man and involving him in a personal way. Experience is always an intimate thing, so much so that we can only convey the experience to others by leading them to have a kindred experience themselves. In the final analysis, this is the only way in which knowledge can be communicated.

Everything that happens to us is an experience. There are mental experiences, emotional experiences, bodily experiences, artistic experiences, and many others besides. The important part of the description is that experience has a personal reference and that we have an intimate association with what it is all about.

But experiment is something different. Man is here not an actor in a drama, identifying himself with a situation in a personal way and knowing its individual character for himself. He is rather a passive spectator. In empiriological physics, he is called the observer. He is really far outside the parade of events, watching them file by.

Secondly, experience does not involve the artificial isolation of facts. We take it as we find it, and we cannot avoid doing so. Experiment, however, always interferes with what it studies. Experiment may be defined as a controlled experience.

Thirdly, in experiment there is a reference to certain selected characters of experience. The chosen realities are in the order of quantity. Experience, on the other hand, is more qualitative and inclusive. It does not pick out certain facets of the world and ignore others. It finds everything somehow meaningful and profitable.

What we call experience is something more profound, significant, and convincing than what we call experiment. Experiment requires a greater superstructure of interpretation from outside it, while experience carries its own evidence more within itself. For experiment indeed is but a special form of experience. In the final analysis, an experiment must always be experienced to be apprehended, a proposition that cannot be converted. In reading an instrument, the experimentalist sees a number colored on a dial; he does not see pure number. Logically then, experience is more important and more ultimate than experiment, and if experience is unreliable, as is often declared, then experiment is not trustworthy either. If a camera is substituted for the eye, the eye must still be used to view the picture.

All the data of empiriological physics must eventually be reduced to the familiar world for verification. If experiment is a controlled experience, what is doing the controlling? Basically, it is the qualitative world which is used to control the quantitative, since the mechanical features of the experimental apparatus are fashioned in accordance with the sense world of quality which creates all problems and, in the empiriological zone of knowledge, is the only signpost for the reading of answers. It is because of the sense of weight, the feeling of effort in the hand holding a stone against the pull of gravity, that a scale is made and calibrated. Without that sense of weight, the principle of the scale would never have been alighted upon by its inventor and communicated to others. Time must be understood before the clock becomes meaningful as a measure. As C. D. Broad says, there is nothing in a clock which indicates that it is for telling time.

Experience is prior to experiment. Man's first contact with the world makes him aware of something more than quantity, and it is only later that he selects quantity, when he does it at all, from the experiential whole. There is a quantified something that experience discloses in its initial stages, and it is this *something* rather than its quantity which ought to be given an ampler attention in studying the world. Quantity cannot be equated to the thing that has quantity, any more than a foot is the same thing as a piece of silk a foot long. An apple and an orange might be of equal weight, and if quantity alone matters, they ought to be called the same fruit. The mathematics of color does not introduce a blind man to a knowledge of what color is. A map of Mexico is quite different from Mexico itself.

Experience, in spite of modern experiment, is still the best teacher. In fact, since all knowledge begins in the sense world, there is a profound way in which experience is the only teacher. All knowledge, in empiriological as well as philosophical physics, is eventually ground out of the data of sense perception, and if this common sense world is ultimately declared meaningless, as learned thought often says, the meaninglessness must apply as well to the world of empiriological physics. Everything is meaningless in such a case.

Eddington, Jeans, Russell, Northrop, and in general the whole modern temper tend to tear apart the familiar and the empiriological worlds and to label the common sense picture of things as an untested illusion. But if such thinkers did not use this familiar world which they call unreliable, they would never have been able to make their statements.

ALL KNOWLEDGE BEGINS WITH BEING

The primary idea which experience forces man to form, at least in an implied and unreflected way, is that of being. This raises a serious problem. If the philosophical physicist studies being, has he not jumped not only to the second order of abstraction like empiriological physics but all the way to the third order which is the territory of metaphysics? Having divided philosophical and empiriological physics, at least to a general extent, in the two preceding sections, the philosopher of nature ought also to be compared with the philosopher of being.

The nature of the being studied in the philosophy of nature is a matter for dispute among those who still discuss the study of being. Some of them abandon the philosophy of nature to empiriological physics. Others take comfort in the third order of abstraction, making the philosophy of nature a deduction from metaphysics as Descartes and Wolff proposed. The philosophical physicist must be defended not only from his enemies among empiriological minds but also from his friends among the metaphysicians. The first group denies the philosophical science of nature, the second sometimes seeks to absorb it.

It would be truer to the spirit of Aristotle and Aquinas and, more importantly, truer to the demands of reality to regard metaphysics as a developed philosophy of nature rather than to turn the philosophy of nature into an applied metaphysics. But neither view is correct. Metaphysics makes a higher and even different kind of abstraction which is not reached by simply inflating the first order. Metaphysics is wider than the philosophy of nature only because it digs deeper into reality, and it can no more be attained by expanding philosophical physics than a well can be made deeper simply by enlarging its mouth.

But that does not free metaphysics from building on experience, and to that extent, it is materially dependent on the philosophy of nature, as Maritain puts it, at least with regard to the more basic truths which the philosophical science of nature discovers and proves. In the opinion of Aquinas, metaphysics, though superior in dignity to other branches in philosophy, uses truths which these lesser lights have searched out.[2] Aquinas terms other branches of philosophy preambles to metaphysics since they contain truths that metaphysics more fully reveals.[3] But are we not involved in a vicious circle if metaphysics depends on the other sciences for its preambles and then purports, as the director of the sciences, to defend the principles of the other branches of philosophy?

No, such a vicious circle does not set in, for the reason that the being studied in the philosophy of nature is not exactly the same thing as the being of metaphysics. Genuine philosophy discerns two notions of being. The first is the view of the ordinary man who, even though not formally a metaphysician, has a spontaneous conviction that being is. It is this idea which, at least in implied form, appears in the first concept of the mind, as will be presently shown. It is vague, confused, unconsciously accepted not only for itself but in the principles which it immediately exhibits. The other notion of being is that of the metaphysician. This is a refined, reflex, scientific notion of being, explicitly recognized as being and rigorously defended as to its reality and its principles. In these two notions of being, one is simply a refine-

---

[2] *In Boethii de Trinitate,* q. 2, a. 3, ad 7; q. 3, a. 1, ad 9.
[3] *Ibid.,* q. 3, a. 1, ad 2.

ment of the other. For the average man thinks about the same world as the profoundest of the metaphysicians. The metaphysician, however, has a reflex and scientific knowledge of the subject, probing it deeper and wider by the hard steel of proof.

Like all other thinking, the philosophical science of nature must begin with the pedestrian notion of being. The very office of philosophical physics is a cultivation, a clarification, a purging, and to a great extent a defense of this ordinary man's notion and what it entails. After clarifying it in the first order of abstraction, the philosophical physicist turns the being over to the whiter light of the metaphysician. Hence, the philosophical science of nature is not a preamble to metaphysics and metaphysics a preamble to the study of nature. Philosophical physics begins with the coarse notion of being and refines it. The metaphysician works with being as such. There is a constant purification and progression rather than a circular movement. If, in the end, there be any doubts about the exteriority of this being, as the philosopher of nature and the metaphysician study it, these questions are settled in that branch of metaphysics which has to do with the value of knowledge and which, like metaphysics itself, comes after the philosophy of nature rather than, as in Kant's plan, precedes it as a prolegomenon.

But this section, from the very beginning, has assumed that the first idea drawn from experience is that of being which, in an implied, vague, and general form, is the starting point for all intellectual knowledge. This point must now be proved.

Modern thought, of course, does not tend to admit that man's first intellectual attainment is the general idea of being. Hegel held that thinking starts with the individual, and Hume and Hobbes had the same view, though they drew different conclusions from it. Following Hegel, in the so-called dialectical philosophy, Marxians would likewise argue to the primary datum of mind as something individual. This is true also in the case of Mill, James, Dewey, Russell, Carnap, Northrop, and all others who, following the empiriological method, deny abstraction and set out to reconstruct the world from atomistic units, the true backdrop of all empiricism in philosophy.

A number of arguments, from both experience and reason, attest that the general notion of being is formed prior to an intellectual knowledge of what is individual about things. Child psychology, for one, supports the point. An infant may learn to identify a dog in his baby language, imitating perhaps the bark of the animal. At first, he will be found to apply the barking sound to all subsequent animals either in life or in picture, showing that he did not apprehend what is specific to the dog but gleaned only a vague, general notion that is later differentiated. For the same reason, he at first thinks the picture of every woman to be his mother and of every man his father. Gradually he learns to identify the distinct and differentiated features of the world about him. He moves from the general to the particular.

No one remembers his first idea, and fortunately, it is not a matter for memory to decide. But inspection shows that knowledge always moves from the universal to the particular, and if this is so, then the most universal of all ideas must be fashioned first, at least in implied form. Perfection is always a movement from potency to act, until a reality is at last in an actual way all that it is capable of being. A perfect circle is as round as a circle could be expected to be. A perfect game at bowling means the highest possible score. A lover says that his love is perfect when he finds in her nothing that is wanting. Growth in knowledge is like organic growth, the development of capabilities, a movement toward the actual possession of all that one is capable of having in the intellectual area, a movement from the potencies of the subject to their actualization.

What is universal is potential. It is crude and vague in content and hence applicable to many things. The universal book, as universal, exists only in the mind. All the books which actually exist deal with some special subject and in some special type and on some special paper. With regard to actual existence, book in the general sense is only potential. It depends on individual circumstances to make the book actual, and then it is no longer a universal book. In this plan, universal and particular are related as potential and actual. The perfection of knowledge requires the movement from potency to act, from the universal to the particular.

A visual spotter of aircraft during the war would see a plane first as an object in the sky. When it came closer, he would see it as a plane. A little closer in, he could tell whether it was multi-engined or not, and later on, he could see what kind of plane it was. Finally, when closer still, the plane could be identified by its number, and its individuality could be established. This is an analogy to the way in which intellectual knowledge always moves.

All genuine science would be impossible if intellectual knowledge did not go from the universal to the particular. The reversal of this process involves a movement from the unknown to the known, just the opposite of how true knowledge ought to march. Intellectual knowledge cannot move from the unfamiliar to the familiar. Classification, a phase of every scientific enterprise at least in its initial stages, requires a knowledge of the general class in terms of which the particulars are organized. Without that prior generality in intellectual knowledge, the similarities which are the threads weaving things into classes become impossible to detect. To declare, for instance, "this is a tree" implies that we know "tree" in general, recognizing "this" as a particular instance of it. Setting up a general class from a limited observation of particulars, skipping from the part to the whole, violates the principle of causality and forms the central problem in modern argument by induction. It is as though one were to conclude that a whole dress is white, simply by observing its fringe of lace.

Adding all the "this-es" cannot generate the concept of tree. Only what is relevant must be added, otherwise under the aspect of "this-ness" one could add books, trees, hot-water bottles, electrons, and anything else in the universe. The general idea must be formed before embarking on a statistical summation that is supposed to yield the idea of a tree.

It need not be argued, at least at this point, whether classification is possible. Classification exists, and hence the only conclusion is that the universal is known before the conscious and reflex intellectual knowledge of the particular. Otherwise, classification would be impossible, and so would all thought.

This does not mean that there are innate general ideas or *a priori* general forms in the human mind but only that, given an individual in experience, the intellect adverts to its generalities before sailing after its singular character. The farmer holds that his horses and cows are animals, because he has perceived some basic likeness among them. The empiriological physicist classifies also. He has never had the experience of electrons in a Moscow laboratory, but he is sure that they have the same properties as the electrons which turn up in his own experiments.

This whole argument toward the primacy of the general in human knowledge and, in the limit, toward the idea of being as the first of man's intellectual achievements can be put in another and perhaps even more forceful form. If intellectual knowledge had to begin by grasping the individual, then it would have to be radically inductive, and if it is radically inductive, it never begins with the individual because it could never begin at all. If a so-called individual is given in experience, how can the knower be sure that it is truly an individual unit? On radically inductive premises, he cannot. Thus he splits the "individual," say a molecule, into atoms. But uncertain whether the atom is an individual, he charges into it with his particle guns and breaks the atom into neutrons, protons, electrons, and other microscopic entities. Radically inductive and compelled to begin with the individual, he cannot logically even accept these subatomic entities as realities that are ultimate and given. So his process of division goes on and on *ad infinitum*. His empiriological physics becomes an eternal quest after premises, a constant effort to begin. Contemporary existentialism, especially in Heidegger and Sartre, has actually carried through this radical spirit of the analytic method, and it has ended its voyage by deciding that nothing can be known at all.

Parenthetically, it might be remarked that radical deduction would likewise make a beginning of intellectual knowledge impossible, and the chapter on mathematics and the infinite, accepting the challenge of inductive and deductive extremisms in modern thought, will show that they deal a death blow not only to all common sense knowledge but to all scientific inquiry.

The point for the present can rest simply that if radical induction cannot initiate intellectual knowledge, the individual as such cannot be known in the primary idea of the mind. It can be known and recognized as a member of a class only if this class is known beforehand. Since knowledge moves from the general to the particular in the intellectual area, the most general idea, at least in implied form, must be had first, and this idea is that of being, which cannot be made more general because beyond being is only the non-being or nothingness.

A final argument might be drawn from the necessity of the principle of non-contradiction to differentiate one thing from another. Without it, all other intellectual knowledge would perish. Since it is necessary for all intellectual knowledge, it must therefore be primary. In the light of this principle, since it relates being by contrast with the non-being, differentiating the *is* from the *is not,* being is revealed as the primary datum of all intellectual knowledge.

EMPIRIOLOGICAL PHYSICS DOES NOT ATTAIN BEING

The philosophical science of nature builds on the ordinary man's notion of being. The *mobile being* of philosophical physics is quite close to the being which is known crudely and confusedly by common sense. For mobile being is extremely potential also. Motion, as the next chapter will show, is the actualization of what is in potency as far as it is in potency. This last specifying clause is of considerable moment. Motion pertains much more to the potential than to the actual since only the potential can be moved. Motion thus appears most strikingly in the world of mineral matter which is almost inert, so much so that by using the principle of inertia developed by Galileo and by Newton the empiriological physicist has achieved a remarkable string of successes on the inorganic level. The mobile being in the philosophical science of nature is thus akin to the plain man's idea. It is a refined and purified version, like ore that has been smelted into a shinier metal.

In considering mobile being, the two-termed reality of the being and its motion must be taken together. The being and the mobility should not be separated into rival corners or a Kantian universe of noumenon-phenomenon results. Whatever apparent separations are made in the following discussion may be justified for purposes of better exposition, just as for the sake of studying man the psychologist breaks him down into parts like his senses, emotions, intellect, and will. But the parts must not be simply united atomistically after the study is over and then deemed equivalent to the whole. Philosophical physics studies mobile being as a unit, thinking it into parts only, paraphrasing Maritain, to reunite it. But neither the being nor the motion can be fitted into the canons of empiriological physics. Evidence for this neglect of both the being and the mobility of mobile being will be brought forward in this section and the next.

In asking whether empiriological physics attains to being, an important distinction must be made between the empiriologist as a man and as an empiriological physicist. The learned minds today who boost their empiriological physics into a philosophical status not only fall short of the idea of being; they openly renounce their interest in it, denying that it is a meaningful and valid idea in the first place. They cannot attain to the idea in empiriological physics, and they do not wish to do so. But as men, they cannot escape what they often believe they have vanquished.

The ordinary common sense notion of being is not simply

known to the philosopher and ignored by the empiriological physicist. It is a prescientific idea, attained by man as man. To renounce the idea of being, as the empiriological extremist is often prone to do, is an arbitrary decision, and if he believes that he has done away successfully with the idea, the only answer is that he is guilty of make-believe. It is empirically impossible to avoid the notion of being. The empiriological physicist who denies this notion and the reality for which it stands, must use the notion and the principles cascading from it in order to accomplish the denial. Even Bertrand Russell admits that this procedure is against all logic. It is as though one were to use his voice to inform others that he had none.

In this connection, a distinction should be made between empiriological physics and what is commonly called scientism. With genuine empiriological physics genuine philosophical physics can have no quarrel; truth can never contradict itself, and true philosophy and true empiriological knowledge can become incorporated for the progress of man, though empiriological physics, as the sequel will show, is the junior partner in the firm. It is scientism, where empiriological physics is turned into a philosophical science, with which forceful issue must be taken. Empiriological physics rightly flowers only on the ground of measurement; it goes to seed as a philosophy. To believe that the empiriological methods alone have access to the real world is one of the great fallacies, the great absurdities, the great tragedies of our age.

In the present context, it should be pointed out that since Kant's time, scientism has subscribed to the dogma that common sense tends naturally to illusion. The philosopher defends and purifies the spontaneous convictions of the plain man in the reflex metaphysical analysis which vindicates the value of knowledge. Such pedestrian convictions, the empiriological spirit attempts often to explain away, taking its own approach as the ultimate one. But the empiriological physicist cannot assume the task of either proving or disproving the reality of being as known to the ordinary man. Such a reality cannot help being recognized, and even when it is rejected overtly, it is used to do the rejecting, surviving its apparent death as the surest proof of what it has of the timeless.

The empiriological physicist, who takes his work as a traffic with the ultimate reality knowable to man, ascends to the second order of abstraction without pausing on the ground floor to see whether such a leap is justified. This is an *a priori* and anthropomorphic attitude, neglecting as it does the demands of reality and imposing on nature an arbitrary human standard that reality is asked to fit in order to reveal itself.

In climbing to the second order of abstraction, the empiriological physicist makes an option to consider nature only as quantified, and it is enlightening to note the extremes which this view must eventually bring about if there is nothing knowable outside it.

The empiriological physicist, as such, must ignore being. His view of reality feeds on the notion of inertia, which thins a material thing into an indifferent state, depending for its reality wholly on the transeunt forces acting from outside of it. Such an inert and indifferent thing, when considered in itself, is really nothing. Hooke's law of elasticity says that stress is proportional to strain, and thus the entire reality of stress is exhausted by the reality of strain. Empiriologically, it could be said that stress causes strain or that strain causes stress. Emile Meyerson simply convoyed empiriological physics to its logical end when he argued that it aims at abolishing distinction and at identifying cause and effect. According to the empiriological method, the action of an atom is exactly equivalent to its component parts and how they act, and the subatomic particles in their turn owe what they are and do entirely to extrinsic forces as well.

Cause and effect tend to be absolutely equivalent in empiriological physics, as Meyerson showed. If irreversibility is argued by an appeal to entropy (the fact that the universe is running downhill and that causal action will always tend in this direction), this is not a valid way of differentiating cause and effect.

For the law of entropy is abstracted from the very causes and effects whose order it is supposed to regiment. Hence, according to strict empiriological physics, the distinction between cause and effect cannot be made. If it is actually made, the physicist has gone beyond his empiriological frontier and has ventured to speak as a man.

The being of the empiriological world, since it is completely inert, is wholly passive, and there is a second way of showing it to bolster the foregoing argument from inertia. If real being has no status of its own but is entirely the sport of outside pressures and forces, then an infinite dynasty of intermediate causes rules the world. This means that the world becomes an undifferentiated continuum. Distinction, identity, definiteness—these could never arise where nothing has anything of its own but is forever determined by forces and factors outside of it and these in turn by other forces and factors, without limit. In this impossible world of infinite division, the whole of matter would thaw into a Heraclitean flux. Nothing would have the character of being but only of between-ness.

In such a continuum, being and nothing become the same things in both reality and the knowing mind. If the principle of inertia eventually compels the empiriological physicist as such to regard the universe as a continuum, then, except for preëxperimental and metaexperimental thinking, he does not come to grips with being whose opposite is nothingness. He does not understand being, in his pure empiriological physics, i.e., understand it with respect to nothingness, which is to understand being with respect to its own evidence and its own self. He understands being in terms of what is outside it, and since outside of being there is nothing, it is only the idea of being which he has as a man, apart from his technical method, which keeps his universe from crumbling into a vacuum. Whatever the empiriological physicist may be explaining, if he explains at all, it is not the being of that which is.

The empiriological physicist is sometimes met with problems

involving discrete data, and from this fact, it might seem as though he were actually coming, even in his technical work to something besides the undifferentiated continuum. Quantum physics, for instance, employs the Heisenberg principle of indeterminism which holds that position and velocity have a discrete relation to each other and cannot be exactly measured at the same time. This same quantum system involves probability equations which make it possible to predict the destiny of an aggregate of particles but impossible to state the position and velocity of individual particles except in terms of probability. For instance, in the Bohr theory of the atom, which to a great extent still backgrounds the contemporary empiriological view of matter, an electron may leap from one orbit to another, emitting radiation in the process. There is no halfway point in such an event. Either a complete unit of radiant energy called a quantum is emitted, or none is emitted at all. But the empiriological physicist cannot deal with a situation that involves a discrete leap. The individual particles in such a system are said to be indeterminate. Unable to understand discreteness because it would involve being as contrasted with non-being and as therefore evident in itself, the empiriological physicist devises wave equations to describe the total, hence continuous, aggregate, abandoning the individual or what the philosopher would call being, to the laws of chance.

A genuine realism claims that we know something of the being of material things from within. Our knowledge is vague and general, but it happens to be about the ultimates, being versus non-being, the nature of cause and effect, the general difference between matter and spirit, the dignity of man. The philosopher is poor in knowledge, but the man with a real penny in his pocket is richer than scientism with a million dollars of counterfeit philosophy. In this realistic universe, there is an explanation for distinction and differentiation and a recognition that distinction is fundamental, in arguments for the continuum and in arguments for anything. The opposite to being is nothingness, and only in a universe where being is understood as not-nothing, as standing out (*ex-sistere*) from nothing, do we have a truly plural world. Where being is conceived in terms of pure passivity the continuum results; the distinction between being and non-being is blurred. Hence the empiriological physicist with a method that treats matter as wholly passive could never attain to being through such a method even if he wished.

Unable to cope with the being of mobile being, how does he stand with respect to mobility or motion?

EMPIRIOLOGICAL PHYSICS DOES NOT ATTAIN MOTION

Motion is a fact of experience, and to explain its causes and its principles is the sole office of the philosophical science of nature. Anyone who denies motion can simply prove it to himself by following the historic footsteps of Diogenes who replied by simply walking when Zeno argued that motion is impossible.

In the world of living things, there is a perpetual cycle of birth, growth, and death. In the mineral world, the seasons change, days come and go, clouds sail through the sky, rain falls and then evaporates. No one who has put to sea, flown in an aircraft, or experienced a tropical storm can deny that motion occurs. In his proofs for the existence of God, Aquinas stated that the first argument, the one from motion, is the more manifest way of proceeding. In the accelerated tempo of the twentieth century, motion is so prominent that it has become almost something for its own sake. The music and dance of our entertainment offer proof of this. The plant engineer is always looking for faster work on his assembly lines. Many lives have become aimless, insecure, fearful, in this age of distraction and speed. Our whole civilized edifice threatens to crumble. From the blast at Bikini to the pecking of a typewriter, motion is everywhere apparent. Philosophers like Marx and Engels, Santayana and Whitehead, Hegel and Alexander and Bergson, have regarded motion as the very stuff of the universe.

But how does the empiriological physicist study motion? To cite Bergson, whose criticism of the empiriological method is a lasting monument in spite of his counterproposals to replace it, the modern physicist studies motion by ignoring it. But before hearing Bergson's indictment, let the empiriological physicist offer his own testimony.

The general approach to reality in empiriological physics is largely lighted up by the mathematical techniques of the calculus, and various of its leading interpreters, from Henri Poincaré to Bertrand Russell, have set the aim of empiriological physics as the description of the world in terms of differential equations. These brilliant and powerful tools of modern mathematics state the way of computing the instantaneous rate at which one quantity in an equation changes with respect to another. To explain this statement, which is the fundamental concept of the calculus as treated in any sophomore book on the subject, two concepts are needed, that of a function and that of a limit.

One quantity is said to be a function of another if, when the second (called the independent variable) takes on a given value, the first (called the dependent variable) takes on a corresponding value. For instance, if $y = x + 1$, y is said to be a function of x or to depend for its value on the value of x; thus if x is 3, y is $3 + 1$; whenever x takes on a different value, so does y. That y is a function of x is written $y = f(x)$. Pressure, for example, is a function of temperature, and when a gas is heated, the pressure increases, diminishing of course when the gas is cooled. The fall of a body in free space is a function of time (distance $= 16t^2$). Causality tends to mean mere functionality in empiriological physics. But a function is by no means the same as causation in the philosophical science of nature. It is more a mathematical paraphrase of Hume's associationism or the method of concomitant variations in John Stuart Mill's logic. There is no true causal interplay in functionality; there is only a parallelism between one quantity and another.

The second concept needed to clarify the calculus and the differential equation is the notion of a limit, which is defined as a quantity which another quantity approaches indefinitely near. A polygon, when its sides increase indefinitely in number, approaches a circle as a limit. y is a limit of x if, when x increases indefinitely, the difference between y and x gradually becomes smaller than any assignable value.

In terms of these two concepts, the fundamental feature of the calculus, so deeply imbedded in empiriological physics, can be sharpened into focus. If $y = f(x)$, the calculus proposes to measure how y changes when x varies by very small amounts, positive or negative. Suppose that $f(x) = x^2$; then $y = x^2$ by a simple matter of substituting in the preceding sentence. Now let x increase by a very small amount written Δx (delta x) according to mathematical convention. Then y changes also by a very small amount, written Δy. The calculus measures the ratio of Δy to Δx when Δx becomes smaller and smaller and tends to zero as a limit; in this manner, there is measured the instantaneous rate of change of two increments. In more symbolic terms, this is written as:

$$\frac{dy}{dx} = \lim_{x \to 0} \frac{\Delta y}{\Delta x}$$

This expression dy/dx is called the derivative and is defined as the limit of the ratio Δy to Δx, as Δx tends to zero. Any equation in which a derivative occurs is called a differential equation.

The apparently simple concept of the derivative is the pavement of the mathematical approach to motion which the empiriological physicist takes when he measures matter. The derivative or differential equation imparts knowledge of the instantaneous rate by which one quantity changes with respect to another. But to study rates is at most to measure change rather than to probe what it is. Moreover, x and y represent quantities, and $\Delta x/\Delta y$ represents ratios of quantity. But quantity is not motion; change is not a ratio or relation. In Humean terms, motion is a series of states, but a series of points is not motion in the real world any more than streetcar stops are moving trollies.

Bergson saw the modern approach to the moving world as a

series of still pictures developed in empiriological darkrooms. He hammered home the important truth that motion escapes the mathematical physicist, that mathematical time is only a line, that time is spatialized in empiriological physics, and that the general dynamism which ignites our material universe becomes, for the mathematician and physicist alike, a static juxtaposition of points. This spatialized time, Bergson went on, is only a phantom of motion, as though corn were studied by examining only empty husks. Time and motion in empiriological physics are not mobile, he concluded; they are the immobility of points in geometrical space.

It is the ambition of empiriological physics to begin with quantity and to deduce motion. The natural movement of the mind is along the opposite lane of traffic. Immobility can be abstracted from motion, but motion can never be deduced from the immobile. That is why, contrary to Hegel and Marx and Nietzsche and other historical determinists, history must always be experienced rather than deduced, and that is why also, creation is ultimately an act of Divine liberty rather than a necessary emanation. The empiriological ambition to deduce all things would be at home in Plato's world; it would be an alien in Aristotle's.

The picture of a photo finish can determine which horse was ahead at the end of a race; but without an idea of motion gathered elsewhere, the picture could never inform an observer that the objects shown were moving as the camera snapped.

It can be seen then that motion eludes the empiriological physicist and that he cannot claim to be a rival of the philosophical physicist in the study of the mobile world. The empiriological method is a mixed assault upon reality. Not that taken in its proper place it is invalid. But for whatever value it bears as a means of knowing things, it hoists the matter of the first order of abstraction to a formal treatment in the second. There is much to be said for Maritain's view that, at least in its knowledge character, empiriological physics is an intermediate science as Aristotle used this expression. It is materially physical, formally mathematical. It uses the physical world to suggest its theories, test its deductions, and apply its conclusions in the field of engineering. But in its precise formulation, empiriological physics tends to stress only the quantified aspects of this physical world, and it does so with mathematical accents. Why empiriological physics does not become pure mathematics can be explained by the fact of its material object which is the mobile world and not pure quantity. Material and formal objects cannot be torn apart any more than matter and form, to be studied later, any more than body and soul. Hence the material object contributes to the originality of a science which ought not be defined in terms of form alone.

But the empiriological physicist is forbidden by his method from grasping mobile being under the prominent and all important aspect of its motions. He is unable to penetrate to the being of mobile being; mobility also gets away from him. The study of mobile being belongs to the philosophical science of nature.

PHILOSOPHICAL PHYSICS DOES NOT SUPPOSE THE EMPIRIOLOGICAL

The philosophical science of nature need not cast its moorings on the data of empiriological physics. Such a procedure would be fatal to philosophy itself since it would then be as dated as the empiriological shoreline, shifting from one age to the next. The empiriological mentality of our time asks philosophy to build on the foundations of the empiriological method. But if this dependence of philosophical on empiriological physics is acknowledged, then the philosophical science of nature becomes in the end as nomadic as the theories of the empiriological domain and just as shaky in its life expectancy.

The origin of philosophical physics is that prescientific experience of things which is common to all men and provokes them to the idea of being and a recognition of motion. The philosopher develops the principles which flow from being and from motion. The empiriological physicist ignores both. The crucial phase of empiriological physics is thus this prescientific set of notions, especially the idea of being which initiates the career of every thinking man but is neglected by the methods of the empiriological physicist as such.

✓Empiriological physics begins on the assumption that whatever is meaningful is measurable, without being able to measure this original statement or to find a basis for it anywhere else in reality. The philosophical physicist has no preconceptions of this sort. The being of mobile being cannot be measured, for there is nothing outside of being to serve as a yardstick. Motion in mobile being also escapes measurement, since only quantity can be measured.

In experiment, the empiriological physicist does not attain being. To control it, turning it into something else, would make it the non-being. Nor does the empiriological physicist attain to ✓motion by experiment. To the extent that motion is controlled it is stopped. Both in measurement and in the control which experiment brings into experience, being and mobility evade empiriological physics.

It is only to be fully realistic that the philosophical physicist, rather than rest his principles on the conclusions of the empiriological method, should insist that the riches of experience be explored at their own level and in their whole reality rather than subjected to a method where only specialized, abstracted, measurable, and controllable portions of experience are considered. In this way, the philosopher can make good his claim as a critic of the empiriological approach, since he has preserved contact with original experience, entitled thus to measure the empiriological report with respect to it. This report can be made meaningful only by asking its relation to that experience which the empiriological physicist controls and thus turns into something else, but which the philosophical physicist keeps wholly and as it is.

It will be later argued, especially by reflecting on experiment, that the primary aim of empiriological physics is not knowledge as such. To the extent that we control a thing, we do not know it objectively, uncontrolled, and as it is. In this later treatment (Chapter 5), empiriological physics will be shown as an art of discovery, not a method of proof, reaching its fullness not in speculative knowledge but in the order of making inhabited by the engineer.

Apart from this primary aim and as a consequence of it, the data unearthed by empiriological physics are of great value to the philosophical science of nature, exhibiting its principles and priming it for fresh insights. But the data as such are powerless to further the philosophical science unless seen through their relation to experience, which empiriological physics neglects but philosophical physics preserves. The data in themselves are not true scientific knowledge which is always in terms of causes. And when they are involved in true knowledge, it is because they have passed over into philosophy where they are related within the network of the philosophical and experiential whole. Experience thus retains its primacy in yielding ideas and contributing to their verification. In a truly realistic philosophy, experimental data ought to confirm experience and to bolster the philosophy taking root in it. That these data do so is one of the theses put forward in the later portions of this book.

Experiment is less convincing than experience which, despite its malignment by overscrupulous scientism, is a simple thing that by its very simplicity diminishes the margin of error. Experience is more self-revealing and self-supporting than experiment. Pain is an index to a person that he is sick. He is convinced and needs no further evidence. Experiments must be multiplied and complicated; they must constantly be revamped in search of new evidence which is really outside the experiment. Knowledge tends toward the simple.

No one needs a criterion like an experiment to determine whether he is conscious. He is conscious, he knows, because he is conscious of it. No experiment is needed by a farmer to recog-

nize that the hay he is pitching requires effort or that his plough
is heavy and hard to lift. Experiments always demand interpretation. Experience is more self-revealing.

An aboriginal who saw a cyclotron for the first time could
never grasp what it was for. But the meaning of pain could be
taught to him by pinching him, the meaning of knowledge by
simply pointing out an object and asking him to describe his internal impression, the meaning of being from which all knowledge builds by asking him the difference between being alive
and being dead, between whether a house is or is not on the other
side of the street, between whether the people of his dreams are
real men or creatures of the world of fancy.

Suggested Readings

Aquinas, Saint Thomas, *Commentary on the Trinity of Boethius*,
   Lesson II, Questions 5 and 6.
Maritain, Jacques, *Les degrés du savoir* (Paris, 1932), chs. 2, 4.

2

Motion and Its Principles

The most striking feature of the sense world is its motion. Everywhere it is present, and our very search for it often involves another of its myriad manifestations. Something new is constantly being born into our universe, while old things pass away. The seasons come and go, and the universe from heaven to earth bears witness to the changes. The soil is hot one day and moist the next. Thunder and lightning are but aspects of the movements of the clouds. Living things are in constant process of being born, growing, aging, and dying. The wind and the waves, the twinkling of the stars and the melting snow of the spring, the river in the valley and the slow erosion of the eternal hills—all reveal the perpetual motion astir in nature, and man sets his clocks, and therefore his life, by the movement of the earth around the sun.

The empiriologist, when he roams behind his measurement to explore its background by non-metrical means, bears similar witness to the reality of motion. Chemically speaking, his universe consists of nearly a half billion different kinds of stuff which he calls substances and which he envisions as in constant kinetic molecular motion. What goes on among the molecules is but a larger sign of a subtler rhythm stirring in nature, that of subatomic particles. In this infinitesimal world, which empiriological physics attempts to predict by theory and command by experiment, matter and energy have now merged into the same thing, and energy is power, work, force, tension, movement. In the last analysis, empiriological physics determines the possibility of chemical, atomic, and nuclear reactions by an appeal to the energies involved and to the directions in which they tend to flow. Much more than the nineteenth-century emphasis on mass and quantity, twentieth-century empiriological physics presents evidence of nature as basically a dynamic thing, and such concepts as field, waves, entropy, surface tension, and electric forces play a greater role in the empiriological vision than they ever did before.

But empiriological physics only measures matter without studying its motions and mobilities in truly causal fashion. This is the business of philosophical physics and can only be settled by transcending measures to the realities that instruments presuppose. In an age like ours, the first question would not be to define the reality of motion but to establish the fact that motion is a reality. Aristotle faced a similar question from the Humes and Kants of ancient Athens. Yet it is not the office of the philosophy of nature to deal with this question, Aristotle argued, since it can be treated only in that part of metaphysics which defends the value of knowledge. However, Aristotle faced the problem in his *Physics* because of its importance for his study of nature, and the twentieth-century realist in like circumstance is invited to pursue a similar course.

Before embarking on the journey, a distinction might be drawn between change proper (*mutatio*), which is instantaneous, and motion proper (*motus*), which is primarily continuous and successive. But in a wide way, the two can be taken as equivalent, and their technical differences, when they become important, will be mentioned in the pertinent passages. After all, it is more important to point up general truths than to squander space on technical detail.

After a discussion of motion, the next hurdle will be the definition of motion; then will follow a more precise characterization of mobile being or nature and the principles of nature; these principles next will be applied to changes of substance with a defense against other views on substantial change.

MOTION IS NOT DEDUCIBLE

When Aristotle said that motion is known by induction, he was calling attention to its character as given in experience. The fact of motion cannot be proved and moreover needs no proof, if proof is taken to mean syllogistic inference. It is nonsense to try to prove motion since there is nothing more obvious in the sense world from which motion could be deduced.

All philosophers require a starting point. Some begin arbitrarily, using a precooked notion of the subject matter. A realist takes reality rawly as he finds it, without preconception or hypothesis. He begins in experience—the hard, fast, stubborn data which cannot be contradicted with impunity and which will, if contradicted, attack the philosopher who tries to deny them. That is why false philosophies continually come and go. To ignore the obvious is to inhale the lethal germs of skepticism, a state that would not only render science false but make it impossible.

The realist cannot help beginning with the obvious. To deny it means to know absolutely nothing in the end. To attempt to prove the more evident by the less evident is not only invalid as a reasoning process, but the less evident, which is the premise of the proof, can only be known and recognized in terms of the more evident, which is presumably to be established. You cannot prove that you see something by deducing it from the fact that you have never seen anything; for you have already seen something or you would not be asking the question.

The empiriological extremist has the habit of shrugging off the familiar world as an illusion and enshrining his own technical world of atoms, quanta, and tensor fields as the only world that is real. But he has constructed all his concepts by reference to this familiar world; he expresses his thoughts basically in its language; he uses the familiar world in order to read his instruments and to communicate his thoughts. No one can avoid beginning in experience, and if that is so, more attention ought to be paid to it. If the empiriological approach is used to explain away experience, it is only in terms of an eventual appeal to that experience itself that the explanation is thought to be valid.

Motion does not need proof because of its obvious experiential character. What needs proof is always the obscure and the questionable, the unseen and the unknown. Motion is so apparent that to demonstrate its existence is unnecessary. The proof consists in opening our eyes, feeling the moving keys of a typewriter, taking a ride on a subway. If motion does not force itself upon us, the only recourse in the proof would be to deduce it from the non-moving or the static. But the static is less obvious than the moving, and the senses can detect it only by reference to the moving which is more obvious. Perhaps the senses best confirm the verdict of the intellect on the exteriority of the world by an appeal to the facts of motion. If a thing moves against us or we move against it, and if we thus feel the interaction between its reality and our bodies, we are spontaneously sure that it is real and objective. The static, for example the world of mathematics, is harder to grasp than the moving; it can be taught to beginners only by instances from motion, the physical adding and the physical taking away of apples which a teacher uses as first examples of addition and subtraction.

MOTION IS DEFINED BY ACT AND POTENCY

The definition of motion is more difficult than its discovery. The most effective approach to the problem might be to face squarely the historical dilemma that challenged Aristotle and to rethink the struggle that his definition arbitrates since both warring parties have today risen anew from their tombs. There were two opposing views that urged Aristotle's genius into action. One was the doctrine of the Eleatics, led by Parmenides and Zeno. The other was the view of Heraclitus.

Parmenides and his school declared that motion is impossible, pointing for proof to the principle of non-contradiction. Their argument ran thus: Being is, and non-being is not. Between the two there cannot be a middle term, and since motion would appear as an intermediate between being and non-being, it turns out to be an illusion. Nothing can come from being, Parmenides went on, since being already is and whatever comes from it would already *be* in it, incapable of becoming because it already is. Nothing can come from non-being either: *ex nihilo nihil fit.* Zeno's arguments will be discussed later since they presuppose an understanding of the problem of the infinite and can best be deferred until after this problem is formally put into the forum. Like Zeno's world, the universe of Parmenides is radically static and monistic.

Heraclitus, on the other hand, denied the reality of being and claimed that all is motion. As in the case of Parmenides, some plausible arguments seem to conspire toward this view. Take the case of time, so subtly emphasized by Bergson, a modern Heraclitus. The past has already been; the future is not yet; and the present passes. The only real thing in this triad is the present, and its reality is flowing constantly by. On such evidence, Heraclitus declared that motion alone is authentic, motion as symbolized by fire which he took to be the basic texture of matter. No man can swim in the same stream twice, he is supposed to have said; Cratylus, his disciple, said that no one can swim there even once. Heraclitus thus proposes a philosophy of radical dynamism and pluralism. It stands in polar contrast to the cosmic picture of Parmenides.

Aristotle was too loyal to experience to allow sophistry to rule on the real and to validate these extreme views. Despite their argument, they are out of touch with the rhythm of daily life which discloses both permanence and change and does not ratify a view of the world as either wholly fluid or wholly fixed. The problem is to find a suitable definition of motion that will agree with this experience which the true science of nature must explain rather than explain away. Such a definition Aristotle formed in terms of the twin concepts of potency and act.

Potency and act are so intimately interlaced that they should be unraveled together. Act, in the broad sense, is synonymous with existence; to be actually something is not to be an imagined something. Kant pointed out that there is not a cent more in a dollar truly existing than in a dollar conceived by the mind. But the dollar existing is an actual dollar. Our wealth is proportioned to it, to the money we own and not to the riches we imagine.

Potency is the capacity to be actual. It has the meaning of possibility, an aptitude for existence rather than the existing itself, a readiness to be influenced by a cause. Shopping downtown, a person has a real capacity to be at home, and later on in the day, he will be actually there. The water in the Ohio river has an aptitude to be in the rain clouds, and if the evaporating heat of the sun is turned its way, some of it will actually be in the heavens by nightfall. The acorn is potentially an oak tree, and the parts of a car in a Ford storage plant are potentially an automobile. Before a radioactive substance emits an electron, it must have the potentiality for so doing, otherwise the emission would be impossible. Potential energy is energy poised and ready for action, like a lion crouching for a kill.

The difference between potency and act is the gap between a capacity and the fulfillment of that capacity. Both are real things. Both refer to existence. The actual is that which is; the potential is that which can be. To discover their deep meaning has formed the historical career of genuine philosophy, and their importance, appearing in full dress at the level of metaphysics, cannot be printed boldly enough. Because they are so basic, they are elusive and have given rise to numerous blunders of a far-reaching character.

Potency is not a simon-pure logical concept, as Northrop suggests nor, as Santayana puts it, a mere name invented to disguise our ignorance. It is a real thing, though not actualized. If it were not real, it could never be a source of the actual. The match has a real capacity for being struck, or the actual striking could not be real either. The airplane has a real capacity for flying, otherwise it could never leave the ground. If the potentialities of our parents were mere figments of an imaginary world, all of us are dream stuff. And if the skeptic declines to believe that atoms have a real potentiality for destroying civilization, why does he discuss the problem of atomic energy control?

Before the loam is dug by the farmer, it has a real capacity to be spaded. The solid coral of a Pacific atoll has no such potencies. Oxygen has a genuine aptitude for union with hydrogen, silver does not. The potencies of things, especially in the experimental disciplines, are in a large measure the way in which we identify them and divide them off from one another. They are thus real and objective. Energy, the power to do work, assumes a deeper meaning when it is remembered that power is a potency. Inertia is likewise a way of saying potency; and inertia, passivity, the controllable, are alone enfranchised in the empiriological world, where potency, far from a purely logical or nominal convenience, is considered in a deep and genuine way to be more real than act.

MOTION IS A MIXTURE OF ACT AND POTENCY

The actual is that which is. The potential is that which has the capacity to be actual. Through the bifocal lens of these two realities, philosophical physics can now recognize motion for what it is. Aristotle says, "The fulfillment of what exists potentially, in so far as it exists potentially, is motion."

Dissecting this definition into its parts provides a conclusive answer to the dilemma of Parmenides versus Heraclitus. Motion belongs to a thing only so far as it is in potency, for whatever already has a perfection does not move to acquire it. Motion essentially involves the production of novelty. Thus iron does not tend to become iron since it is iron already; and a dog does not tend to become a dog but to satisfy its animal urges.

Motion thus entails the fulfillment or the act of the thing that is in potency, but this alone is incomplete as a definition of motion. It must emphatically be added that motion is the act of the potency only as far as the thing moved is still in potency. Why this clause must dominate the definition is clear from another example. Marble has a potency to be a statue, and oxygen has a tendency to unite with hydrogen. The fulfillments or acts of these potencies are a statue in one case and water in the other. But both the statue and the marble are actual beings. Far from being process, they are more the terms or completions of the motion. So potency and act are not fitted together to form motion like the shingles on a roof. Taken simply, they are not enough to define what motion is.

Motion is the act of being in potency as far as it is in potency. As Aristotle writes: "The actuality of the buildable as buildable is the process of building." Had he simply said "actuality of the buildable" or "the act of a potency," he would not have defined a process but its completion. When the buildable is no longer buildable but built, it is a house not potentially but actually; a house is "the actuality of the buildable." Likewise, when the rusting of iron is considered as a process, it goes on only so long as the iron is oxidizable, as opposed to being actually oxidized, and when the iron is worn away by the process so that the capacity for oxidization ceases, the motion likewise comes to an end.

Motion is not act, and it is not potency. It is really a mixture of the two. What is in motion is partly in act and partly in potency, and this twofold character which it owns will lead to some tremendous consequences in developing the philosophical science of mobile being. As far as the moving thing has made progress toward its term, it is in act: as far as this process is not complete, the moving thing is in potency. Before a house is finished, it is in various stages of being partially built. But the stages are not motion, any more than motion is simply the sum of its positions. As far as the house is being built, there is a gradual character to the process. The house does not leap out of a void. And if a traveler, leaving New York, could arrive in London instantaneously, he would in some way have to be in New York and London at the same time since an instant, like a point, has no before and after within it. Motion in the proper sense is a continuous process, and empiriological physics acknowledges this fact by the stress which it leans on time factors. The house that is in process of building, the ocean-goer en route to London, and any other thing that is moved has to take a longer road than the instant provides. As far as such moving things have advanced to their terminal point, they bespeak that reference which motions make to act, but as far as this point has not yet been fully attained, the reality of potency still asserts itself. Potency is a kind of drag that the moving thing must overcome. Whatever progress the thing makes toward act records the various stages of its success. Potency thus shows itself as a separating and plural factor in matter, an element of division and discord.

Motion is midway between potency and act. A thing in motion is neither potential, lacking all entitlement to being, nor is it actual, possessed of its ends and not inclined to a movement that would acquire them. That a man works for a living does not mean that he has nothing on which to live; he may not be rich, but he need not for this reason be in utter poverty. The failure to do justice to that midpoint between the capitalist and proletarian extremes is one of the fallacies of dialectical materialism. When the astronomer plots the position which a star will occupy five minutes hence on the cross hairs of his telescope, he does not use the purely potential as his datum; what is actual in the present position of the star is an index of what the star will be doing in the future. The astronomer must consider both the potential and the actual. Motion is their go-between.

WITHOUT ACT AND POTENCY, MOTION IS ABSURD

Ripened by the sunlight of potency and act, the philosophical science of nature may now weather the Heraclitean-Eleatic dichotomy. Parmenides emphasized only the actual, failing to see that being can also be potential. Heraclitus completely overlooked the actual, making for a universe of indeterminism and pure potentiality.

The truth runs squarely on the center lane. Parmenides said that nothing comes from being, and if being is simply actual, he is right. But something can and does develop out of being as far as it is potential. Motion comes from potency, not from act. Within limits, Heraclitus was also right. A constant state of change besets things as far as they are potential. But motion likewise involves the actual, and what is in act, to the extent that it is in act, does not change. If there is no actual character to motion, no being that moves, then movement becomes the movement of nothing and would be rendered just as impossible on Heraclitean principles as in the philosophy of Zeno.

Parmenides and Heraclitus were by no means the last of their breed, and it is a timely task to reflect anew on their truths and on their errors. Heraclitus stalks through recent thought in men like Bergson, Santayana, Spencer, Hegel, Whitehead, dialectical materialists, the existentialists, and the whole chorus of naturalism from Alexander to John Dewey. The reduction of reality to static categories and algebraic forms is the general tendency of empiriological physics and of its interpreters like Russell and Carnap, who dilute their final account of reality into logical and even linguistic forms. Potency and act are at the heart of the hierarchy in our universe and in the realistic report of it by genuine philosophy. Such a hierarchy is not admitted into philosophies of pure motion or in the approaches, more typical of the empiriological temper, which are dominated by the equality sign and by the equivalence of action and reaction. Potency cannot be added to potency, attaining act as a sum. Act is on a higher level, invested with a degree of being that potency cannot claim.

Empiriological physics, it was said, seeks to measure the real by quantitative techniques, but quantity is not the equivalent of motion. It is on a different rung in the ladder of abstraction where motion is absent and only the static remains. How then does empiriological physics define motion? Poincaré depicted it in terms of a differential equation of the second order—a mathematical account. The empiriological physicist generally views motion in terms of a series of positions, encouraged by Hume's verdict that causality is simply a succession of states. But a series, a sequence, positions—these are not motion. Motion is not positions but between them, and a series is a disconnected thing, like pearls on a necklace. Such a mathematical embrace of matter neglects the dynamic heart that throbs in motion, and this is the reason why strict empiriological physics suggests the staticism of Parmenides, who began with a principle that was preconceived instead of taking experience in the raw. In the theory of relativity, where in driving our car, for example, it could be said that the street is moving relative to us or we are moving relative to the street, motion becomes a matter of relations, and it is impossible to say absolutely whether anything is moving at all. In this connection, the empiriological physicist sometimes forgets that he is only measuring reality and that it is dogmatism in its densest form to equate the metrical with the existent.

ART AND NATURE ARE OPPOSITES

The philosophical science of nature is interested primarily in natural motions, and in this light it is of paramount importance to decide what nature and the natural are all about. Nature is often taken in a wide sense to include the whole mineral, plant, and animal universe, and the term "Mother Nature" is but the poet's testimony to this usage of the word. But nature is not taken in such a setting here. Individual things also have claim to the title of nature, and common speech bears out this fact by referring to the nature of man, the nature of a dog, the nature of iron, water, a pear tree, the nature of the intellect and will and emotions. For a long time, the empirical disciplines went by the name of natural history. It is this second usage of the term as applied to individual things, that is important here.

Like so many other things, the meaning of nature can be best illumined by playing it against its opposite. That opposite is art. To forge anew the distinction between nature and art is perhaps the central problem of the twentieth-century philosophical science of nature. What do we mean by saying that art imitates nature? Where does art part company with nature?

Velasquez painted a famous picture of King Philip of Spain

upon a horse. Philip and the horse were living beings in a given time and place, but what is the relation between the originals and the representation on dead canvas? The painting never was Philip himself, but only a picture of him. Philip was a man, endowed with a life-giving principle that we call a soul and integrated as a result into a unity and self-possession that we define as personality. He had something from within himself, an ability to think about his own being and to determine his own actions. He was thus not entirely the algebraic sum of forces acting on him from the outside. If this were true, if his being were determined completely from without, it would be nothing in itself, and being nothing, he would certainly never have existed, let alone rule a kingdom, command an army, and attract an artist. Much of this analysis could also apply to the horse if animal soul is substituted for human soul. For even though devoid of thought and of freedom, the horse is likewise not completely determined by outside forces. In that case, the horse would be nothing in itself and hence nothing at all. Philip and the horse have this in common that they have something from within themselves.

But what about the picture by Velasquez? Analysis discloses it to lack the inwardness that marks its subject matter. In its status as a picture, it is nothing but the mechanical arrangement of a series of pigmented solids on canvas. The chemist would announce that the colored surface is an aggregate of molecules bound together by mechanical forces. If sand could be colored and the various grains patiently juxtaposed on a table top to represent a man and a horse, a similar effect could be produced. A picture is but a mosaic on a microscopic scale.

What is important in the analysis is that the picture does not own the organic unity and wholeness of the original beings. There are no interior bonds between the molecules of the pigmented surface as there are between the parts of a living body. The picture *qua* picture has nothing from within itself. It owes whatever reality it owns as a picture to forces acting on it from the outside, coercing the parts into their proper position. A being like Philip or the horse is not fashioned by the painter. A series of beings is merely juxtaposed. Having no unity from within itself as a picture, the picture derives its unity from what is extrinsic to it. It is easy to see how truly Aquinas spoke when he said of a golden vase that it is truer to call it gold than to call it a vase.

At this point, it might sound premature to say that the parts are outside the picture too. Later discussion will beam a stronger light on this, and it need here simply be noted that the parts are not combined like the soul and body of man, where there is mutual compenetration. Since the parts of the picture are separated from each other, they are obviously outside each other, so that the picture cannot be called a whole, a unity, a being in the proper sense; therefore the parts lie outside the reality of the picture, just as the furniture of a room does not form the walls but stands exterior to them. In general, nature is interiority, and art is exteriority.

But what about the beholder of the picture? How does he relate it to nature?

It should be remarked simply that the artist, by carefully ordering his medium from the outside, creates the impression of reality for the man and his horse; and the more perfect he is an artist the more perfectly he can represent his subject matter with pigment. He depends on the beholders to coöperate with him, using their insights into what a man is and what a horse is in order to appreciate the painting that the art has provided. Without an idea of man derived beforehand from nature, the spectator could never get such an idea from the picture. The art could never portray alone what it means to see, feel, taste, touch, think, will, and experience emotions. Without an idea of life, the horse would remain a dead patch on dead canvas, unassociated with any meaningful thing beyond itelf.

A person congenitally blind can never get a remote idea of what color is, even when skilled in the mathematics of spectroscopy. To be appreciated, art must be related to the original, to life and nature as understood from within. Servicemen on Ta-

rawa, after the island was taken and made so peaceful that even movies could be shown, used to wonder about the attitudes of the natives in a labor battalion who were allowed to see the films. For example, what did they think, in their tropical background, when they saw pictures of falling snowflakes? It turned out that in American mess halls they had seen machines produce a chipped and frosty type of ice which they linked to the falling snow in the picture. How otherwise would they even have known what snow is?

No matter how well a dog is acquainted with its master, it can never recognize his picture.

What the spectator does in viewing the Philip of art is to bring to the appreciation his own idea of man derived from elsewhere. The full unity of the picture, by contrast to the sheerly mechanical union of juxtaposed parts on canvas, thus comes to art from the logical order. As in the making, so in the appreciation of it, the principle of unity and being comes from the outside. John Dewey says as much when he writes that "with the perceiver, as with the artist, there must be an ordering of the elements of the whole that is in form, although not in details, the same as the process of organization the creator of the work consciously experienced."[1]

Art, for both the creator and the beholder, has its principle outside itself. Philip and the horse had such a principle from within.

But if this is good reasoning, how can art be anything at all in view of a prior verdict that what is completely and inertially determined from the outside is nothing? The answer involves the apparent paradox that art is never pure art. It is simply a rearrangement of nature. Logic is never pure logic and purely formal; and the real picture is not an ontological zero, deriving everything from the painter who made it and from the beholder when it is appreciated. Pure art would be pure nothing in itself since

---

[1] *Art as Experience* (New York, 1934), p. 54.

its total reality would be owed to the agent producing it; it would be entirely outside itself and hence something contradictory. Art for art's sake is a principle of subjectivism. The artist must draw upon nature for his materials; it is from nature too that he derives his ideas. The artist simply replants in nature ideas that he has plucked from it, and it is in this sense that Aquinas realistically explains the principle that art is an imitation of nature.

But an imitation is, after all, an imitation. An imitation flower is an artificial flower. Art cannot be a perfect imitation of nature because the artist must use nature as his medium, and such a medium limits the purity of the art, while at the same time guaranteeing, through the natural parts that comprise it, that the work will wear claim to being. Composed of natural parts, a work of art is supported from becoming a pure nothing emerging from pure subjectivity. Its objectivity is from nature. Its "subjectivity" is from art.

This brings out the fact that nature has a wider ambit of meaning than its use to describe man, a horse, or any other animal. Every plant has a nature charged by its vegetative soul. Elements and compounds all have natures, as Chapter 6 will display. Iron, copper, water, salt, sugar, kerosene—all are invested with distinctive natures. They all have something from within. Each has a certain electromagnetic character, a definite specific gravity, a melting point of its own, and especially in the case of the kerosene, a fixed point of combustibility. Each tastes differently and acts differently. When each is exposed to sunlight, it selects certain wavelengths of the incident radiation and reflects others. Thus copper absorbs all the sunlight except the wavelengths in and near the yellow band of the spectrum; it has a brownish-yellow color. If the empiriological physicist insists that the copper has nothing from within but, measure for measure, simply gives back what is put into it in obedience to the fact that action and reaction are equivalent, the consideration of his arguments must be postponed to the discussions of efficient causalty. Here it is enough to point out, with promise of later proof, that the elements and compounds of our universe have natures that make each an original thing, acting and reacting in styles determined not entirely from without but also from a selective principle that can be only within.

Just as nature stretches not only to life but to the mineral world, so art, as used in the foregoing example, was employed in a narrower sense than it actually can boast. Art is not only fine art, like music, sculpture, painting, and literature. It can be a liberal art like logic, which aims at correctly organizing thought. It can above all be a mechanical art, the entire area of human production. Carpentry is an art, so is shoemaking and all the other trades. Farming, driving a car, running a lathe, hitting a golf ball, mining coal, cooking, sewing—all of these are arts. In all of them man imposes something on nature; man determines nature from without, casting it according to the image and likeness of his own thought. Art, in general, may thus be defined as the production of any exterior work by the mind and will of man.

A simple analysis could show that all the arts have in common with the case of the picture that they organize nature from outside it; their principle is extrinsic. All the arts are limited by nature which yields their ideas and by nature again which affords them a medium to shape. Like any other pure art, a perfect machine, say a device for perpetual motion, would be a nonentity entirely since its whole reality would be exterior to it, leaving it a perfect zero in itself. Thus while nature limits the artist, it also sponsors his aims by providing whatever stability, permanence, and objectivity his work possesses. Marble is the natural part of a statue, and iron, of a stove. The statue of Venus de Milo has survived passing time not because of art but because of the stability of its natural parts. In this light are Augustine's profound words to be understood that a pure picture (pure art) of a horse would be a false horse; and a tragic drama becomes a false play if it is a true tragedy.

Aquinas neatly boils down the exteriority which art implies by his insight that art exists for man, who is outside of it. Man is its end and purpose. Its principle is not in nature but in man. The same statements could be made about the machine which is simply a work of art in the mechanical order.

But how is nature itself to be defined? Inspecting the word reveals that it comes from the same stem as "nativity" and therefore has the meaning of birth or being born. *Physis*, the Greek work for nature and the parent of our word *physics*, means broadly the same thing. If a corsage of gardenias is buried in the springtime, a plant will sprout up surely enough, and it will later bear gardenias. But they will not be in the form of a corsage. Art, as in the artifact of the corsage, has no tendency to reproduce itself. Nature has the meaning of the innate, and what is natural has tendencies of its own and from within itself, impulses that are not all imposed on it inertially from without. Art has no tendencies as art; it lacks a final cause in the outer order. The gardenias have tendencies; the corsage as such does not.

In a more formal sense, Aristotle defines nature as "a source and cause of motion and of rest in that to which it belongs primarily in virtue of itself and not in virtue of a concomitant attribute." By calling nature a source and a cause, Aristotle simply portrays the fact that the action of a thing is not due entirely to outside forces but that the mineral, the plant, the animal, man— the subject responding to such outer factors—contributes something of its own to whatever results; the nature in question has tendencies of its own and is not indefinitely pliable to outer agents that would mold it. Such a thought, that nature is an identity with itself and not with what is wholly outside, is underscored by insisting that nature is primarily in the thing that has it; it is there by virtue of its own power, it is not an accident. Hence nature is not ingrafted into a preëxisting subject by forces acting from without; it is not like champagne held in a container not itself, by a cork exterior to both. It would be more correct to say that it *is* the subject. Far from being an attribute, it is immediately itself and, so to say, in itself. It has an interior, original, independent, and ultimate character that does not inhere in a preceding subject or derive from a higher transeunt cause.

Nature is a principle of action and of rest. It is a source of action and of stoppage, of movement and of repose. As long as the sun beats down on the copper wire, the brownish-yellow color will be reflected. But after dusk, the reflections will cease. It is the same copper that has reflected the color and ceased the reflecting. The reflections are not due to one force in the copper and the absence of them to another. In such a case, there would be two beings to the copper rather than one. The same thing that is in motion can, at a different time, be at rest, and the principle in the two states must be unitary. Copper in a natural state and copper at white heat in a blast furnace is the same copper. How empiriological physics confirms this view will be apparent in the sequel (Chapter 6).

Chance should likewise be clashed against the notions of art and of nature. But this subject has many implications in the science of today and will be discussed separately in connection with final causality.

This contrast between art and nature, apparently so long, is really too brief to emphasize its importance. It is not simply dragged from the mortuaries of medieval thought. Perhaps in no age has the distinction between art and nature been more timely than in the mechanical epoch of contemporary man. Empiriological physics, for instance, discloses its affinity with art by its profound attachment to the principle of inertia which states that a thing is entirely determined from the outside. This is precisely how a realist defines art as art, and hence when the empiriological physicist reports on matter, it is in the light of art rather than of nature that his words must be weighed. His inertialism prompts him to view the world as a mechanism or a work of art to be understood entirely in terms of parts; he is authorized by his method to explore a thing only in terms of other things constraining it from the outside. He aims to control the world, imposing his command upon it exactly as other artists marshal their media. As every artist must study the laws of his medium, so the theoretical part of empiriological physics is concerned to know the medium in order to get more out of it, "to get results" as pragmatism says, to build bigger and better bridges and power plants and radar ranges and atomic devices for peace or war.

Empiriological physics does not envision nature as having a principle within itself. Art is what nature becomes, in the limit, for the empiriological method when it is taken purely. The philosophical science of nature, on the other hand, is interested in nature primarily to know rather than to bring it under control. What nature has from within man must obey rather than command. Just as there is no pure art, so there is no pure empiriological physics in practice, and it is because of this mixed character which the empiriological approach takes on in the concrete that it provides a rich mine of data for the philosopher to refine. Making the distinction between art and knowledge in the purest sense empowers the philosopher to explain the difference between his own approach to reality and the one used so brilliantly by the empiriological physicist. Empiriological physics views nature as art; philosophical physics views it as nature and therefore as it is. The one seeks primarily to control, the other to acquire speculative knowledge.

How this character of empiriological physics seeped into western thought appears in the historical origins of the so-called scientific movement. It got up steam at the time of the Renaissance, in Europe. But when the leading spirits of the Renaissance, reverting to the Greek world, were shouting "back to nature!", it was to ancient art rather than to nature that they eventually went. The older account of nature, with its inner tendencies and its fixed objective laws, slowly withered into a fossil, and nature, considered as art, came to replace it as a living attitude. Nature grew to be studied more and more by interfering with it rather than by taking it as it is, until at last Heisenberg called attention to this fact of interference as the trick that makes empiriological physics to be experimental; he put the interference principle at the very base of empiriological physics in its dissection of matter.

Empiriological and philosophical physics are like two hunters in the forestry of nature. The first can bag its game only by killing it; the philosophical science of nature seeks to capture its prey alive.

NATURAL MOTION INVOLVES MATTER, FORM, AND PRIVATION

The philosophical physicist is concerned with the motions of nature, and the concept of nature as a source of motion is simply a synonym for the more precise term changing being (*ens mobile*) which the philosophical science of nature has for its only interest. Since any branch of philosophy must aim to discover principles, the question may now be asked as to the principles of natural motion, just as the law of inertia is the principle of motion in art.

A principle is that from which anything flows in any manner whatsoever. Principles must be ultimate, mutually exclusive if there is more than one, and potential in what follows from them. A principle may be a cause, as neutrons moving with the proper speed produce fission in the uranium nucleus; or it may not be a cause, as a point is the principle of a line.

The concept of a principle since Kant's time has been stripped of its ontal status and is today viewed more as a regulative idea. Philosophies, like logical empiricism, want to reduce empiriological physics ultimately to a body of rules for verification, and theories, viewed as tools for predicting laboratory results, have tended to become only rules for multiplying experiments and guiding the experimenter. In this sense, the empiriological physicist speaks of the principles of least action, of least time, and even the principle of gravitation. Principles at best mean laws for the empiriological physicist, and a law is simply a generalization of inductive results rather than, like a truly scientific principle, an account of origins, terminations, and the processes transpiring in between. A law is always expressed in equational form, and in this static dress it is not suited to clothe the real mobility of motion.

A principle of motion corresponds to the facts or factors responsible for its origin and especially for its end result. The analysis of motion unveils three such ultimates in the thing moved.

First, motion involves the arrival of something new in the universe, and this emergence of novelty cannot be sufficiently stressed since it marks a point where the mind must abandon empiriological physics with its apparatus of equations, and call on philosophical physics for an answer. A billiard ball wins a new position by being rolled to the other side of the table. Oxygen gains a new status in being when it is united with hydrogen. All change involves this element of novelty, and without it, as John of St. Thomas emphasizes, there is simply no change or motion at all.

Secondly, there must be a subject which changes. For if there is nothing that has changed, quite obviously no change has taken place. Without a subject, as without the novel element, motion is not only unexplained, it is impossible. A billiard ball to be rolled across the table must be a billiard ball; it must be something. Oxygen, if it is to be transformed into water by union with hydrogen, cannot be a non-existing thing.

The third principle of motion is the subject's original lack of this new perfection which the element of novelty represents. Obviously the billiard ball must not be in the new position to which the motion is to displace it, and oxygen cannot be made to unite with hydrogen if it is already combined with it. If the ball is already in its new position and the oxygen is already united with hydrogen, no motion occurs. And hence, for this negative reason, the factor of lack or, more technically, privation, must be reckoned among the principles of motion. A principle has to do with *origins*, and privation is necessary if motion is to *originate*.

The subject of motion Aristotle labeled matter, and the perfection which the motion begets is called form. Because of the jumbled meaning of these words in a tongue like English where the spirit and style of expression are no longer set by the classic temper and where old words have shed their old meanings, it is important to pause upon the definition of matter and form, as Aristotle depicted them. Matter is not simply what is massive and weighty. Form is not the same as shape, and above all it is not the misty, almost mystical thing that its opponents accuse it of being. Form is simply the term of motion, and when this term has been admitted, it is all that the philosophical physicist means by form. Matter is that out of which anything is produced in the motions of nature. Matter is the raw stuff of process, whether the motion be the compounding of elements, the digestion of food, the manufacture of shoes, the splitting of an atom, or the carving of a woodcut. After all these processes have run their course, something remains of the original subject, but something has also been changed. When the various motions of nature have been completed, there is something new in the universe, but there is also something that has persisted. This new factor, consorting with the original raw material and corresponding to something novel in the matter's being, is called form.

Form is not to be confused with shape or figure, despite the first impulse to treat it thus. Even though, as in the case of the woodcut, it may have this meaning, there are other cases where much more has been changed than the sheer geometry of the subject. Digested food, for example, becomes part of us; it forsakes its character of sugar, tomato, water, and becomes assimilated into our own being. Sodium and chlorine when united become a new entity which we know as salt, and in the fission of atoms, it is well known that the elements are trans*formed*.

There is nothing mystical, supernatural, *a priori,* or dogmatic about this matter-form dualism. It was not dreamed up by an unenlightened Greek, who let the dummy world of logic dominate his cosmology or simply softened up the Platonic myths without destroying their mythical character. Experience and abstraction, motion and being, all of them team together to form the realism of Aristotle's report on change. Admitting it is only to agree that motion requires the emergence of something new and a subject, from which the emergent comes, which originally lacked the new reality.

Privation is likewise the prey of misunderstanding as a principle of motion. Whereas matter and form are essentially involved in change, privation is only accidentally implied. It is not a positive reality, and the negative cannot be part of the essence of anything. So motion involves privation only in an accidental way. It simply happens that the subject does not have the form which the motion will beget; another being of the same type, say another billiard ball, might have it. If in the absolute and essential sense the subject could not have this form, motion would be impossible because the term of the motion itself would be absolutely and essentially excluded from the realm of the subject's possibilities. The marble must have been deprived of the figure of *David*, or Michelangelo would not have carved his statue. It would have been given. But the marble, while lacking the chiseled figure, had the possibility of being chiseled, and this, for anyone wishing to go into the technicality of the problem, is why the principle is called privation rather than negation.

Privation is not simply nothingness. It is a denial or a lack, within a determinate subject, hence not simply a negation. It is matter regarded from the viewpoint of what it lacks. But matter is never without privation. When it has one form it is deprived of another since its limits are such that it can enjoy only one form at a time. This is why matter is restless and changing and why the mind must graduate into metaphysics for the truest satisfactions of philosophy. The contracted character of matter which forbids it to own more than one form at a time must be taken into account in philosophical physics. That is why privation, even though an accidental thing, must be counted among the principles of motion.

Form and matter, each in its own way, are often called nature since they are intrinsic to the thing moved. But nature can also mean their composition, and this was the sense of the word in the preceding section. Form especially is worthy to be called nature since it determines the matter to be this or that, an interior and original thing, as the ensuing sections will show.

SUBSTANCE IS A NATURE EXISTING

So much can be said about matter and form in the general sense. There are various degrees and various kinds of changes in the world of nature, and it might naturally be suspected from this that matter and form appear in different kinds and degrees. Such is actually the case.

There are four kinds of being which display motion and therefore recommend themselves to the philosophical physicist. These are substance, place, quantity, and quality. Substance, as chemical changes show, may be generated or destroyed; place may be changed by what is called local movement; quantity is augmented or diminished in the realm of life where things grow larger or smaller; quality may be altered as water which has different sonic properties in a solid and a liquid state. Of these six species of motion—generation and destruction, local movement, augmentation and diminution, and alteration—only substantial changes will be treated for the present, with local and qualitative motions to be explored later and quantitative changes left to that part of the philosophy of nature which opens the door to psychology.

Naturally the first question is, what is substance and what is its relation to nature which has been set up as the only stock in trade of the philosophical physicist. As in the whole of the philosophical science of nature, motion is the frame for the definition, and substance is not considered, as in metaphysics, by the light of being. Substance is contrasted with accidents or attributes. Silver is a substance; its accidents are its color, its specific gravity, its melting point, its electropositive character, and its magnetic properties. Water, radium, sulfuric acid, a cow, a man, a neutron —all are substances. Substance corresponds to the question, what the being is, and an accident is what the being has. An accident has thus been called *ens entis*—the being of a being.

Treated in the climate of philosophical physics as the being of a thing, substance seems at first sight confusingly like the cause and source of motion and of rest that Aristotle called nature. The difference between the two is that nature is a universal community of a given kind (often called second substance), whereas substance proper (first substance) is the individually existing thing within the kind. Thus, all iron has the same nature, but it does not all have the same substance. Each atom of iron is different from every other atom and does not inhere in a common all-pervasive nature that would lead to a monism in the world of iron. In the strict sense of the term, an individual atom like an individual man *has* a nature; it *is* a substance. Similarly of the other examples mentioned above. Substance for present purposes may be taken as a nature existing, a nature that is no longer universal but invested with all the requisites to be an independent existing thing. It is being concretely existing.[2]

Substantial changes involve the generation of a new substance, the change from non-being to being, and the destruction or corruption of the old substance, the change from being to non-being. It is from its changes, substantial and accidental, that substance is known to the philosophical physicist in his strict limits, and to explain such changes Aristotle saw the necessity of matter-form. This dualism in the substantial order is emphatically not a doctrine to explain bodily essence but to explain substantial change. Philosophical physics is not a philosophy of essence but a philosophy of nature, which is essence viewed as a principle of operation.

Are there substantial changes in the world? Experience answers with an unqualified yes. Certainly there is a much greater change in silver when it unites with chlorine than when it is cut and stamped in the mint to become a ten-cent piece. Wood changes much more when it burns than when it is carved into a

---

[2] What makes a substance individual (so-called signate matter) is being omitted from the discussions in this book and is usually treated in psychology in connection with the problem of personality.

leg for a table. An atom changes much more when it is split than when it is heated. And the evidence is very obvious that an apple changes much more by being digested in man than by its variations of color in the autumnal sun. Clearly there is a difference among the various changes. In some of them, only accidental properties are modified, while in others the identity of the original entity is lost, and a new being can be recognized. A substantial change is a change of substance, and a substance is not the attribute of the being which is transformed but the very being itself. This is the best definition which the science of nature can give of substance, and its fuller elaboration has been adjourned until now because the philosophical physicist can only work it out from the changes that matter goes through.

The empiriological temper would not admit the existence of substantial changes, choosing rather to nail down all the motions in the cosmos in terms of quantity and local displacement. Parts are simply rearranged into new configurations. The universe becomes a game of Chinese checkers.

In Chapter 6, it will be seen that Aristotelian dualism is required and mechanism is refuted by the contemporary achievements of empiriological physics. It may simply be stated here that the changes in accidents which occur in growth, local motion, and alteration are not in the same class with generation and corruption. Substantial changes show not only variations from the outside working inward toward the interiority of the changing being but the reversal of this direction. An accident is directed from the outer to the inner structure of the being and of its motions, whereas substance is just the opposite. Accidents and substances thus cannot be reduced to the same principle, and if a change results in a new intrinsic principle of operation, a new nature, then the original substance has been substantially changed. Chemical changes in the living and the lifeless and nuclear transformations in nature and in the laboratory—all of these are substantial changes. The new substances have different principles of motion from the old ones. They are new beings.

SUBSTANTIAL CHANGES INVOLVE PRIME MATTER

The form and the matter of substantial changes are called substantial form and prime matter respectively; there are also accidental forms and second matter, which are involved in accidental changes.

The general discussion of the principles of motion will underwrite the conclusion that matter, as the subject, is the principle of potency, and form, the term of movement, is the principle of act. What makes prime matter different from second matter is that it is not only potency but pure potency.

Why do Aristotle, Aquinas, Augustine, Bonaventure, and nearly all of the later scholastics agree to the matter-form report of substantial change? First, because substantial changes occur; and secondly, nothing can come from nothing.

To account for the second truth, prime matter is required in its role as the first subject of change. If prime matter were not a reality abiding through the change and appearing in both the old and the new beings, substantial change would be a matter of annihilating the old substance and creating the new. But this sequence of annihilation and creation cannot be accepted. If it actually occurred in nature, it would be impossible to explain the dispositions which a substance possesses to be changed into *this* other determinate something rather than *that*. Oxygen and hydrogen have an affinity for each other, and zinc combines with sulfur, though not with gold. These dispositions and determinations, poised for action in one direction rather than another, would lack a sufficient reason and be self-contradictory if the ingredient substances of a new being had to be annihilated and the new substance created out of nothing.

Something in the original has an influx into the production of what is new. Otherwise, new substances would be only the successors of the old, not their effects. Hume's definition of causality as mere sequence would carry the day in philosophy, and the universe of modern mathematics would replace the changing physical world studied in the first order of abstraction. Peano, translating Hume into mathematics, attempted to elaborate a theory of number in which one number is related to the next lower one in terms of the unique relation "successor of." But if substantial change is not a case of annihilation and creation, then prime matter must be admitted as an abiding substrate.

√ Aristotle defined prime matter in two ways. In a positive sense, he called it "the primary substratum of each thing from which it comes to be without qualification, and which persists in the result." It is the first subject of change, and from it there results not a substance-accident union but the constitution of the substance itself which is then ready to receive qualification or accident. It is not an outside cause, separated from its effect; it persists in the effect, since it is that *out of which* the effect is made.

In a negative way, Aristotle described prime matter "as that which in itself is neither a particular thing nor of a certain quantity nor assigned to any other of the categories by which being is determined." It is not a particular thing since it has no actuality; it is not a quantity since quantity is an accident and can only inhere in a particular thing; it is not a category since a category is a determinate something and prime matter is indeterminate—determined by the form which is united with it.

Prime matter is an elusive reality to grasp since there is nothing like it that could act as its substitute in a full definition. Though every analogy limps, to suggest prime matter is to ask an analogy to limp rather far. The best way to exemplify its nature is to take an instance from the accidental order.

A handful of putty can be shaped into any number of geometrical figures. It can be rolled into a ball, it can be squared neatly into a cube, molded into a cylinder, an oblong, a model airplane, the figure of an animal. A hole can be worked into it until it resembles a doughnut, or it can be squeezed into irregular form to plug up a hole that worms have eaten into a tree. The same marble that Michelangelo used for his Moses might have been used to sculpture any one of the billions of human beings, animals, and plants which, in various sizes and shapes, have appeared or will appear on this globe.

The putty and the marble may be likened, but likened only, to prime matter, and their various configurations to substantial form. Nothing could be more fatal to the matter-form account, however, than to lift these analogies from the window cases of example designed to lead the mind to abstract the substantial principles. Matter in the cases of the putty and of the marble is second matter (composed of prime matter and substantial form), and the form is an accidental one, far removed from the form that goes to make up a substance. Prime matter cannot be imagined; and like all potencies, it can only be understood from its actualization accomplished by form.

Prime matter must be pure potency in order to explain the difference of being which substantial changes produce, differences from the core out and not merely in the accidental order. Generation is the change from non-being to being, and corruption is the reverse. If prime matter were not pure potency, a substance would be an aggregate.

Prime matter is incorruptible; it subsists through all changes. Unable to exist by itself since of itself it bears no actuality, it is incomplete and indeterminate. But it is not simply nothing. Its reality is as a potency, pure potency,—potentially any material thing that is but none of them by itself. Prime matter is in the substantial order since it is a constituent of substantial being and is called its intrinsic cause like form. Like form also, it is an incomplete substance, and the two incomplete substances together compose the complete one.

Since prime matter is the fundamental changeless element in change, it can only have been created. None of the species of motion which the philosopher of matter explores can account for its origin. It is not a product of change but a principle. Substances are generated and corrupted; prime matter is not. This changeless element cannot be produced from a preëxisting matrix since there is nothing more potential than pure potency, from which it could emerge.

SUBSTANTIAL CHANGES INVOLVE SUBSTANTIAL FORM

Form is the first act of the prime matter. In a substantial change like the fission of uranium into barium fragments, the change of iron and oxygen into rust, and the furious fuming and spitting when potassium is dropped into water to form potassium hydroxide—in all these the identity of the initial being is lost and a new identity emerges. The prime matter has lost its old form and gained a new one. In the examples from the accidental order, the putty and the marble could be cast into an indefinite number of shapes. One shape differs from another by a principle that is called its accidental form. In a parallel but only analogous fashion within the substantial order, one being differs from another by means of its substantial form.

Substantial form, according to the slant taken on the world in the physical order of abstraction, is the term of generation. It is defined by motion not by quantity. In metaphysics, form is considered as the principle of being which makes a thing what it is; there it is a broad synonym for essence or quiddity just as the philosophic science of nature often interchanges the words *nature* and *form*. In a secondary, indirect, and improper sense, the philosophical physicist may consider form not only as the term of generation but in the light of its origin since substantial change does not begin absolutely but from a matter here and now invested with a form that the change will overcome.

The primary meaning, however, is not as the origin of generation but as the term since the office of form is precisely to inform matter, terminating it so to speak. Matter is directed to form as to a final cause which will later be more clearly defined. Moreover, it is only as a term of generation that the philosopher of nature comes to a knowledge of form since both matter and form are recognized from substantial changes. It is in these senses and for these reasons that matter is properly defined as the subject of generation and form as its term. Form is that which makes iron iron; it makes the elements and compounds what they are; the vegetative and animal souls are forms of their respective matters and the soul of man must likewise be considered as the form of a matter.

When a form is acquired in a substantial change, it is educed from the potency of the matter. Similarly, when a form is lost, it reverts to the potency of the matter to emerge anew whenever external conditions conspire to cause its reappearance. Such a stand may sound like an appeal to magic rather than to realism in the light of modern misconceptions of form. Yet it is only in such a view that the appearance of substantial novelty in our universe can be accounted for. To resume the analysis of the putty which must still be kept within the limping body of example, it may be asked where the spherical form existed while the plastic mass was actually shaped like a cube. Since a sphere can be rolled the next minute out of what is not spherical, the putty is capable of rotundity. The spherical shape comes from such capacities, and when in turn it disappears, the putty is still really and truly capable of being rolled anew into a ball. The same principle applies, divested of its accidental references, in the substantial order. Otherwise, the novelty involved by changes from being to non-being, and vice versa, is impossible.

Augustine held that forms were actually precontained in the matter in a kind of seminal existence (*rationes seminales*)—a hint, it has been said, of modern morphological evolution. Such a view where forms are actually present within the matter does not account for the substantial unity of the composite being, and it churns substance into an aggregate. A much shallower opinion of how novelty occurs in the world is found in contemporary scientism. There, cashing in on the Cartesian currency that all mutation is but local motion which is now called displacement, the opinion thrives that novelty results from the simple shifting of particles, those of atomic and subatomic dimensions and finally pure quantities. Differences become a matter of differently related points, in a coördinate system of geometry, where the subject of motion is ultimately quantity alone. It is as though a woman could change the kind of her powder by simply shaking the box.

In a mobile universe principled by pure quantity and its displacement, nothing new could ever result, and hence no motion could occur and no mobility be detected. In this far-fetched cosmos, everything must remain what it is and do nothing but, in an extremely mysterious fashion, change its position. But novelty is not explained in being when only quantity and place are allowed to change. If a ton of coal is shoveled into a bin, it is still coal on arriving at its destiny and it would still be coal if a half ton were taken away. Local movement and quantity are not enough to account for any novelty if they and they alone exist. If newness occurs in experience, something that was present before has vanished and something new has been gained. In the homogeneous universe of mere quantity where only position changes, the same homogeneous something that is in the new position was there preceding the change by the very premise of homogeneity, and no change has really occurred. There must be something more than the displacement of the same by the same if novelty is real. Act and potency must be involved, form and matter. Something goes out of existence and something comes into it. Something goes from act to potency in corruption and from potency to act in generation.

No actual precontaining of the new can explain novelty nor explain why the old form has vanished. This is but another way of stating that the new form must emerge from pure potency since it is not actually precontained; it must return to pure potency when it gives way through another change. No references are being made here to the external agents which act upon substances from the outside and cause the substantial changes to occur. The whole question is here the intrinsic principling of motion in substantial changes, where the change is an inward

change, a change of being. The form of the new substance is said
to be educed from the prime matter, and the old form returns to
the bosom of matter's pure potencies. Lest eduction be taken as a
verbalism to cloak a medieval ignorance, it simply states, as
Aquinas remarks, that "something becomes actual that was previously potential." It is tempting to use the contemporary term
emergence as a synonym for *eduction,* but the shadows of confusion have closed in around this word in the doctrines of "emergent evolution."

Form and matter must be immediately united, and on this
point, the Thomistic position diverges from that of Suarez who
envisioned the union as occurring through a medium. The medium wedged in between the matter and the form would have to
be actual, if it differed from the matter, and hence would have a
form of its own. But one form cannot be intrinsically united to
another when both preserve their actuality, any more than a car
becomes one with the street by being parked on it. The Suarezian
union of actual forms, the one mediating, the other terminating
the substantial composition, would be only accidental. The result
would not display the intrinsic unity characterizing substances
and changing when they change.

The problem of the plurality of forms was one of the big questions which beset the middle ages from the controversy between
Abelard and William of Champeaux in the twelfth century to the
full decadence of scholasticism at the time of Ockham. The issue
was alive in Aquinas' day, and in meeting it, he departed sharply
from the Franciscan scholastics like Bonaventure and Alexander
of Hales and even from his own master, Albert the Great. Only
when matter and form are immediately and intrinsically united
do we have one substance. The doctrine of the plurality of forms
would seek to argue that things like man, the maple tree, the
elements, and the compounds are simply aggregates of many substances, like a tapestry which is an aggregate of threads. But
substances show, each in its own way, an immediate and an intrinsic union, a unity of the parts. How this immediacy of union

is possible can only be explained by the fact that matter is pure potency, and any act that it owns must therefore be united to it immediately. Between pure potency and any act there is no middle ground that could mediate their intrinsic union.

Substantial form, like prime matter, is an incomplete substance; like matter, it is also an intrinsic cause of mobile being. It is neither generated nor corrupted since these changes occur only in the composite. Substances are generated and corrupted but not the principles of change.

Natures do not change; substances do.

Matter and form are concreated; neither can exist without the other (except in the case of man where the form, being spiritual, cannot be educed from a material potency nor return there when it can no longer exist in the matter).

But if form and matter must be created, how can any change of substance actually have occurred after the first instant of creation when a world burst into being? How explain all the subsequent motion which the facts of experience verify beyond doubt? Was this not the ultimate question that prompted Augustine to posit his "seminal reasons"?

The only possible explanation is the definition of motion in terms of potency and act. Forms are not generated or corrupted, but they are brought from a potential to an actual condition and vice versa. New forms were in the potencies of matter from the moment of its creation, and they are educed in time into an actual status.

This is one of the natural mysteries that the mind may continue to meditate but never exhaust. Potency and prime matter cannot be imagined or even directly known by intelligence. They can only be apprehended from act. A curtain will always be drawn over the direct view of them which would permit a glimpse of all that matter could achieve. By intelligence—never by our imagination—we know that prime matter is and we reach an indirect knowledge of its nature by way of negating what act is. Therefore, we in a sense overcome our own ignorance by accounting for its reasons.

Widely speaking, no form ever returns to pure potency, in the sense that the fact of its existence has altered the face of the actual and left its trail for all time upon the universe of existing things. Motion is not neutral; all of it makes a difference in the cosmos. Succeeding chapters will show that all motion is not so much a return to an origin as a development toward an end. In this respect, it is much more natural and rewarding not to look "backward" into matter but "forward" into form.

An emphatic note in connection with substantial change is its instantaneous character. In this respect, substantial motion differs from all others and is not properly motion at all. It is better called change (*mutatio*). Because a new being comes into existence, it cannot be evolved from its privation in gradual steps, any more than being can come from nothing on a graduated scale. Substantial change involves an abruptness that other motions do not require. In originating substantial changes, alteration and local motion are always necessary, as will be later seen, but they are more in the manner of dispositive influences. They are continuous processes, shortening but never bridging the gap between the old substance and the new. For the rupture is there. The new substance is not divided from the old by a scale of more or less but by a change of inner principle. This is another indication that matter must be pure potency since any act united with it would make all changes affairs of addition and subtraction, never permitting that change of inner being which substantial transformations exhibit.

Finally, the form of a substantial thing is present wholly in the whole and wholly in every part of it. The whole of an iron atom is iron, and every part of it is iron. The so-called virtual presence of elements in compounds and of subatomic particles in atoms will be discussed in Chapter 6.

SUBSTANTIAL CHANGES PROVE MATTER-FORM DUALISM

The proper and convincing argument for the matter-form dualism is substantial change. Such changes occur, and nothing can come from nothing. These are the twin principles on which the proof depends. There are, however, some confirmatory evidences that, if they lack pointedness, may nevertheless carry a certain expository appeal:

1. Material substances reflect unity and multiplicity. There must hence be principles of unity and multiplicity within them. The first corresponds to form, the second to matter. Wood, for instance, has a certain extension, an extraposition of its cellulose molecules in space. Yet all of the wood is wood. An atom of helium has quantity, but it is all helium.

2. Material substances display both passivity and activity, and there must be a corresponding principle for each. Passivity is ascribed to matter and activity to form. Water has a certain reality from within which makes it what it is; yet it is also passive, capable of being drunk, evaporated, frozen, decomposed, combined with carbon to form organic compounds.

3. Time and space are often differentiated. Time reflects the dynamism of things and space the drag that resists change. Time, runs this argument, has the flavor of form and space of matter.

4. There is a determination (form) and an indetermination (matter) in everything. A material thing is something, but it is always struggling to be something else.

5. There is a principle of limit (matter) and of limitlessness (form) in corporeal reality. Man is fully man in individuals, but individuals are multiplied so that any one individual does not possess the full perfection of the species.

Such arguments are exceedingly suggestive in their own way, but the way does not lead necessarily to matter-form dualism. The arguments show, to use a Whiteheadean term, that matter is bifurcated. But they are not of themselves sufficient to rank with substantial change in proving the dualism of matter and form. This doctrine is drawn from motion, not from essence or quantity or even being as the metaphysician studies it. The metaphysician uses arguments similar to all of the five listed to introduce his doctrines of potency and act, of essence and existence, of substance and accident. Unless the arguments are based on the pivotal issue of substantial change, they do not localize substance which, from the standpoint of the philosophical science of nature, can be established only by motions.

Thus, in the arguments above, unity and multiplicity, time and space, passivity and activity, determination and indetermination, limit and what is limited—all show the bifurcation of matter, but by themselves, they do not report whether atoms or molecules are substances or whether these might not be just the mechanical aggregates of fundamental particles inhabiting a sub-atomic world. The problem of the continuum (1) involves in the proper sense more the divisibility in quantity than motions in substances. All such arguments are, in a realistic view, simply aspects of the basic argument when they are convincing, and though often used, it is in the larger context of motion that they should be taken.

ATOMISM AND MECHANISM ARE INERTIALISMS

The dualism of matter and form, to put it mildly, is not generally accepted. In its stead, modern philosophy has tended to waver between mechanism (atomism) on the one hand and dynamism on the other, attempting by such principles to deal with the problem of change.

Mechanism and atomism are ancient doctrines, dating back to pre-Aristotelian philosophies like the views of Anaxagoras, Anaxamander, and Empedocles, and ripening into classic form with atomists like Democritus and Epicurus. Democritus, for instance, held that everything is made up of tiny individuals called atoms, differing among themselves in shape and size and forming our qualitative universe by chance differences of order and position. In mechanism, atomistic or otherwise, a thing is viewed as a machine without intrinsic unity and with all its principles, art-like, outside it.

Descartes' mechanism takes its rise from his definition of body in terms of extension and of all corporeal change in terms of local movement. Prompted by Descartes, Gassendi revived atomism as a philosophy, and the atomic theory, though developed independently of earlier philosophical atomism, carried off such great stakes in chemistry that atomism as a philosophy seemed to win strong academic support. Clerk Maxwell, Helmholtz, and Du Bois-Reymond, empiriological scholars of the first magnitude, were among the leading advocates of mechanism in the nineteenth century.

At the turn of the present century, Max Planck originated the quantum theory which eventually showed that not only matter but energy as well could be studied as a phenomenon of particles, which he called quanta. Atomism was migrating from chemistry to empiriological physics. In the twentieth century, the study of matter by breaking it up has reached such a kindling point that the atom itself was finally split in laboratories and even over cities, and today's empiriological signposts lend credence to the belief that the subatomic particles are being experimentally divided.

All of the successes of this atomism in both chemistry and empiriological physics might seem to sanction the mechanical view of reality which the empiriologist, by adhering rigidly to measurement, is compelled to adopt. Quantum physics is puzzling in this respect because it has concluded that exact measurements of individual particles are hopelessly out of range and that the only reliable account of nature can be given in terms of aggregates, where individuals are grouped in a statistical whole. But quantum mechanics still amounts to an atomism by regarding wholes in partitive terms. All processes are referred to smaller ones. What happens in the visible world is only a forest of microscopic trees, and the microscopic in turn is explainable in terms of the submicroscopic, making matter into a labyrinth where the paths become narrower for man to tread but never run out. The claim of quantum mechanics to dispense with mechanism because of the rank it assigns to wholes cannot be made good for another reason. Like the rest of empiriological physics, it is still mechanistic in viewing whatever is and whatever moves as entirely the result of outside forces. As empiriological in temper, it cannot proceed otherwise.

The hylosystemists incline to shrink philosophical physics to fit the empiriological world picture, and in this respect hylosystemism is but a philosophical mechanism dressed in scholastic terminology. This view maintains that empiriological physics studies corporeal substance and descends to the fundamental constitution of bodies. It forgets the difference between the methods of the empiriological and philosophical attacks on the universe, and it overlooks almost wholly that the philosophy of nature is not primarily concerned with body and its constitution but with motion and its principles.

Hylosystemists want philosophy to pitch its camp on empiriological terrain, without remembering the prescientific experience (contrasted with experiment) that is the beginning of all knowledge and that gives the philosopher a positive and critical prestige with respect to the empiriological physicist. If experience is banned as a source of knowledge, even metaphysics must become either a continuation of empiriological disciplines or an *a priori* dogma like that of Kant or Plato. Hylosystemic mechanism thrives on the confusion between the philosophy of quantity and the philosophy of nature, and like the grosser mechanisms it eventually supplants the view that matter is nature with the dogma that matter is art.

DYNAMISM REDUCES MATTER TO THE IMMATERIAL

Dynamism differs from atomism by tending to reduce the material to the immaterial. Its final report declares that the universe is made of points, the inextended, motion, energy, field. Heraclitus was the greatest of the ancient dynamists, and his thoughts are countersigned, in many respects, by the twentieth-century systems of Bergson and of Edouard Le Roy.

Leibniz, reacting to Cartesianism, distilled out a doctrine known as monadology in which the cosmos is resolved into inextended substances called monads, each of which is different from every other and all of which are close to living. Boscovich held that matter is composed of indivisible points, and Kant took a similar view. Hegel was a thoroughgoing dynamist by his view that the universe is but an idea in pure motion. His philosophy is usurped by Marx and Lenin, who viewed matter as possessed of its own contradictions and hence capable of accounting for its own motion, like an explosive mixture in a cosmic carburetor.

Herbert Spencer, by his doctrine of evolutionism; Samuel Alexander, by his view of all things as the radical motion in a space-time matrix; Santayana, impressed only by the fertility of things and describing matter only in terms of its forward tensions; Whitehead, for whom all reality is formed of monadic units called "actual entities" and the world is shot through and through by a "creative advance into novelty"; emergent evolutionists, like Jan Smuts and Lloyd Morgan who view matter as essentially spontaneous or emergent—all of these men are dynamists. For whatever is of interest to the philosophical physics, Dewey and his naturalistic school are likewise dynamists, presenting the universe as a continuum of ongoing tensions where life is ever "perilous" and "precarious."

Ostwald in the last century is the classic example of the view that all is energy, a statement that Einstein was to solemnize in his theory of relativity a half century later. In this respect, relativity physics diverges from quantum physics, and one of the major empiriological struggles of the age is to seek which of these two systems is fundamental or to try to transcend them both. The space-time *continuum*, even in its expression, reflects its variance with the quantum system where the leading idea is the discrete energy packet. Whitehead acknowledges his debt to Einstein's theory, and Alexander, though apparently independent of both thinkers, has constructed a system strikingly like that of the relativity continuum of space-time.

MECHANISM AND DYNAMISM ARE INADEQUATE

Mechanism and dynamism have the general common denominator that they deny substantial changes, either reducing them to local motion or calling them an illusion of mind. Experience refutes both for that reason. Dynamism, in general, has caught a glimpse of the truth that motion involves the novel, but it cannot account for the persistency factor in change. Mechanism in general sees the abiding ingredient of change, but it cannot explain the production of the new. As a result, neither accounts for motion. Change becomes a shifting of position; in some cases as in that of Leibniz not a reality at all but only an appearance; in other cases as in those of Hegel and Marx the union not of contrary principles but of contradictory ones; sometimes the sheer burst, with no reason, of a material spontaneity called "emergence" or "creative advance"; in still other cases as in that of Einstein an affair of relation or relativity. However subtly they may be defended, these views fall by their own weight either because they are extremisms as philosophies or because they are the children of empiriological method that cannot survive outside it.

It should be noted that there is no unanimity of opinion among modern thinkers on the things that count most, the ultimate reality on which their thinking bears. Mechanism and dynamism are in polar contrast. Chapter 6 will put forth evidence to show that such fluctuations should not be a scandal in empiriological physics but are a fate, natural and normal to the method it employs. The real scandal of our times is to inflate empiriological physics into a philosophical science.

Error is more than often a truth gone madly to extremes, and this is the case with mechanism and dynamism in philosophy. Mechanism emphasizes the inertial aspect of things and dynamism, matter's activity. It is a kind of vindication of the matter-form dualism that it keeps its feet on the firm ground of experience and can hold in each hand all of the truths which dynamism and mechanism propose while avoiding their unfortunate extremes.

A material substance is bifurcated. The same material substance is both active and passive, dynamic and inert. Form points up the truth which dynamism has detected, while the reality of prime matter can account for the successes of atomism. Modern philosophy is at the same impasse as Greek thought before Aristotle's time which faced the dilemma of Parmenides and Heraclitus. Aristotle did not compromise, patching up a soft mechanical union between his opponents. He dug deeper into things than either of them and found principles of potency and of act that could unite both. In a kindred dilemma on the modern scene, the answer to the conflict of atomism and dynamism will only be found by probing deeper than sensism and scientism are capable of searching. Beneath the senses and beyond scientism lies the genuine dualistic answer of a genuine realistic philosophy.

Suggested Readings

Aristotle, *Physics*, Bks. I, II.
Aristotle, *Metaphysics*, Bks. VII, VIII.

3

Motion, Its Origins, and Its Ends

"WHATEVER IS MOVED IS MOVED BY ANOTHER"

When man has discovered and defined motion, he is a long way from closing the book of nature as a finished story. Like a hunter tracking his game until he finds the lair, the mind presses after the fact of motion until it yields the secret of its causes. Man is truly a cause-seeking animal, unable to wonder at the difference between night and day without asking its reasons. What produces the lightning and thunder, the swing of the tides, the shooting of the star, the cry in the forest? What is responsible for the universe as it now is? Such are the questions that man puts to nature, confident that nature and not his own fancies will answer them. Man does not close his dealing with motion when he defines it, any more than he solves a robbery without asking, Who did it?

Motion is the fulfillment of the potential as far as it is the potential; or, taking the dualism of nature as an account not only of substantial change but of all movement, motion is the process of the eduction in matter of a form that the matter hitherto lacked. But what brought about the actualization of this new form, changing the material thing from privation to possession? And why did this change take place? The answer to the first question is the definition of the efficient or motor cause, and the second question is settled by defining the final cause. These two causes are said to be extrinsic, as opposed to matter and form which are intrinsic causes. They will be treated in order in the present chapter which will be kept more or less introductory in character.

With an ear toward modern difficulties the two extrinsic causes of motion will again be a theme in Chapters 7 and 8.

The logic of the mind, as it looks beyond the moving thing and settles upon the necessity of an efficient or motor cause for all motion, is a rigorous one. If anything could move itself, the mind would be relieved of its worry about the mover; but if nothing can move itself from within then there must be a mover acting from the outside. The reasoning from a movement to a motor thus pivots upon the question of whether a moving thing can move itself. If it cannot, then motion must come from what is not itself, from a mover outside of it. There are two ways of showing from motion the absolute necessity of an outside mover.

That a form is united to matter by any motion, neither the form nor the matter can explain. The matter, to repeat, is always potential, and in the case of prime matter, it is purely potential. It cannot *act* to bring about its union with form because it is not *act*ualized itself until this union has come to pass. Form is also powerless to account of itself for its dualistic union with matter. It is the term of the movement in its proper sense, and it would have to exist at the beginning of the movement to originate the change. Since motion can come from neither of the components within the thing moved, it must of necessity be the outcome of an extrinsic agent.

In an even more basic sense, a proof that a moving thing receives its motion rather than produces it can be drawn, with a magnificent simplicity, from the definition of movement as the fulfillment of the potential as far as it is potential. At the risk of tautology, motion may be described as the reduction of a thing from potency to act or as the actuali*zing*, in the dynamic sense, of a potency. The point is that at the origin of every movement there is a potency which is a capacity to be actual but not the actual existence.

Now if a moving thing were self-moved, the potential would have to be actual while at the same time potential—actual because it produced the motion and potential because it was being moved. Self-motion, involving the potential that was not potential and the actual that was not actual, would violate the principle of non-contradiction. If a thing were its own cause, it would have to exist before it existed to do the causing. If a thing were its own mover, it would have to be actual before it were being actualized, arrived at its term before it even started from its origin. A Californian could never travel to New York if he had to be there before he started. Self-motion, like self-causation in general, is absurd and impossible. Since potency is a form of non-being, self-motion would turn the non-being into a positive and causal agency.

This means then that if movement occurs, as it obviously does, the moving thing must be moved by something outside of it or, as it is put in more polished form, "Whatever is moved is moved by another." In philosophical physics, this is a statement of the principle of causality, the mover being called the motor cause. The metaphysician of course must probe the nature of a cause so that it can be applied to all being, mobile and immobile, material and immaterial. But the philosophical physicist is unable to get above the water line of motion. For his purpose, a cause is always a mover, the agent that brings about the union of matter and form which neither of the components can explain.

There is a frequent illusion about the mover's influx into moving things, an error that is best symbolized in Newton's metaphor that the universe is a giant clock wound up in the beginning by God and then abandoned to unwind by itself. The unschooled mind of the average man is oftentimes persuaded that a mover is necessary only to provide an initial impulse, like an archer shooting the arrow, and that once the motion has started one need not seek another mover outside of it.

But this view, both in classical, Galilean-Newtonian physics and in the frequent homespun philosophy of the ordinary man, is seriously in error. So long as the moving thing has not yet reached its term, it is still in potency and cannot actualize itself. It cannot confer a form which it has not yet gained, spending its riches before it earns them. There is no credit in the bank of nature.

Thus, if the line *AC* represents the trajectory of a moving thing and the point *B* divides it into two segments, the movement is just as inadequate to account for its own coverage of *BC*, the last lap of the trajectory, as for its coverage of *AB*, the first part of its path which begins with rest. The archer moves the arrow, and when his motion ceases, the dart is carried forward by concussions in the air and dropped earthward by so-called gravity. Every moment of its motion requires a mover as much as the initial moment does. By day or night, in summer and in winter, in large changes or in little ones, a mover is always required wherever there is motion and for every moment that it endures.

MOTOR AND THE MOVING THING ARE IN CONTACT

Motor causality brings with it a number of subsidiary issues. Hume reduced causality to sequence in time, and in general, modern thought has followed his lead by insisting that what the philosophical science of nature calls an effect simply follows after the so-called motor, without causal influence between them. In this caricature of causality, the so-called cause is completely extrinsic to the effect with no dominion whatsoever over its motion.

From a slightly different direction comes another stream in modern thought which likewise puts the cause too exterior to the effect and even favors action at a distance (*actio in distans*). Can a moving material thing affect another without direct or indirect contact? Can a body at one point move a body distant from it, without going through a medium? Ordinary experience would give a negative answer to these questions, but a dissenting vote is cast by empiriological physicists like Faraday and Maxwell and by philosophers like Bolzano and Kant and, to a certain degree, Leibniz. To a great extent, action at a distance is also favored by the quantum theory and by statistical physics in general. In Bohr's theory of the atom, for instance, there is a jump of electrons from one point to another, without an intervening medium.

The whole quantum theory from Planck to Heisenberg and Schroedinger seems to sanction the discontinuity of matter. Empiriological physicists likewise single out the so-called spontaneous character of radioactivity as an indication that matter does not move through media but suddenly and as though there were no motor contacting it.

Yet coming down from Descartes in his spirit though not in his words, there is also a tendency in modern views to make a cause too interior to the effect. Though he exaggerated when he went beyond a criticism of empiriological methods, Meyerson argued very brilliantly, that the inquiring mind tends to identify cause and effect. To bring this thought to a point, it might simply be observed that the empiriological physicist adopts the equations of mathematics for his language. When he relates cause and effect by equation, it is clear that in the limit there is no more reality on one side of the equality sign than on the other. In fact, the two quantities can be transposed. Empiriological physics inhabits an equalitarian universe.

Wedged between these opposing extremes which overdraw the exteriority or the interiority of the motor is a third alternative which discerns neither distance nor overlapping between a motor cause and its moved effect, but contact. The truth of this third report can be tested by refuting the two extremes.

Hume's opinion topples when compared to experience. There are simple sequences in nature, as shown by two cars which move bumper to bumper on the highway because they are moving at the same speed; and there are causal sequences as when one car is pushing another, not only following it in time but influencing it in its motion. The Humean view, taken in all rigor, does not account for the difference between these cases, the one a sequence, the other a causation.

It is also an easy matter to dismiss the logic that would identify cause and effect, by turning it loose against the relentless facts of experience. Such an identity would lead to a static universe, where difference is at most only an illusion. No true novelty could emerge because there would be nothing in the cause that did not appear in the effect. Equating the pair means to deny all differences and to restore Parmenides to the philosophical throne.

Finally, there are several arguments which stand with common sense against the claims of quantum indeterminism that there are leaps in nature, and against the views of philosophers like Kant that a motor can move its subject without contacting it.

First of all, action at a distance presumes the existence of a vacuum, and a vacuum cannot possibly exist (Chapter 10). It is thus not possible to have that mediumless influence which action at a distance requires. A second attack in the same direction can be mustered from the limited character of matter. The forms of mobile realities are limited. They cannot soar out of their dimensional captivity to act upon what is distant. Man, of course, gets outside himself, in a way, when he thinks, recognizing other as other. But lower forms are much more limited in character, being determined to one place at one time. If a distant thing is really moved by a motor which is not compelled to pass its causal influx through an intervening medium, there is really no causal influx into the thing to be moved, and if it is moved, it would have to move itself. Belief in action at a distance is based upon a false notion of what a limit is and how substantial form is restricted to its own matter. Denying contact between motor and moved, it must reject their causal influx if it is at all logical.

Simply stated, action at a distance would make the motor so extrinsic to the moved thing that a Humean universe would result, and it would not be possible to have that intrinsic conjunction between motor cause and moved effect which any motion requires. Matter is limited and must stay within its bounds. Moved and mover are not separated, transcending quantity like spirit. They are together.

EMPIRIOLOGY TENDS TO FAVOR EVOLUTION

The mind cannot linger long on the problem of how matter is moved without asking what, if anything at all, provides the initial motion. Is motion possibly eternal, and if so, does not its eternity explain it, absolving man from a search after an Unmoved Mover? The problem of the eternity of matter and of the creation of the world was one of the critical questions in the middle ages, dividing the Greco-Arabic Aristotelianism from the Platonic preferences of the Latin West. How the universe got its start and how it came to be as it is today is also a favorite theme in modern thought.

The study of the origins of the universe is called cosmogony, and an outline of modern directions in this field will make the realistic solution of the problem, when it is outlined, more significant and compelling.

Long before Darwin published his famous views on biological evolution in *The Origin of Species* (1859), the idea of prehistorical transformations in the cosmos was abroad. Kant outlined a so-called Nebular Theory in which he traced the present constitution of the solar system from a pristine nebula of hot gases which for some reason or other cooled and contracted. At first, as in steam that is cooled, the gases became liquefied, and then, like ice, turned into solids. Laplace, a famous empiriological physicist, wrote out the details of this process and gave Kant's theory an empiriological eminence. For that reason it has become known historically not as the Kantian but as the Laplacian Nebular Theory.

The Laplacian idea worked well enough in describing the general motions of the heavens, but there were certain non-uniformities (especially the distribution of angular momentum among major planets) which indicated to empirical physics that a primeval nebula could not account for the present universe. Such facts pointed to an agency outside the solar system as its originator and led to the so-called Planetesimal Hypothesis of Chamberlin and Moulton. This theory held that the sun was originally without planets. Then for reasons which were never quite explained by Chamberlin and Moulton, a colossal star passed very close to the sun and, by the mutual attraction of gravity, pulled out of it myriad masses of matter that began to rotate about the parent body. They were fragments of a solar explosion and were called little planets or planetesimals. As time went on, the theory goes, gravity began to exert its pulls, and the planetesimals in various points of space tended to draw together until they formed the huge solids which constitute our present heavenly bodies.

A third popular account of how the solar system reached its present form is the Tidal Theory of Jeans and Jeffreys. They agreed with Chamberlin and Moulton that a giant star swept close to the sun, which at first had no system of its own, creating a terrific solar disturbance not in the form of explosive fragments but in the form of a huge tidal arm. This fiery mass then disintegrated with time into the planets, their satellites, and other bodies. Jeffreys has since decided that there was not only a near collision between the sun and the tide-raising star but an actual crash.

Finally, in very recent days so much so that at this writing the chief source is magazine clippings, some American astronomers, among them George Gamow, have decided that the universe could have been formed inside an hour from some pristine gases, making it seem as though a form of the Nebular Theory is about to be revived.

It is not necessary to decide among all these theories from the angle of philosophical physics, nor is it simply an evasion of the question to remark that all of the accounts are questionable and, so long as man was not on the scene to witness them, will always so remain.

After the solar system has been accounted for, at least hypothetically, geology begins its story about an evolutionary earth that went through various stages of fire and ice, floods and eruptions, before it reached its present state. Empiriological physics believes that it can find the date of the earth's origin from a birth certificate of radioactive deposits. From a quantity of lead which is the end product of the uranium series of radioactive elements, it can be estimated how much uranium was necessary to have formed the present residue, and, because of the temporal constants in radioactive decay, how long it took the original uranium to do the job. Strata of rock formations also indicate to the geologist that the earth was not always as it now is and that by a fabulous margin its age exceeds the traditional 6000 to 8000 years.

All of this might well be true, but it has always been theory, still is theory, and always will be theory in contrast to the certain truth which the philosophical science of nature attains.

It should also be remarked, just to complete this topic, that the biologist now comes upon the empiriological scene after the evolution of the mineral cosmos has been made a tenable theory and proposes that life has also gone through evolutionary stages. It is biological evolution that has received the most attention in the twentieth century and has won the most approval from the empiriological wing. However, where mineral evolution might be admitted, though never as an established fact, there are strong arguments against complete biological evolution—the crossovers from the mineral to the plant to the animal and to man. But this is not the proper place to discuss biological evolution which can be best studied in connection with the psychologist's definition of life.

Here, only mineral evolution—the origin of the solar system and the stages of geological development—can be an issue. And in solving the issue, it may be observed that although such a cosmic evolution may well provide the empiriological physicist with a backdrop for unifying and classifying his data, it can never enjoy the dignity of a settled fact or a certain principle, and in all logic, it must be excluded from the philosophic science of nature as mere guesswork in however academic a form. For the philosopher, evolution is more of a problem in logic than in philosophical physics and will always involve the fallacy of affirming the consequent. It is, for example, illogical to proceed like this: A is mortal, if A is a man; but A is mortal; therefore, A is a man. A might be any plant or animal which, like man, is mortal and the conclusion would be: A plant (or animal) is a man. In similar fashion runs the argument for evolution: The data measured in astrophysics and geophysics can be organized into a system if evolutionism is true; the data can be organized into such a system; therefore, evolutionism is true.

THERE IS A PRIME MOVER

Hence, in a study of cosmogony another path must be sought wherever certainty is to be attained. This rigidly scientific account is less detailed and from such a standpoint more impoverished than the empiriological hypotheses, but, what is most important about it, it is certain and true. The empiriologist, engaged as he is in the infinite regression, never really attains to origins and absolutes. He pushes the history of the cosmos to an early date but cannot push it to its origins. What moved the nebula in the Laplacian Theory? Or what, in the Planetesimal or Tidal Theory, accounted for the sun and the star which approached it? If empiriological physicists answer these questions, as some of the more recent astrophysicists like Gamow have attempted, they make the causal agent out of some preëxisting material and view this material in turn as formed from a still earlier material, applying the law of inertia, which they exploit in the laboratory, even when they are chronicling the stars. There is an infinite regress in the empiriological account of origins and hence no account of origins at all. Nothing in an infinite series has the power to originate anything.

How there can be any originality in the empiriological universe has been a frequent question throughout these pages, and one of the theses of this chapter is that empiriological method alone cannot possibly account for novelty. A belief in evolution is incompatible with a method that admits not the advancement of one stage of process over another but only their stark equality. Empiriological physics must make its choice: either evolutionism or equalitarianism. It cannot include both in its strict world view, for they are as different as the quantity which empiriological physics studies and the motion which it ignores.

Unlike empiriological physics which is interested in metrical structure, philosophical physics is primarily occupied with the question of what moved matter to its present form. There are two principles which solve the question, and one of them has already been established with the other to be copiously confirmed in later chapters. The first is that whatever is moved is moved by another which this chapter has shown, and the second is that in a series of movers, subordinated to each other, there cannot be a regression into infinity. It remains simply to apply these principles to the present problem.

Since self-motion is impossible, for the potential not being actual is not an agent, it can be taken as certain that motion can occur only where there is an extrinsic motor cause. If this motor in turn is in potency and cannot be the agent of the motion unless it is moved extrinsically, a series of motors is necessary to account for the motions of experience. But this series cannot be infinite. So somewhere, there must be an end to the chain of motors, an Unmoved Mover, free from potency and thus plenary in act. Without this Mover, nothing could ever move.

It should be pointed out that this terminated series of movers is not reckoned by going backward through the past and eventually reaching a Deistic and Newtonian God. One might call this a horizontal search after a Prime Mover.

The real logic reposes in the fact that here and now, in the motion of a typewriter or the pelting of the rain, a Prime Mover is required, exerting His motive power in the very present over anything that is moved. This is the vertical search for the Unmoved Mover.

But this proof which ends the series of movers does not end the questions which it raises. Though to account for present motion, this Unmoved Mover must be operative here and now and was operative when any motion occurred in the past, there is still a question of when motion actually began. Aristotle held to the eternity of motion, and for that reason until the thirteenth century he was rejected by western theologians who preferred to think philosophically in terms of Plato, with his preference for creation in time. It was Aquinas who really settled this problem. Though creation in time is known by revelation, it cannot be established by reason. This can be shown by an examination of the Prime Mover as well as by a reflection on what He moves. From all eternity, God had the power of creating the world, and from all eternity He could have created it. On the part of the series of moved things, there is none of them as we search back through the past, which requires that it be the first thing moved and that no other motion could have preceded it. Hence, the Prime Mover could have moved matter from all eternity. That he did not is known not philosophically but theologically, not by reason but by revelation.

The term creation has entered into this discussion, but it takes more than the science of nature to discuss it. The philosophical physicist deals only with motion, the fulfillment of the potential as potential. But creation involves something infinitely more than this. It requires no preëxisting potency on the part of the material object. It is not properly motion or even mutation. It is the production of something out of nothing (*ex nihilo sui et subjecti*). The Prime Mover, as the metaphysician clearly proves, did not have a raw material to actuate. He was not simply a Mover like river water floating a barge downstream. He was a Creator. If matter is completely caused, completely contingent, completely moved, completely unable to explain itself, then everything in it was produced from an extrinsic agent, and if everything, absolutely everything about it, was produced, then it was produced out of nothing.

The imagination balks at all this, and reason has to solve the question by its own forces. In an age that thinks in terms of images, man puts them aside only with difficulty. He would like a picture of the absolute. But the imagination breaks down in tracing back the history of the cosmos. It wants a preëxisting matter and a preëxisting time as a matrix to picture the fact of creation. The intellect states problems and asks the imagination to answer them. Knowing where to look for an answer is the only way of finding it.

In the philosophical science of nature, three sides of the larger picture have thus far been framed. Matter and form, intrinsic causes, are united by an extrinsic mover. But the question arises, why does the motor cause produce this union of matter and form rather than that? Why does the rain fall instead of spouting upward toward the sun? Why does the fire transfer heat to a chimney instead of absorbing more heat from the bricks to grow hotter and hotter while the chimney is cooled? The probing of these problems swings open the study of the fourth and last of the causes, that of finality.

Baldly put, finality means purpose or aim. It represents the telic cause (from the Greek word, *telos,* for end), and the study of it is teleology. The final cause is the purpose for which the agent acts or the goal toward which a nature marches. Philosophical physics is distinguished by the fact that it alone studies all four causes. The formal answers the question *what;* the material, the question *out of what;* the efficient, the question, *whereby;* and the final, the question, *why* or *wherefore?* The principle of finality, as the philosophical science of nature considers it, means that everything which moves tends toward a goal, or simply that motion is not aimless.

To define the meaning of a name and then to ask if reality owns any counterpart to the term is a part of sound method. The initial inquiry here is to search out whether there is such a thing as end, aim, purpose, goal, and true determinism in the movements of nature, and if so, to what extent. The dissenting opinions of various thinkers may then be hailed into court and cross-examined to sort out the true from the false in their reasoning. Final causality breeds such mighty questions as that of physical law and the order of nature and the element of chance. It involves a whole host of modern problems that will be faced in Chapter 8.

The classic form of the principle of finality runs: "Every agent acts for an end." There are variants like "nature acts for the best" and "nature does nothing in vain." But these alternate forms, though synonymous with the first, will be side-stepped in the following development.

Every mover *tends into* a goal, and hence *intention* is another way of translating the causality of the end. It is indeed a very apt expression, since the burden of proving that final causality is real is to advert to the tendencies or aptitudes in a given nature and to ask why one is actualized, under given conditions, rather than another. Final causality does not make the tendencies. They owe themselves to form. But the end determines which one will prevail under the circumstances. A nature, when moving, intends these results rather than those. In the literal sense, it has intentions.

The end is that for the sake of which a moving thing moves, and the principle of finality can be anchored by showing that natures will move only if they have fixed ends. The dynamism of the world is not a pure one because it is not indifferent.

The fact of finality in nature emerges from a sketch of what motion would become without it. To paraphrase Dostoyevsky, what begins in a falsehood must end in one; what must always lead to absurdity is absurd. Now if a moving thing had no end and if it did not lean to this effect rather than that, there would be no sufficient reason why one effect should be produced from its efforts rather than another. If water did not tend to boil at 100 degrees centigrade under ordinary conditions, why does it always boil at this point? A moving thing that did not slant to one determined end rather than another would be indeterminate. Any effect ought to be realized from its movement rather than this one or that one which actually and—under like conditions—always occurs.

At a tier deeper in the proof, it is obvious that a moving thing that did not tend to one goal rather than another would be neutral and inert, hence wholly passive, hence not only unable to act toward this end rather than that but unable to act at all. What is totally inert and purely indeterminate is, like prime matter, not even an actual existent, and the denial that a moving thing has fixed tendencies, when moving, is a denial that it even exists.

From still another angle, since a tendency is an aptitude or inclination, whatever did not tend to anything by its motion would tend to nothing, and the motion of course would never even start. There would be not only motion without aim but a universe without motion.

Still another entrance into the science of finality is the conclusion that if a thing did not tend in some directions rather than others when it moves, it would tend in all directions at once. Matter would blow up. A pluralism would result since the tendencies, bidding for expression, would be infinite in number. If a thing had an infinity of goals, none of them would ever be attained. The infinite, the indeterminate, the purely passive, and the totally inert will be shown in Chapter 4 to lead to a chaotic universe which is certainly not the one that man experiences and that his thinking ought to explain.

Here, as often, philosophical physics accords with the pedestrian view that there is order in the world. This is a cosmos, not a chaos, and teleology accounts for the order rather than, like modern methods, ignores it. The order of the universe, witnessed by the experience of men and used to regulate their lives, is a kind of inductive proof that finality is something real and that mechanism, which is the opposite, is not. Even the empiriological physicist makes an undercover bow before this order as a fact, in spite of his denial of it as a principle. In a universe of chaos, even empiriological physics would be sucked into it.

The evidence that finality pulses in nature is not just a projection of man, comparing purpose in his own life with the workings of the world outside that resemble it. The tests are rooted in motion and in the prerequisites for motion. Intentions reign not only in man's activity but wherever there is motion, and for as long as the motion endures. It is mechanism that warps reality and projects man into it. It is mechanism that is anthropomorphic.

The proof that a moving thing is purposeful does not hinge on our ability to discern always what that purpose is. Shallower views of nature have proposed such arguments as the one that flies are black in order to be better seen and swatted and even that God put the earth at the center of the solar system bcause its rational animals are the center of visible creation. Such anthropomorphisms have done much to discredit the principle of finality and to encourage the secession of the modern mind from the whole kingdom of speculative science.

Certainly one of the ends of rain is to water the plant life of the world. Carbon dioxide from animals is breathed in by plants which in turn manufacture oxygen for their benefactors. But the principle of finality is not proved from such observations, though it may be strongly suggested. It is tested by reason, so that if we are not always able to discover the purpose of a nature's motions we are still entitled to say that they are purposeful.

A universe directed by end is far different from the static formalism that empiriological method depicts in its mosaic. The moving world is dynamic, though never purely so. Heraclitus was a better student of nature than Parmenides. Because the potencies of prime matter are pure potencies and, as the unity of substance shows, possess only one form at a time, the world is always more in potency than in act. It is a world not merely of inertia and quantity but of tendency and striving. All moving things are tense with aptitudes or appetites, and their motions are made goalward by the fact that some are favored more than others under given conditions. Natures do not do or seek or realize everything of their potencies at once.

FINALITY IMPLIES LAWS OF NATURE

The general decision that a moving thing has aim in its motion and does not obey the law or rather the lawlessness of chaos is by no means all that finality means in philosophical physics. The natures of the world spell out the conclusion that their goalward march is perfecting and progressive and not a degeneration. This truth follows because nature is invested with its tendencies and fulfilled by their actualization. For nature is a cause or principle of motion and of rest. When moved, it responds not as an inertia or a pure passivity but with pattern and originality and stubbornness. It tends to move in this way rather than that, depending on outer conditions, like smoke which tends upward on a still day, and not sidewise. What is a nature has definite goalward tendencies which express and reveal it when it is moved. Nature is defined by its tendencies. We know it by its motions. To be original is to have definite tendencies, and nature is an original cause and source. The fulfillment of these tendencies, with the end deciding upon the ones which a given impact will actualize, is natural motion. The advance of such tendencies from their potential status to their actual ends enables a moving thing really to acquire what it has a natural bias to seek and to possess.

The nature of a thing is thus fulfilled or perfected by tendencies actualized. Its motions fill the vacancies in its house. By being moved, it grows to a greater fullness of its being. It makes progress as an individual, and where all the individuals of the world have fixed ends in motion and fulfill their tendencies, the universe as a whole makes progress too. Natures do what is good, what is fitting, for them under the circumstances, and where every nature acts thus, there is a certain good in the universe as a whole, which is realized.

A tendency of a moving thing toward a fixed end and not to a merely indifferent fate is certainly a determination, by contrast to an indetermined web of inertias. On this basis, the philosophi-

cal science of nature is a determinism, where the pure (hence indefinite) potencies of matter are finited or de-terminated by form
and where form in turn is de-terminated in its motions by ends.
Sheer mechanical determinism to be discussed later would make
progress impossible by equating causes and effects. But in the
hierarchical determinism seen by philosophical physics, progress
is not only possible but implied.

Form is educed from matter by the motor cause and returns
there when another cause overcomes it. But the vanquished form
has left its footprints behind it, having, while it existed and
operated, moved other beings, herding them onward to their fulfillment. The universe is greater, after a corruption, for the fact
that the form existed even for a twinkling moment. The action of
even a fleeting form has entitled it to what Whitehead called
"objective immortality." And the motor which triumphed over it
fulfilled its own goalward tendencies in the motion, thus enrich-
ing the universe with something greater than what it removed.

A nature's penchant toward a fixed end under a given set of
conditions is called a law of the nature. There are laws of nature
in the general sense and in the case of the nature of man, the
natural law. Laws are natural appetites, natural inclinations,
goalward tendencies that natures own and that are broken only
at the price of destroying the natures themselves.

A law expresses the nature which, so to speak, has it; in a genuine sense, since a nature is defined by the tendencies expressed
in given circumstances, a nature and its laws are synonymous. To
follow the laws of iron, combining as it does with say, sulfur,
chlorine, or oxygen is simply to be iron, expressing its natural
tendencies. For man to obey the natural law is merely to be true
to his nature. It is to be fully natural. The laws of any nature can
be amended only by changing the nature they are. Iron obeys
the laws of iron, copper the laws of copper, animals the laws of
animals, and man the law of man.

A nature is necessarily subjected to law because it is not indeterminate. And it is not indeterminate because it has tenden-

cies. And because it is finalized, some of these tendencies are actualized by a given agent rather than others.

The ultimate reason for determinism in the motions of nature is finality.

FINALITY EXPLAINS THE ORDER OF NATURE

The empiriological mind has been hard put to reconcile its plea for autonomy with the order or uniformity of nature that measurement alone must leave not only unexplained but, today, unperceived. The confusion is almost as serious in vocabulary as in doctrine. With a faith in Hume's dogma that causality is ordered sequence and ordered sequence is causality, the order of nature is taken today to define causation. So-called disorders in nature are alleged by scientism to be exceptions to the principle of causality.

The whole problem is as baffling to empiriological physics as it is to modern logic. Empiriological physics seeks to generalize its measured facts. For example, Ohm's law, saying that current is equal to voltage divided by resistance, is not regarded as a single fact, applied to matter at a given time and given place and not valid thereafter. It is pumped into a general principle, applying, in the empiriological view, wherever there is electric current.

Such generalizations of measured data are called laws by the empiriological physicist. They involve a pivotal problem in logic concerning the grounds for extending a fact, measured several times and ideally only once, into a generality. How can it safely be concluded that Ohm's law measured in Paris in 1960 will hold in Tokyo in 1961? The empiriological physicist extrapolates his facts, in the framework of nature's uniformity which he cannot explain but uses anyway. This uniformity simply means that under the same circumstances a moving thing will always move in the same way.

Empiriological physicists are frank to avow that their chief aim is to predict fact and that their theories are nothing but tools to facilitate the forecast. Prediction involves the time element, a foretaste of what tomorrow will bring and a faith that the future will resemble the past. But how can the empiriological physicist, whose only business is measurement, patrol the area beyond his instruments to decide about the future or about order? It is here that empiriological physics must be rescued by a rational knowledge outside itself or sink into a complete skepticism.

Scientism has preferred to sink. But the fact remains that philosophical physics provides a backdrop for empirical physics to reinforce its conclusions. The philosophical science of nature has not retreated to an instrument panel but kept its feet on the ground of experience. Empiriological physics can be propped up if it does not care to sink.

To explain the order of nature requires the sternness of final causes. In the realism of a truly scientific view, a nature is shown to have tendencies or determinations to a fixed goal in all of its motions and in every moment of them. These goalward drives draw out the nature in the same way whenever external conditions repeat themselves. They reveal what that nature is. It is ordered, determined, fixed by its end which but incarnates the sufficient reason for the effect which is realized. Such goalward determinations, which motions reveal and which define a nature, draw the nature into almost being a synonym for its laws. To be tin is to follow the laws of tin, reacting under the same conditions with a fixed valence, a definite melting point, a specific gravity, a conductivity of this or that magnitude, a magnetic permeability of so many units; to be tin is to follow the laws of tin, and to follow the laws of tin is to be tin.

Hence, it can be assured that tin under the same set of circumstances will always produce the same effects. If a metal did not produce them, then it would not be tin that was being tested.

A physical law, as the expression is used, is the same in content as a law of nature but not in form. A physical law is established in empiriological physics and states a fact; a law of nature is studied in philosophy where reasons are discerned for the regularity of the empirical fact. The difference between "is" and "ought" dimly emerges in the contrast.

Physical laws are measured by experiment, and experiment, though controlling reality, is not something unreal. A physical law is a generalization of measured fact. But to the extent that it involves fact, such a law is the locus where the empiriological physicist greets reality and feeds data to the philosophical science of nature to be interpreted. In a regularity of fact, the empiriologist may discover the fact but will be unable to account for the regularity. He is thus unqualified to extrapolate his facts.

Without the light of teleology as studied in philosophical physics, the faith in the future which experimentalism adopts darkens into a blind faith. Measurement can never measure order. It can never pronounce on the relation of what is measured to what the future will bring. Measurement is only of fact. In particular it is only of quantity. It is never of relations as such, of tendencies, of ends, and of motions.

The problem of nature's order, together with the need to examine and express it, looms so vastly on the present-day horizon that it might profitably be rethought from another angle. There are four causes in nature, and each of them ought to be sounded out on the issue of determinism or uniformity.

The formal cause, the form, makes a thing what it is. It is the principle of operation in the thing, a synonym for its nature. Now the question to be asked and answered here is whether the form in material reality requires action in a fixed pattern or whether the form, while abiding as the same form, can vary its actions. The answer is decisively against the power of a material form to remain what it is and vary what it does.

Mineral matter has only one form at a time. Knowledge, for instance, involves that the knower retain its own form and become the forms of other things; the knower thus has more than one form, and the motions which follow upon this multiformity of knowledge are varied accordingly. But in the mineral world, which is of primary interest here, things have one form at one time and can achieve only the motions flowing from this single-ness of character, when they move at all. There is a uniformity (one-formedness) of motion because there is a uniformity of its principle.

Matter's limitations are drastic. It is determined to one form or one kind of motion, when it moves. Chapter 6 will show more lucidly that matter does not have the interiority and immanence of living things; it is much more inert and transeunt in nature. If it could vary its activity from within itself, it would have the self-possession and self-determination of man who is free. But it lacks this inwardness of man, with his power of reflection and of self-determination. From within itself, matter therefore cannot vary its actions, and differences in its motion will turn out to be not matters of its own choice but differences outside it. The form of matter, limited and localized as it is, is not a source of variety but of uniformity.

Resolved from the aspect of motor causes, the same determinism turns up. The motors of the mineral world do not have a source of variation in themselves but a principle of uniformity that is drawn out into fixed and finite patterns of action. Minerals do not pick out the raw materials on which they will turn their causation nor select their mode of affecting their matter. They are limited to one form and hence one type of action. If they varied their motions from within themselves, they would have more than their own limited form as their principle. They would be immanent and even intelligent. But like the matter on which they work, they are actually limited and hence determined by their oneness of form to a oneness of action, a uniformity of nature.

It is the final cause which crowns the determinism of the formal and motor causality in nature. Both the form and the motor in matter are limited to a uniform pattern of action, and the final cause fixes what pattern it will be. It does not make the tendencies. It is more of a selector. Given that matter has plural possibilities but, in its limited and localized character, can only exercise one of them, the end determines which one. In one sense, it converts what is uniform in principle to what is uniform in fact. For natures, under the same conditions, will always move in the same way. Destroy that fixity imposed by ends, and the nature itself must be destroyed. If sodium unites once with chlorine, it will do it again under like conditions; if it did not, it would not be sodium. By the intentions of natures we know what they are.

But what about the problem of material causality as an argument for uniformity? Since matter is pure potency, it takes its measure from the form which it owns, and does not have the power to determine either a nature or its motions from within itself. Prime matter, as such, is the locus of variability in nature, but it requires the form united to it in order to make the variation actual. By its own inner resources, prime matter can vary neither itself nor its form. It is to the form that a mobile being owes its unity of nature, its uniformity, and matter under the tyranny of form has no power to deviate from the course which is charted for the form by the end.

Aristotle said that matter is finalized by form. It follows the form as the form follows the end; and the motor cause, invested with its own form and obeying its own end, completes the circuit of causality in motion which is everywhere ordered and determined.

With this scientific equipment, the philosophical physicist can join fact to law or principle and particular cases to general truths. He can solve the baffling problem of induction.

CHANCE IS EXTRINSIC TO NATURE

But despite this logic, dictated from a view of the various natures in the cosmos all taken singly, the hard fact remains that there are abnormal events in the universe. Monstrosities are born into animal and plant worlds. Instead of the expected rains in the springtime, there are occasional droughts. Volcanoes, quiescent for long periods, suddenly erupt. There are tempests and plagues and landslides in nature, and in the human world there are accidents like the collapse of the bridge of San Luis Rey. Experience attests that there is no rigid algebraic determinism in nature but that the ordered, purposeful movement of the world is apparently violated at times. Natures move for the sake of ends in the usual case, but there are aberrations, admittedly rare, when such ends are not attained. A science that claims to be a realism must take these variations into account, endeavoring, if it can, to plot their sources.

By almost a paradox, the study of these rare events is not just a rare and incidental aspect of philosophical physics but one of its crucial tasks on the contemporary scene. Empiriological physics is equalitarian; it refuses to admit a dualism in nature. If it studies order it cannot account for disorder, and vice versa. It has to choose its targets, and it has chosen today for disorder, chance, and chaos at the base of the world as Chapter 8 will show.

Here, at the introductory level, the general philosophy of chance will be outlined with the principal objections adjourned to Chapter 8. Chance is distinguished from fortune. Chance is a rare and unexpected variation in the sequence of cosmic events, like a tidal wave or a Florida hurricane. Fortune is a subdivision of chance. It is chance in human affairs, as in the attendance of two people at a college convention which leads to friendship and later to marriage.

The ordinary man thinks of a chance event as something rare, but he also gives it a teleological slant. It is always favorable or unfavorable, just as fortune is never indifferent but always good or bad. This verdict of common sense is extremely realistic. Things have tendencies to seek what is proper, fitting, proportionate, perfecting for their natures, in short what is good for them. And a chance event, where a nature's tendencies do not realize their normal and natural effect, should be considered in the light of final causality. A chance occurrence may be defined as an event which happens beyond the intentions of whatever produced it. It belongs to the present discussion as the contrary to final causality and because it is beyond the intentions of its agents, it is a sort of contrary to nature. A chance happening, since it is outside the tendencies of its producers, lacks a final cause.

But chance does not destroy the determinism in natures. Taken in themselves, the four causes of natural motion were marshaled to show that each nature has definite tendencies and operates in fixed and predictable ways. That thesis still holds. Chance arises not from natures taken singly but from their compresence in a universe where existing individuals cannot be altogether reduced to the rationality of law. More specifically, chance results when two or more natures, following their own laws and hence moving according to their native tendencies, cross one another's paths. This intersection of two causal series happens obviously when two friends, who have been separated for years, suddenly meet in a strange city. It happens when two clouds, where each particle within them is acting fixedly and finally, draw near enough to each other to produce lightning. Such a causal congestion takes place in more complicated form when there are earthquakes, magnetic storms which disturb compasses at sea, and charges of static electricity which accumulate on woolen clothing if the temperature and humidity are just right. Natures are determined by their four-ply causality, but chance arises from outside of them, that is, from their clash with other agents. Chance is the opposite to natural movement since it originates, like art, outside the natural agent. But chance lacks a final cause and is unforeseeable for this reason. Art does not lack purpose or intention. Its final cause is in man and it is not foreseeable, to an observer considering it in advance, because it is a distinctively human product.

It can easily be objected, of course, that chance is merely a matter of ignorance. Fundamentally this is true. For God, omniscient and omnipresent, nothing happens by chance. But the question remains whether man, if he studied the universe long enough, could eventually arrive at a rationalization of events that now seem chance occurrences? It is true, of course, that chance can often be explained in retrospect. The weatherman who has predicted a sunny day only to see his sunlight drowned by torrential rains can reason back to explain the factors which ran counter to the weather that he had forecast. Also what was formerly called chance, like spontaneous generation, has since been shown to be not chance at all but, for instance, the natural gathering of maggots on decayed meat.

But even with the continued march of knowledge, chance could never be ruled out of material reality. Man can know the basic character of natures taken singly, and he can reach a certain, though general, knowledge of the four causes which their motions imply. But the conquest of chance involves something more than a knowledge of law. It involves a knowledge of fact, a knowledge not only of what a nature *must* do but also of what the natures outside of it *are* actually doing. Fact is as indefinitely great as the potencies of prime matter are pure. The search after the ultimates will forever be a disappointing one, if like the modern empiriological drift it pursues matter in order to map all actual and possible fact. Atomic physics, for instance, not only puts off till tomorrow what it can do today. There will always be a tomorrow in its account of matter since there is always a residue to be divided after today's divisions of atomic and subatomic and subsubatomic particles have been achieved. The whole empiriological method proceeds thus, leaving a surplus of its subject that evades its present efforts but that it hopes to reduce in the future. It is a kind of protest by nature against art.

But if it is agreed that a chance event arises beyond the intentions of an agent which is at least partly responsible for its existence, it does not lack a causal element altogether. If that were so, it could never come into being. Obviously to the extent that it is something it analogates a material and formal element, and it is also necessary that there be efficient causality to unite the matter and the form. But the motor cause in the case of a chance event is an accidental one. In fact there are at least two causes so that the true and intrinsic unity of being, which is a nature and a natural cause, is really missing where there is chance. Two causal chains, each aiming at a certain end through the natural tendencies of the agents and patients that are involved, cut across one another and, though not intending the chance event, produce it accidentally. The event so produced is an accident of nature. It is a disorder, and lacking the unity, interiority, and order of determination which are found in a genuine nature, a chance event lacks being to the extent that it is chance. If it did not affect a substance, as accident does, it would lack the title to being altogether.

Since chance is lacking in order, unity, and nature, to that extent of its constitution which is chance, it cannot be a source and principle of operations. Whatever positive and permanent results it produces, like the eruption of Vesuvius which buried the ancient city of Pompeii, are owed not to the chance character of the event but to the nature which the chance affects. The permanent ruins which the tourist sees in Pompeii are ruins because of chance, but the permanence is derived from nature.

Chance is extraneous to nature; it does not itself have the intrinsic principle of a nature. Nature is a fullness. Chance is a privation, the impeding of natural tendencies which are thereby obstructed from achieving the intrinsic good which the tendencies seek for the nature that bears them in its bosom. Apart from man, whom it might affect for the better, a truly chance event is always a degeneration of the mineral nature affected by it, because the nature is thereby prevented from attaining its intrinsic goal. Disordered, degenerate, owing itself to extrinsic fact rather than to intrinsic nature, a chance event does not endure or tend to reproduce itself, to the extent that it is chance. Monstrosities die out; nature tends to throttle down its typhoons and prevent their cyclonic centers from growing to envelope the entire earth in their devastation; an atom, ionized by collision with another, seeks immediately to neutralize itself and to return to its natural state. Arguments that chance produced the universe or propel the animal world along an evolutionary path are the products of minds too inflexible to note the disorder, degeneracy, and extrinsicness which chance involves. Chance would not tend to order an original chaos but to make the chaos more chaotic. Chance is something secondary, presupposing natures that interact to produce it and that are affected by its disordering influence.

A chance event is unforeseeable and it is rare. But neither of these characters can define chance. How tall a sapling will grow is not foreseeable and yet it is not chance, at least not wholly so.

Though a chance event happens infrequently, rarity is not its essence. Many events are rare, like the completion of the sun's orbit around its galactic center, and are not chance. Decay of some of the radioactive elements, uranium for instance, is rather rare, but it is not disordered. On the contrary, it is law-abiding. A chance event is rare because the natures of the cosmos are almost inert, and the near inert does not have the power to make variations a routine. A chance event is rare because it would be contradictory if the natural tendencies of natures were naturally and normally frustrated. Such an event is unforeseeable because only a natural thing is truly predictable, endowed with the stable and persistent principle called nature which flowers into a persistent and stable course of action.

The natures of the universe are of mutual aid rather than mutual impediment. Though there is an element of what the Darwinians call struggle in the cosmos like the destruction of plant life by animals, there is a higher element of coöperation. The universe is unitary primarily by its finality and order, and in the nature of an ordered cosmos, the lower must sacrifice for the betterment of the higher.

A chance element is rare because natures have final causes which chance contravenes. But if the finalized tendencies were not normally fulfilled, there would not be a sufficient reason for their existence. This would become a universe of privation to the extent that it were dominated by chance, and the order which thought discerns would be left wholly unexplained.

A universe that underneath experience were mere chance could not produce the regularity which that experience witnesses, and it is these hard, burning, undeniable facts of experience that the true scientist ought to face rather than flee. With little difficulty, it can be shown that the unity in the universe arises from its order, the tendencies of all natures to one ultimate end which alone explain their coöperation in the balanced aquarium, terrarium, and planetarium that is our cosmos. The universe can be a universe only by its order, and this means that chance must be a minority within it. The minority has its voice, but nature overrules its resolutions.

Suggested Readings

Meehan, Francis X., *Efficient Causality in Aristotle and St. Thomas* (Washington, 1940), *passim*.
Simon, Yves R., *Prévoir et savoir* (Montreal, 1944), ch. 1.

4

Motion and the Infinite

INFINITY IS A LIVE CONTEMPORARY ISSUE

The substances in the world of motion are genuine ultimates. To range beyond them, dissecting them into parts, would really be to destroy their originality since the separated parts would then be substances in their own right. The chicken with its head chopped off is not the same thing as the chicken alive. Smash an atom, and its character is likewise changed. To be a mobile substance, charged with a principle of interiority called a nature, is to be an indivisible unit, divided only at the cost of a substantial change.

Dug in against this view of the universe as a manifold of natures which are undivided and individualized, the empiriological mood has worked out a different slant on matter in terms of its infinity. The new account in general ignores the realism where a nature is a center of originality. It makes a substance simply an engine with parts that are ever more finely tooled as they diminish in size but that never quite dwindle to zero. The empiriological direction tends to explore a mobile being by dividing it and then subdividing the components, until at last an infinite series must be hurdled before any ultimate answer can be reached. Is mobile reality explained by viewing it as an infinite number of parts? If infinity rather than the triad of matter-form-privation the genuine account of motion? Can motion take place if it must plow through an infinite series? If not, what is the relation of infinity to matter? Such are the questions that the present chapter must consider.

In the study of the mobile world, there are so many conflicting and confusing opinions today about the really big things, despite the apparent concord in the empiriological fraternity, that the philosophical science of nature instead of taking a straight-line path to its positive truth is tempted to go to its objective by the roundabout way to answer objections as it moves along. In this chapter, an effort will be made to keep the road reasonably straight. If present discussion does not take the circuitous route, it will at least attempt a glimpse of the countryside that is being passed, without the actual detours into its byways. After a prefatory treatment to show the timeliness of discussing infinity and to provide some definitions and distinctions, this chapter will then prove that infinity as the actual bedrock of the mobile world would lead to a chaotic rather than ordered universe. Motion will then be shown as the opposite to infinity. Next, the famous maxim that an infinite regression is impossible will be defended. Though matter is not actually infinite, it is potentially so, and this must be explained and established. Such a potential infinite, it will next be shown, is the infinity studied in mathematics. A concluding section will sketch how the modern notion is an attempt to substitute infinity for form.

The problem of infinity in nature is one of the oldest issues in western thought. In pre-Aristotelian Greece, for instance, Anaxagoras analyzed matter into a primeval infinity of similar parts which were afterwards separated by Mind and shaped into the various entities of the universe. Democritus explained matter as an infinity of atoms, alike in quality and forming the distinct objects of experience by their geometry alone. Plato held to the existence of the infinite in his separated heaven, and Pythagoras, for whom material reality was a slide rule of number, brought infinity down to earth, in the sensible qualities around us. That motion could not truly occur because it would have to span an infinite series of points to gain its goal was a favorite argument of Zeno. Even Aristotle, though he dealt heavy blows against his predecessors, was baffled by an important issue in regard to the infinity and so was prompted to declare that motion is eternal.

However puzzling was the idea of infinity to the Greek mind, it is not a problem that the ages have hung among the moth balls. When Descartes defined matter as mere quantity, he invited mathematics to replace philosophical physics, and in mapping this new territorial annexation, the mathematician naturally applied his time-honored tool of mathematical infinity. In the view of Leibniz, a mathematician as well as a philosopher, the world is an infinity of indivisible substances called monads. "Each portion of matter," he writes in his *Monadology,* "may be conceived as like a garden full of plants, and like a pond full of fish. But every branch of a plant, every member of an animal, and every drop of the fluids within it, is also such a garden or such a pond." Paulsen has a similar analogy of the world in terms of bricks that are composed of smaller bricks until the bricks finally become so small that man does not worry about their natures.

Theoretical as well as empirical in interest, Newton sketched a universe that was purportedly finite, but his law of inertia rules out the notion of nature in favor of a system where one thing is moved by another which in turn is moved by another, and so *ad infinitum.* Kant honed the whole problem into pointed form when he argued, in one of his famous antinomies, that reason could conclude along one channel of thought that matter is infinitely divisible and, by another chain of argument, that it is not.

By the middle of the nineteenth century, the controversy on infinity had migrated almost wholly to mathematics. First Dedekind and then Cantor proposed a bedrock for arithmetic in which numbers are envisioned as an infinite succession of points on a line. Cantor finally blueprinted a whole algebra of transfinite numbers in which there is not only one non-finite quantity but a whole hierarchy of them. The work of Dedekind and Cantor tends to support the belief that the infinite division in a quantity of matter is not only possible but actual. Their methods and their conclusions, their successes and their failures are lively contemporary issues that the matter-form dualism must face. With the exploits of atom smashing in physics, it appears only a question of time until the nuclear particles themselves will surrender their inner secrets. Is this division, in the words of P. W. Bridgman, "essentially infinite"? Is it logical to adopt a philosophy like the naturalism of Dewey which sees no term in motion but simply proposes to lead experience "ever onward and outward"? F. H. Bradley, the British neo-Hegelian, likewise saw no finality in our knowledge of matter, claiming that thought must take the road of "indefinite expansion."

Now there are various ways in which the word *infinite* is used, and it is urgent to screen out the senses of the term which are of commanding interest in the study of nature. It is legitimate to define the meaning of a word and then to establish that the reality corresponding to it does or does not exist.

Infinite in general means without limit, and it is known by denying the limits of the finite. McWilliams has compiled a neat table of the traditional notions of infinity. The first broad division includes absolute infinity, which is applied to God as the plenitude of being, and relative infinity, which is found in creatures. The relative infinite is subdivided into the formally infinite, like the human intellect and will which are directed to all being, and the materially infinite. The materially infinite in turn is a broad term which includes such realities as prime matter, unterminated (un-finited) by form; second matter as indefinitely divisible; and number as having no end in the cardinal or ordinal series. The materially infinite, often called the privative infinite since it bespeaks privation more than perfection, was defined by Aristotle as that to which something more can always be added. Bolzano, using the mathematical rule that if a quantity is subtracted from the infinite the remainder is still infinite, defines the infinite as a quantity in which the parts are similar to (equal to) the whole. Bolzano's definition is the one which has passed into the toolroom of modern mathematics. Whether or not it is an improvement on Aristotle's definition remains to be seen.

The philosophical science of nature is not directly concerned with the absolutely infinite, nor even with the formally infinite. The study of number and of extension, in the strict sense of these terms, ranges likewise beyond its ken and in the mathematical, rather than physical, order of abstraction. It is because number and extent are applied in the world of motion that the philosopher of nature has a right to debate about them. Here there are two broad questions that rear up: Is mobile reality nothing but the fireworks produced by tiny, powderlike grains that are infinite in number? Is the universe infinite in its extension? The first of these problems will be handled in this chapter, with the second being deferred until the discussion of place and space in Chapter 10.

PRINCIPLED BY THE INFINITE, THE WORLD WOULD BE HOMOGENEOUS, POTENTIAL, AND CHAOTIC

In general, the empiriological approach to the real has ratified the natural alliance of its principle of inertia and the infinite series. The two go hand in hand, since inertia or prime matter is the materially infinite. Stopping the series, say the series of divisions dusted throughout an atom according to the empiriological picture, would be tantamount to admitting a reality that, in Bridgman's words, is "self-terminating," invested from within by a nature, tense with its own power, determined in its own motions by this inner source, crowned with its own term. But the approach only through inertia puts natures, forms, interiority, self-termination out of bounds. What is terminated, according to the empiriological spirit, is terminated by something else like the pressure of a container which keeps a gas from diffusing, with the containing walls again terminated by forces on the outside, and thus on and on.

Realism reports that form terminates the potencies of the matter. When form is overlooked, the only alternative is to view matter as unterminated or as infinite. Form is the term of generation, and without it there is no generation at all but simply the chancing of inert particles from one point to another. Form bestows a unity on the composite. Since form is intrinsically united to the matter and the two make one being, it is proper to say that the term and what is teminated are the same thing. "Self-termination" is indeed a happy word.

Dialectical materialists are more logical than scientism when they underscore the motion in the world, but denying the reality of form, they remove the factor which terminates processes and they cannot logically hope that such processes will terminate in the Communistic utopia of peace and plenty. Feuerbach, another leftwing Hegelian and an influence on Marx, was more logical on dialectical premises when he held that world processes would simply go on and on, unterminated.

Aristotle has some interesting things to say about infinity in matter, and it is enlightening to review his principles, garbed in modern examples, with a concluding study, centered mainly upon Dedekind and Cantor, reserved to Chapter 9. Such is the natural procedure of genuine philosophy, working up, as work it must, from the study of nature to the study of number, from motion to quantity.

To lead off a long parade of argument, the following is very apt. If there are several components of a physical body, one cannot be infinite while the others are finite; the infinite would completely absorb the finite and make impossible that balance of structure which the body displays. If a nucleon (proton, neutron, or meson) is infinite in the actual substructures that comprise it, how can there be an equation between the nucleus and the electron—an equation that, translated into more physical terms, means the stability of an atom? Fire and air were the examples chosen by Aristotle to illustrate his principle. Supposing fire to be infinite and air to be finite, one could multiply air a hundredfold without giving it a sufficiency to overcome fire and, balancing it, to form a stable compound. Now if a proton, changing Aristotle's example and rethinking his principle, were formed from an infinite number of subdivisions and an electron were not, the electron could never unite with the proton in a stable configuration called hydrogen. It could never balance out the infinity set over against it. Atoms, elements, compounds, where this infinitely divided particle was an ingredient, would thus be homogeneous, consisting of this infinite thing and it alone. Hydrogen, oxygen, uranium, tin—all atoms would be formed of protons only and the world would be homogeneous. Nothing could stand its ground against the omnivorous proton. The other particles could be subjected to the same analysis and the same absurdity.

This leads in to the more general thesis that an infinite series of divisions would abandon matter to an indeterminacy rather than fashion definite objects which experience reveals. Divide motion into various intervals and subintervals, and there is reached eventually a very small element of the trajectory between the state of original rest and the first stir when the body moves. But this element, with the inexorable knife of an infinite division dangling over it must likewise be split, leaving a middle state between motion and rest, say the state m_1 between M and R. But the element of the trajectory between m_1 and R can also be divided according to the premise of infinite division, yielding a middle state m_2—until, when the process is carried to infinity, everything becomes middle, neither this nor that, neither motion nor rest, neither a trajectory nor a non-trajectory.

What happens to motion under the indeterminacy of an infinite regression befalls being also. When being is considered as divided, it must be equivalent to non-beings that would make it up. Being and non-being are thus the same thing. The principle of non-contradiction must make an unconditional surrender if the infinite division of matter is an actual fact. Matter becomes neither this nor that, it is neither being nor non-being. It is indeterminate. It yields a universe of flux where one thing, if there could be things, softens off into another, where everything is middling, and where nothing can either be or be distinguishable. Where permanence is thus outlawed there is, to paraphrase John

Elof Boodin, no mind to say anything nor any world to say anything about.

Probing this point from another angle reveals that a particle or a universe, infinitely divided, would be chaotic rather than ordered. Order, if it is anything, is certainly stability. It is firmness rather than flux, a differentiation rather than an infinitely middling state where everything is *radically* on the march to be everything else and nothing has any identity of its own. Nothing has any definite tendencies if everything is unrestrictedly in the middle state. Hence motion, like being, must be an absolute disorder—absolute, it must be emphasized because middling must be taken in its extremist sense, where it denies all identity, permanence, definition, tendency, stability, unity, intrinsicness, nature, and substance.

Quantum physicists, it may be observed here, reach the conclusion that the basic law of nature is the law of chance. They have simply extended, beyond Newton, the scope of the principle of inertia which is a principle of infinity, both of which flatten out the world of matter as indeterminate. Relativity mechanics likewise removed the classical mask from the idea of inertia and, by applying the principle more rigidly, came up with a view of the universe in terms of a space-time *continuum*. Whatever cannot be inertially treated is empiriologically meaningless, and it is the merit of Einstein, Heisenberg, and Schrodinger to have seen this more clearly than the Newtonians.

It could also be urged that an absolutely indeterminate particle or universe would be purely potential. It could claim no reality of its own but would await determination from the outside in order to become a being and be capable of motion. Where everything is sheer potency, nothing could ever move. When we look at a slow-motion picture of a ballet dance we simply pause longer on each frame as it passes the projector. Slowing the machine down infinitely, which means to stop it, turns the moving picture into a still shot. Where everything is sheer potency, nothing could ever move, and the still picture, capable of moving, but always remaining only capable, would forever remain still. More than that, if the universe is nothing but potency, it, like prime matter, would have no identity or determination of its own and could not even correspond to a still picture. Having no actuality or being, it would be hollowed out to a vacuum.

Potency is the source of plurality in mobile things since it may or may not be actualized, depending on an agent, and since the actualization is determined to a great extent by the type of agent and by the way in which it acts. What is potential can act in this or that way to a notable degree, conditioned by circumstance. The potential is hence the plural, the disorganized, the indeterminate. The actual is determinate and ordered, a source of unity.

Where all is indeterminate, all is potential or plural; and a pluralistic, rather than an organized universe, is exactly what would eventuate from an infinite division in matter. Plurality opposes organization. In a pluralistic universe, things would tear apart from each other rather than hang together, as they obviously do for instance in an atom and in that larger proportion of things which makes the universe something unitary. Radical pluralism would subvert the order in motion, impede all science which is nothing but organized knowledge, and forbid even the semblance of living organism and social organization.

INFINITY IN MATTER WOULD FORBID ITS MOTIONS

With this background, Aristotle's analysis of the fate of finite air combined with infinite fire seems richer. If the proton is infinitely divided, it cannot be steadied with a finite electron to form the hydrogen atom. There would result not stability but flux. The proton—plural, potential, and indeterminate—could not be matched by the finite electron because it has nothing matchable to an electron. It is indeterminate. It is utter chaos. If the electron, like the proton, is likewise infinitely divided—and such is the case in a pluralistic universe—then chaos is piled on chaos, indetermination catches greater fire from more indetermination, when the hydrogen atom is formed. Order can no more result from adding chaos to chaos than an empty tub can be filled with water by merely empty buckets. More and more chaos and indetermination results, and in such a universe, the higher the scale of being is mounted—from nucleons, to atoms, to plants, to animals, to man—the more disorganized things ought to become, the more passive, plural, indeterminate, potential, and the nearer to non-being. That this is not the case indicates that the structure of the universe is not sunk into infinitely divided sand.

The foregoing analysis ought not to be relented. If a neutron, say, is infinitely divided and if all parts of reality are the indeterminacy to which all is alike melted in an infinitely divided universe, then a single neutron exhausts all the potentialities of matter, and it would be impossible not only that there be another particle in the world like the electron or meson, there could not even be another neutron. Nothing is more potential than absolute potency, and a neutron, infinitely divided and purely indeterminate, would appropriate all this potency to itself, making all other material reality impossible.

If the infinite division of matter is a reality, then all things should be formed of the indeterminate substructures which a truly infinite series requires. But this does not account for the fact of difference in the world, any more than simply multiplying pure inertias can lead to anything except pure inertia or indifference. Differentiation cannot arise from absolute homogeneity any more than order can arise from disorder or something from nothing. Indeed, there are as many different entities in the world as there are finitudes, the finiting, terminating principles that we call forms.

Philosophical physics is alert most properly to the problem of motion, and its argument is crowned when it can show that matter, if it were actually infinite, would forfeit all its motion. As Chapter 10 will argue, bodies tend to seek their natural places, and for that reason undergo the change which is called local movement. Water, seeking its own level as the cliché puts it, is but following the same general law of location as a rocket soaring into the stratosphere or a stone rolling down the mountain. In a universe of infinite divisions, where all the parts would be indeterminate and hence all alike, a complete state of rest would reign in the world and all motion would be impossible. A body at point *A* would not tend to move to a point *B* because its like is already there and cannot be dislodged; *B* is the natural place of both bodies and so is *A*; they have no tendencies to exchange seats. This argument can be turned in another way. With no determination and difference, hence no inequality between things, there is no motion. Everything is equal to everything else, and the body does not tend from *A* to *B* because, equivalently, it is already there since it is radically equal to the body at *B*. From still another angle, it could be pointed out that a body would have to move through an infinity of places to get to *B*. It could never make the grade.

As if to show that an absurd principle must give rise to absurd conclusions, Aristotle reasons that infinity actualized in matter would likewise give rise to an utterly dynamic universe where now rest would be completely outlawed. This is simply another way of stating that infinite divisions in matter would turn it into a flux and flow where everything is middling and tends to everything else. Aristotle's own words about an infinite matter can stand today: "It will be at home everywhere, then it will not be moved; or it will be moved everywhere, then it will not come to rest." Absolute motion and absolute rest are both at odds with experience; the fact that both follow alike from a given theory proves that the theory itself must have been wrong to start with. The true notion of nature unites the two contrary aspects of matter by its status as a principle of motion and of rest. Nature's language is not that of split infinitives.

THERE IS NO REGRESSION INTO INFINITY

One of the most important principles of human thought is the impossibility of an infinite series of directly subordinated movers:

non regreditur in infinitum. This principle can be defended in the philosophic science of nature where Aristotle himself arrived at the notion of a Prime Mover. It can also be shown that even in our own universe, there must be relatively prime movers, which we call the natures, as opposed to inertias.

A proton is shot out of an atom smasher toward a target nucleus whose make-up it will change. A leaf is blown from one side of the street to the other in a gust of autumn wind. An infinite series of movers could not account for the rush of the proton or the flight of the leaf. How could an infinity of subprotons or an infinity of subdivisions in the cellulose of the leaf swing into action to accomplish definite tasks? The movements of both the proton and the leaf are finite processes because they are measured by a finite time. The finite cannot measure the infinite; there is no proportion between them. On the hypothesis of an infinite series of movers, it would take an infinite time for all the structures inside and outside the proton and the leaf to accomplish the simple operation of moving the bodies through the smallest thinkable fraction of an inch. Somewhere, the parade of movers, however long, must run out. There must be a prime mover. The philosophical physicist calls this a nature, and in natural theology is shown that such natures require a Supreme Prime Mover, who moves them not inertially but from within, who does not act transeuntly upon them but creates them, who does not guide their actions as a painter does his brush but shares with them His own interiority and Prime Movership making them His participations rather than His mechanical instruments.

A thing can only move at the time it is moved by something else; mover and object must act simultaneously and by contact. But if there is an infinite string of movers, mover and its object are separated by an infinite time. The first could never move the second, because powerless to cross the infinite series, it could never be simultaneous with the object to be moved. The object moved would thus be moved by nothing since its supposed mover could never catch up with it across infinity. Moved by nothing, irrelational because it cannot be affected by anything or affect anything else across infinity, the object moved would thus become completely random, whimsical, and chaotic.

The modern idea of inertia, universally and rigorously applied, contains a fundamental contradiction. On the one hand since empiriological method agrees that nothing can move itself, as Plato said, or be an unmoved mover in the better language of Aristotle, the random explosion into time and space is, according to empiriological physics, what movement would have to become —a blast that nothing can leap infinity to start, stop, or control. On the other hand, the law of inertia, or the principle of equality between action and reaction, which is but the law of inertia in a new costume, requires that any movement be completely controlled by outside forces. This is the basis for what the empiriological physicist calls order. He defines it in terms of predictability, and yet to achieve predictions he employs a principle that in its ultimate and universal sense gives rise to a random and unpredictable universe. Order for empirical physics means determinism, and without it there would be no empirical method; yet the law of inertia, the basic principle of the method, makes for a universe wholly undetermined. This contradiction is alive in the current crisis between classical and quantum physics.

A second ballot of nature against the infinite series of movers reads like this: If there is no first mover, there can be no motion at all. Without a first mover, all movers become intermediate, and the *intermediate* must be taken in its most literal sense. A can never move B because there is a radical between-ness between them, a bottomless interval where every part of it, given the infinite series, is as unbridgeable as the whole. A could never get started to B because their separation is absolute. They are separated unqualifiedly because everything, the infinite, is in between them; they are separated as being and nothing because the between-ness is radical.

Motion would be impossible in such a setting. Things become closed in on themselves, separated in the absolute sense from ev-

erything else. Their isolation is infinite, and thus they are irrelational. They are withdrawn completely into themselves rather
than capable of moving toward goals outside them. If anything,
they would tend to increase their isolation rather than enter into
outside relations. They would tend to pluralism rather than a
universe. There would be a static shrinkage in things rather than
the motion which resounds through the universe of experience.
This pluralism is the ultimate meaning of the attempt to understand matter only by dividing it. The subdivisions of pure empiricism become so infinitely removed from the city of experience
that they cannot commute with it. William James and George
Santayana formally embraced a pluralism, and such must also be
the ultimate meaning of Bertrand Russell who calls his philosophy a logical atomism. It is the logical conclusion of scientism.

Here again, the conclusion of the argument immediately is
that there are prime movers in the universe and ultimately, when
the metaphysician takes over, that there is a Supreme Prime
Mover, guiding creation by premotion rather than by inertia. In
Chapter 7, it will be shown that an inert being, like a scientific
object to use a Whiteheadean term, can be neither a cause nor
an effect at the level of efficient causality. (Inertia and being,
taken purely, are incompatible.) Here the argument simply is
that the infinite is not an actual principle of nature.

A third rejection of the infinite series in matter can be provided by examining the meaning of an instrumental cause. An
instrument is a medium—a pencil, a hammer, a throttle—by
which the principal cause—a writer, a carpenter, a railroad engineer—produces its effects. An instrument actually transmits the
causal motion to the effect. A tool is transmissive, what the scholastics called a *causa vialis*. It is undifferentiated precisely as a
tool, to the extent that it is determined by the mover that uses it.
A pencil could write the diameter of the sun, a love letter, or a
Shakespearean play, being more or less indeterminate as an instrument and taking its determination as a cause from the principal, as opposed to instrumental, agent that applies it.

If there is no first mover, everything becomes an instrumental cause. If all movers are transmissive only, there is no cause or principle of movement. A mover cannot be just radically transmissive; it must be productive and actual. No matter how we might multiply transmissive realities, we can never come to a cause or principle of the movement. A thing would move without a cause or without a mover, and the absolute spontaneity of a chaotic universe again would reign. Everything moved would have to move itself.

A tool in the ideal case must be undifferentiated and indeterminate, completely at the command of the agent which applies it. Now if all movers are simply and ideally tools of agents which themselves are instruments instrumentally moved, then reality becomes completely undifferentiated; everything becomes pure potency; everything becomes absolutely transmissive, yielding once more a universe that is a Heraclitean cataract. What is absolutely indeterminate must take its reality completely from the outside, and thus once more nothing has any reality in itself. Multiplying transmitters does not account for what is transmitted.

A tool transmits. It is directed to something else. It is *for* something else. As the preceding principle yielded a world where there is a radical between-ness between things, so here there is a radical for-ness. Everything is wholly *for* something else. Nothing has any reality in itself, and hence nothing could be. This is the unchallengeable logic of natural theology when it argues that if there is no Prime Mover, then there is nothing. In the universe of instrumentalism pure and simple, everything would transmit movement rather than receive it since reception itself would be a form of transmission. Indeed, not a form of transmission, for everything would be purely transmissive in the instrumental universe, and no different *forms* of transmission could be real.

The empiriological method tends to understand a thing in terms of the results which it produces. Theories are validated by a pragmatic test. Water is understood in terms of what can be done with it or, if analyzed, what particles it produces. The empiriological method thus turns the world into a tool chest of pure instruments. This conclusion is embraced by Dewey and, in general, by the naturalists, even including Alfred North Whitehead (in his so-called ontological principle). Dewey's instrumentalism, as he calls it, is the pivot of his philosophy, repeating over and over again that things are understood or preferably validated only in terms of what can be done with them. James' pragmatism lies along the same road.

This does not categorically repudiate Dewey and James. Indeed, it is in the area of tools that their ideas have an outstandingly valid application. In painting a room, building a garage, doing the wash, why not choose the most expeditious way of getting the job done, evaluating one's material resources in the light of instruments? It is to the extension of instrumentalism through the whole cosmos that the realist must close the door. Carried into the philosophy of nature, instrumentalism means that everything is outside itself; in itself it is nothing. It is only *for* . . . Where everything is radically *for* . . . motion becomes just as impossible as where everything is radically *between*. The universe thaws away into a pure and undifferentiated *for* . . . a single and immobile relation. Differentiation is impossible where all is indeterminate, where all is a tool in the ideal sense. The pragmatism of James is consistent with his pluralistic premises. Both imply flux, indetermination, a sheerly potential and even vacuous universe.

But this is not a purely transmissive world. There is in some way a jamming of the transmitters. Even in radio engineering, a transmitter tube transmits only after a frequency-generating oscillator has actuated it.

MATTER IS POTENTIALLY, NOT ACTUALLY, INFINITE

It is obvious that this is not a universe of formless fluff, divided and moved into infinity. Can it be then irretrievably denied that matter is infinite?

Finitism, as it is called, would categorically reject the existence of the infinite in the world of motion. Such is the thought of Renouvier, a nineteenth-century French neo-Kantian; to a certain extent, it is the gospel of the Marxians who view motion as *terminating* (finiting itself) in their Communist utopia, and to a great extent it is the teaching or the implication of the existentialists, Kierkegaard, Jaspers, Heidegger, and Sartre, who are impressed more or less by the radical limits of things and tend to nihilism.

From certain angles, finitism is suggested in dynamisms like those of Leibniz and Boscovich and Whitehead, who reduce matter to structures where division ends and indivisibles appear. The law of the degradation of energy has a certain flavor of finitism, somewhat at variance with other principles of empiriological physics, and Einstein likewise suggests such a view when he calls the universe "finite but unbounded."

But finitism in general can no more be sustained than the infinitism which the foregoing pages have rejected. Time becomes radically finite, as existentialism would attempt to prove. Secondly, there comes a point in dividing the trajectory of a moving body when an indivisible element is reached on finitist premises, and hence motion is seen not as a continuous process but as a series of leaps from one such indivisible position to another. Number, on finitist grounds, has an upper and lower limit; for example, there must eventually be admitted a greatest possible number, to which no more unities can be added. This would change such quantities as π and $\sqrt{2}$ into rational numbers and rebuke the mathematician for his proof that the diagonal of a square is incommensurable with the sides. The mass of the electron is of the order of 10^{-28} gram, and its radius is of the order of 10^{-13} centimeter. What is to prevent thinning matter out even further, cutting the electron into particles that are fractions of itself? The only reasonable answer is that empiriological physics has not yet developed guns powerful enough to do the job.

Infinity, it was said, could be taken in a formal or material sense. While rejecting the view that matter is formally or actu-

ally infinite, it can speedily be shown that it is materially or potentially so. This type of infinity is broadly synonymous with the
indefinite or indeterminate, and, according to the traditional view
which Dedekind and Cantor will later be shown to dispute, the
most obvious example is that of number. Number can always be
increased into larger quantities, and fractions can always be diminished into smaller ones. There is no limit to the series at either end. This means that any number actually attained is finite,
but it can grow into a greater number with the addition of another unity or shrink into a smaller fraction by division. Properly
speaking, mathematical infinity of the very large is that to which
a new magnitude can always be added, and on the smaller scale,
it is that which can always be further subdivided. Every pace
along this infinite road represents a number, small or large, actually attained; nowhere is infinity actually reached. There is always a potency to further addition or further division, and that is
why this infinity is called potential. The potentially or materially
infinite is that to which new additions or new divisions can always be made.

This position cuts a middle path between the finitist and infinitist extremes, just as matter-form dualism bisected the line dividing dynamism and atomism, as shown in Chapter 2. With the
finitist it agrees that matter invested with a nature is actually undivided and finited by its form; it agrees that any number actually attained by counting or dividing is finite. But with the infinitist, it agrees that matter, organized into undivided wholes
called natures, can be divided, is divisible and that any number
can always be augmented so that we never reach a last number.
Aristotle's realism is able to enfold the truths in both extremes
because it admits a dualism, the bifurcated character of matter.
As far as this dualism implies form as the term of generation, it
is finitist; as far as it admits a purely potential principle out of
which new forms can always be educed, it is infinitist. This is
broadly the difference between act and potency by which motion
is defined.

The divisibility of the so-called continuum will be discussed again in Chapter 12 where the relations of quantity will be more thoroughly examined. But the continuum provides the classic example to illustrate the difference between the potentially infinite and the actual infinity of matter that was rejected in the foregoing sections. There, it was shown that matter is not actually divided into infinity as it stands in nature. But while denying this actual dividedness to matter, the philosopher of nature must affirm its unlimited divisibility. Its dividedness is thus not actual but potential.

In the case of the electron, for instance, supposing it to be a formal unity and not several smaller particles mechanically interstructured, the 10^{-28} gram of weight or the 10^{-13} centimeter of diameter can at least be mentally divided, if the empiriological evidence is not quite clear about electron smashing. The subdivisions can then be subdivided, and so on and on. Nowhere does the process lead to particles of mass and diameter zero. But this does not mean, once more, that the electron as it swings through nature is actually divided into such a series of smaller masses and extensions. It has a unity, an undividedness due to its form. But denying dividedness does not thereby preclude divisibility. A tailor can cut a few yards of cloth from a roll that is thirty yards long. The original was undivided but divisible, potentially and not actually divided. Now it is true that it may not be the same to divide a bolt of silk as it is to divide an electron. As the chapter on quantity will show, the divided silk is still silk, but the subelectron may not be an electron. However, the point here is the same in both cases: the difference between dividedness and divisibility, between actual and potential division. Matter can always be further divided without ever tapering down to an indivisible particle; time can always be dissected without ever coming to an indivisible moment; motion's trajectories can always be pulverized without reaching an indivisible element, as Aristotle argued against Zeno and as Bergson argued against scientism.

The potentially infinite is either that of unlimited addition in terms of the very large or of unlimited division in terms of the very small. Of the two, the second is more fundamental in the world of motion, despite the physical picture which is sometimes drawn from modern Cantorian mathematics. The fuller implications of this point would form a chapter by itself and will be treated again in Chapter 10. Here, speaking from the viewpoint of a mathematics which follows the grain of the human mind and should be examined in its own order of abstraction rather than in the philosophical science of nature, it is sufficient to point out that division is both logically and ontologically prior to addition. The first act of the mind is "analytic," contrasting being with nothingness. Ontologically, the parts at least by nature if not in time are prior to their configuration that we call a universe. Divisibility is more fundamental in matter than additivity. Without exploring this point further in a parenthesis too long to justify it for the present context, it can simply be pointed out that only by dividing matter did the empiriological physicist conclude that it could be lumped together into a spectrum of ninety-two (?) elements. Atom building became a reality after atom smashing, just as arithmetic—despite again the protests of the Cantorians—is prior to geometry.

THE MATHEMATICAL INFINITE IS THE POTENTIAL INFINITE

Infinity in modern mathematics is a complicated subject, and Chapter 9 will attempt to view some of its larger lines. The matter of the mathematician, number and extension, is potentially infinite, and it is quite consistent that he choose as a pivot of his technical universe the model of the continuum. This is exactly what a purely potential universe becomes, as Aristotle urged long centuries ago against Heraclitus.

Briefly put, the mathematician draws a line of any length, provided it is continuous, and argues that the whole number system is analogous to it. The numbers correspond to points on a linear continuum, and there are as many numbers as there are points. Passing over the problem of whether points are potentially or actually on a line, it may be asked, what is solved by analogating the number system to the linear continuum? To such a fund of potency, the modern number theory applies rules which it has disengaged for certain sequences. It can, for instance, give a rule for deriving all rational fractions and even for deriving the rationals plus ordinary irrationals like $\sqrt{2}$, $\sqrt{3}$, $\sqrt[3]{7}$, . . . $\sqrt[m]{n}$. . . . It can likewise give rules to show that there are higher irrationals like π and e, the base of natural logarithms, which cannot be derived in an ordered sequence like the series of rational numbers. If the continuum is indeterminate and potential, which is the only objective reality owned by mathematical infinity, modern mathematics has developed a set of rules for drawing determination out of the potency and thus determining what before was actually indeterminate and only determinable.

Now although objectively the number system remains what it was in Aristotle's sciences, namely, the potentially infinite that a continuum forms, the rules discerned by modern mathematics give the impression of dominating the series which they govern and hence terminating them. This is the reason why Cantorians speak of orders of infinity, as though infinity admits of differences, and the whole discussion backfires into the orbit of logic, where Russell, for instance, is willing to take it up. What is different about the various types of infinity is not something objective but the rules for determining the indeterminate and determinable, in other words the various methods of actualizing, short of exhaustion, what is potentially infinite. According to one rule, the set of rational numbers is developed; another method delivers the rationals and the ordinary irrationals, which are called algebraic numbers. A third set of rules shows that the whole spectrum of real numbers, including π and e, cannot be determined into an orchestrated sequence.

But such procedures do not mean that the rationals, the irrationals, or the reals are actually infinite. What is actual is the rule which is abstracted from the sequence of numbers, like the Aristotelian rule that the series of whole numbers is indefinitely extended by adding unity to the number preceding. These rules, actually the products of abstraction discerning the nature of number, are turned into logical valves by the modern mathematician, applying them to his continuum to get whatever he wants from it according to the rule he is using. It is not for the philosophical science of nature to dispute about such rules, except to point out that they are abstracted from the actual and applied throughout the range of possible being, just as the form of rationality is applied to all possible men. What is of interest here is simply that the reality objectively enjoyed by the mathematical infinite is that of the continuum which is the materially or potentially infinite. What is actual is the rule, and what is infinite about the rule is simply its logical implications which do not concern the philosophical science of motion whose sole interest is how the matter stands in nature. Empiriological method tends to view its subject matter as controllable, and this is the case no less in mathematics, as far as it has felt the influence of this method, than in empiriological physics.

ACTUAL INFINITY IN MATTER IS A SUBSTITUTE FOR FORM

Contemporary scientism has jettisoned the traditional notion of form, as a term, and it is consistent, if contrary to experience, to conclude that the infinity which Aristotle ascribed to prime matter should graduate from this potential state into the all-embracing fact of the universe. The indeterminate, continuous, chaotic, potential, and plural picture of the world is the conclusion of inertia which scientism takes as the nickname for matter and which, in traditional thought, corresponds to the potential substrate in things, the lowest form of being.

Scientism has made matter's actual infinity into a shadowy substitute for the Aristotelian notion of unity, nature, relation, number, and order.

Nature is that intrinsic stability in a physical thing which determines how it will act when acted upon. Numbers have natures in an analogous sense. Aristotle called them species and said they were varied by the addition or substraction of unity. Between the species of number in the Aristotelian account, there is a gap, an abrupt break that makes 1 forever different from 2 in the mathematical order. Modern mathematics has attempted to pack this interval with the infinite series. But the infinite, it was seen earlier, is purely potential, and absolute material infinity, it was also said, would leave the world a vacuum, having nothing in itself. This non-being is the same thing as the gap in the Aristotelian number scheme, the rupture between 1 and 2 or between any other such quantities. The modern view is to take the intervening infinity as something real and actual rather than to acknowledge it simply as an aid to the imagination in crossing the bridge between being and non-being which intelligence alone can span.

The modern notion of infinity is likewise a ghost to haunt the fact of unity which it attempts to replace. Once we abandon the notion that there are wholes in nature or in number, we are forced to the conclusion that what is commonly called a unity is nothing but an infinite sum. A sum can never be a whole, any more than Humpty Dumpty can be put back together again. But when this sum is made infinite, the mathematician has the impression of restoring the broken unity to number and the empiriological physicist to nature. Aristotle admitted that a unity in nature was infinite in potentiality. When, as in the empiriological method, potency is made the only aspect of things, it is clear why unity and infinity have become synonymous. But a sum of potentialities can no more be the understudy of act and unity than the sum of fractions in the foregoing example on number can yield a break (as that between 1 and 2) by simply becoming more solid.

Aquinas was especially emphatic in discussions of mental relations. Such relations do not add to a thing nor subtract from it, and yet they are relations, like that for example, implied by human knowledge, cognizing a thing without altering it. Now in connection with measure or number, mental relations play a major role. For example, a standard like unity or an inch or a pound is measured with respect to itself by a mental relation and then everything else is measured with respect to it. Otherwise, we would search into infinity for a standard. But once the fact of the so-called mental relation is abandoned, a pluralistic universe results. When a thing is set in relation to mind it must change on pluralistic premises, and the change to be known must in turn be altered. Thus the infinite series is opened. Unity known with respect to itself, number known with relation to itself, circumvent the infinite series. Making all relations to be real involves it.

The philosophical doctrine of order is likewise replaced by the more contemporary view that matter is actually divided and that there is no limit to the divisions. In Chapter 3 it was shown that things have fixed tendencies, and if they did not, that disorder and chaos would result, the flux and flow of the infinite series which the non-telic views of modern philosophy suggest. Once teleology was abandoned in the study of nature, as it has been from the days of Bacon and Descartes, it was logical to seek for the order of the universe within the individual realities, and since form was likewise ruled out by the leaders of the empiriological movement, the only place left to search for the secrets of the universe was the indeterminacy of the matter. But order cannot be explained by its reduction to the indeterminate, any more than a railroad track could be laid on the watery surface of Lake Michigan. The sum of disorders is more disorder not less.

Empiriological data tend to suggest and to illustrate philosophical ideas. They do not constitute the ultimate in knowledge. Understanding empiriological physics as a source of analogies to express and to deepen philosophical truth, the four fundamental theorems on infinity may be set down from mathematics to show that material, potential, mathematical infinity is the indeterminate which is indefinitely determinable.

As a prologue to these illustrations, it should be remarked that an expression like $\lim_{v \to o} c/v = \infty$ simply means that if c, a constant, is divided by v, a variable, then as v tends to decrease and to approximate zero the fraction c/v tends to infinity. A second introductory remark is that although the mathematician considers addition and multiplication to be the two fundamental operations of his science today, the fundamental operations are, more basically, addition and subtraction. The mathematician thinks of subtraction as a form of addition; it becomes algebraic addition in which a negative quantity is added to a positive one. But for the philosopher, on the other hand, addition and subtraction differ as the positive and the negative. The non-being is not added to being. The non-being is being, negated. Multiplication is a form of multiple addition. For instance, $3 \times 2 = 6$ answers the question how many times must one add 3 to itself in order to get 6. Division is multiple subtraction. For example $12/4 = 3$ answers the question, how many times must 4 be subtracted from 12 to get 0?

With the preface of these remarks, four fundamental theorems involving infinity may now be stated:

1. $\lim\limits_{v \to 0} c/v = \infty$. This means, in qualitative language that when a constant is divided by a variable and the variable tends to become zero the result tends to infinity. This equation answers the following questions and states the following analogues to physical truth: How many times can one subtract 0 from a constant? An indefinite number of times. A thing is what it is. Zero is absolutely nothing. A thing is purely potential so far as the subtraction of zeros from it is concerned.

2. $\lim\limits_{v \to \infty} cv = \infty$. How many times can you add act to absolute indetermination? There is no limit to the potentialities of matter. It is pure potency and can receive an indefinite number of forms.

3. $\lim\limits_{v \to \infty} v/c = \infty$. How many times can one subtract act from indetermination? How many times can form be evolved from matter? How long can the number series extend? Again, an indeterminate.

4. $\lim\limits_{v \to \infty} c/v = 0$. How many times can all the indeterminates be

taken from a number? How many times can all the potencies, all pluralities be removed from matter? None.

Such examples tend to illustrate the traditional notion of material infinity. They establish that the practical working mathematician tends to analogate the principles of philosophical physics with regard to what the infinite is in matter and how it relates to the more general laws of being and form. From one aspect, it can be seen how the mathematician can use formulae involving infinity and use them indeed on the real world.

Empiriological physics, by considering nature according to the laws of inertia and by arriving at the notion of matter as purely potential, tends away from form and in the direction of prime matter. It is natural then that it should arrive at a picture of things as infinite and as indeterminate. This is exactly what Aristotle said about prime matter. Aquinas adopted Plato's term when he called prime matter a kind of chaos. The indeterminate is a common term applied from the Greeks onward to the material principle in nature.

But prime matter is not the sole constituent in mobile reality. It requires the complement of form, without which reality floats away into the unchartable seas of the continuum. Empiriological physics, when it speaks of the indeterminate and the infinite, is hitting upon something real in nature, but the philosophical account of form must be added in order to portray the reality fully and to portray it as it is.

Modern mathematics has disengaged rules for determining successive members of various series from the number continuum. But the actuality of the rule does not apply to the infinity of the series. Moreover, mathematical rules must be qualified when applied to nature, which is more than mere quantity and extension and hence more than merely mathematical. Objectively, the infinity of mathematics remains what Aristotle said of it, the indeterminate or the continuous. Modern mathematics has simply unearthed rules for carrying out the determination. Any actuality ascribed to this infinity is that of a rule. In the physical and mathematical order, infinity still remains the potential or determinable.

The indeterminate cannot exist. If it alone obtained, the principle of non-contradiction would perish. The indeterminate cannot account for motion because it is chaotic, whereas motion is ordered. It would leave a purely potential universe where motion would be impossible, and hence it cannot provide a philosophical science of motion at all. Motion is not explained by denying its existence any more than a fire department by putting out the fire thereby accounts for its origin.

Suggested Readings

Aristotle, *Physics,* Bk. III, chs. 4–8.
Aquinas, St. Thomas, *Summa contra gentiles,* Bk. 1, ch. 13.
McWilliams, J., *Physics and Philosophy* (Washington, 1945), pp. 8, 135.

PART TWO

5

Motion and Empiriological Physics

EMPIRIOLOGICAL PHYSICS IS MARKED BY EXPERIMENT

The physics so prominent today may be called, in Maritain's term, empiriological, and its definition forms a problem that rivals in both importance and interest the actual study of mobile being in the philosophical science of nature. Scientism, by its addiction to the empiriological method, gives an original touch to the modern mind, and it is largely the seeds of that method which have matured into the mechanical age.

Dewey has promoted the empiriological method into the rank of a philosophy. Lenin claimed it as the basis of his dialectical materialism. Logical empiricism has proposed in general that whatever cannot be known by the method of empiriological physics is not knowable or even worth knowing. Positivism, which is the empiriological spirit let loose into philosophy, is in one form or another the dominant academic mood of the day, at least in America where the empirical test is so often taken as the last tribunal of truth.

It should not be surprising that empiriological physics has not been properly evaluated, at least to the satisfaction of realists. Philosophy spent nearly a thousand years in western Europe getting itself defined. The empiriological disciplines are more complicated than philosophy, more changeable and precarious, less reflective and more avoidable, and of themselves they do not tend to train minds that can dominate technical discoveries and

139

trace them to the larger truths which philosophical physics defines and defends. This complicated character of empiriological physics ought to show, of itself, how little it traffics in ultimate issues, and how little qualified a man becomes, by the mere study of empiriological physics, to relate his work to the simple and certain truths that initiate his thinking as a man.

Science, in its traditional sense and in the only sense that can avert a complete skepticism, means a certain knowledge in terms of causes. Does the empiriological method fit the rigor of these requirements? If it does, a vast region of the philosophical science of nature would have to be rethought and reworked. If it does not, a vaster region of the modern atmosphere must be cleared. Empiriological physics holds today the Promethean power to control the future of our civilization, but the idea of what the empiriological method is can control the physics which espouses it.

This is not the time nor the place to plot the history of empiriological physics. By whatever way its engines started turning in the Renaissance, it was moving with full speed ahead at the time of Galileo and arrived on the high seas with Newton. What distinguished Galileo is the thing that still distinguishes empiriological physics. He experimented, deliberately controlling his subjects of study, and he gave a mathematical form to his results so that they could be extended through a wide range of possible experiments.

The original work of Galileo was actually much more subtle. He formally stated the law of inertia, which holds changes of motion in direction and magnitude, to be entirely the fruit of outside forces. This view of things is more vividly put in his so-called parallelogram law, which means, when carried out, that the motion of a body is the algebraic sum of outer forces in their various quantities and directions.

Galileo's two laws are almost a definition of experiment, and it is in the character of experiment, much more than in the mathematical language of the Galilean approach, that the philosopher is likely to discover what empiriological physics is. It is in experiment, more than in mathematics, that the empiriological physicist makes contact with reality. It is here that terrain is provided for comparing his report with that of philosophical physics, as sketched in the preceding chapters. It is here that reality itself sits in judgment on both versions of what it is. Much more insight can be gained by examining the experimental basement of empiriological physics than by attending to its mathematical overhead.

Empiriological physics must interfere with a phenomenon in order to understand it, and, in its purity, it can grasp only what it can control. Such a view of the empiriological method has been in bright focus among John Dewey and his school of naturalism. Dewey applauds the "aggressive attitude toward nature."[1] In naturalism the empiriological method swallows the whole of philosophy, and the purpose of philosophy is to bring man's cultural and moral life under the same empirical and "active control" that the empiriological physicist clamps on matter. The same instrumental function of the empiriological disciplines thrives in Communism, where they are tools to further the dialectical process.

Galileo's two laws, which on the surface of things look like pure theory, are thus the basis of experiment. Only what is inert is controllable, and control, in the spirit of the parallelogram law, means knowing a thing through extrinsic forces.

Experiment, the core of empiriological physics, is a controlled experience, and it is in this area of the controllable that the startling successes of experiment have been scored. The scruple to control matter and to equate the meaningful with the controllable marks off the modern empiriological approach to nature from philosophical physics.

In its purest form, experiment does not get to things as they are. It disturbs them. Only what wilts before the power of man is deemed empiriologically significant. For example, the law of

---

[1] *Reconstruction in Philosophy* (2d ed., Boston, 1949), p. 116.

freely falling bodies is known by deliberately varying their sizes and altitudes and atmospheric resistances. An electron is experimentally known by what man can do with it.

Croce agrees with Vico that man can truly know only what he makes. Kant said of the great experimenters: "They learned that reason has insight only into that which it produces after a plan of its own, . . . constraining nature to give answer to questions of reasons's own determining."[2] Despite the pleas of positivism, there is radical subjectivity in the empiriological method as such, where its failure to ripen into fullest maturity is owed to the deeper failure of empiriological physics to be true to itself. There is a happy survival, in the mind of the empiriological physicist, of that prescientific knowledge which he enjoys as a man and which keeps him from bankruptcy.

Newton did not change Galileo's methods. He improved and extended them. His most remarkable contribution took the form of his three laws which became the basis of classical mechanics:

1. Every body continues in a state of rest or of uniform motion in a straight line, except in so far as it is compelled by forces to change that state.
2. Change of motion is proportional to the force and takes place in the direction of the straight line in which the force acts.
3. To every action there is always an equal and contrary re-action; or, the mutual actions of any two bodies are always equal and oppositely directed along the same straight line.

Newton was validating again Galileo's method of control, which regards a body as inert and as equivalent to the forces and factors maneuvering it from the outside. This conclusion is written into each of the three laws.

Empiriological physics had fairly smooth sailing in the nineteenth century, but storms began to break in the twentieth. It is not proposed to trace here how Einstein removed large items of the furniture which Newtonians had put into their model of the

---

[2] *Critique of Pure Reason*, English transl. by N. Smith (London, 1929), Preface to 2d ed., p. 20.

world. The important fact here is that Einstein asked: "What is observable, i.e., experimentable?" Relativity emerged from Einstein's purpose to purify experiment from the non-experimental which Newtonians projected into it. Closer attention to how Newton spoke of the world rescinded what he actually said.

This sharper definition of experiment in the contemporary approach is even more forceful in the work of Heisenberg. He reasoned that measuring instruments always interfere with their object and hence never present it exactly as it is. Heisenberg's logic became a blueprint in the newly developing quantum theory, which is now the contemporary rival of relativity mechanics. He simply redefined an experiment, pointing out that when it put the mirror up to nature it was a distortion mirror that was always used.

The philosophical science of nature takes its bearings upon the objective world. It does not interfere with the object; thus it leaves the object unaltered for others to see as we see it and to agree with us on its nature. In philosophical physics, the order is to know first and to control in the light of what one knows. In empiriological physics, the traffic runs the other way. We control first and know later, know in the light of what we can control.

To test knowledge by whether we can control its object is a sign of the deep anthropomorphism in empiriological physics. The science of nature proceeding, as Chapters 2–4, have done, insists on the primacy of the speculative rather than of control in knowledge. It is more objective and realistic and more truly scientific. Empiriological physics often abets a certain pride in the physicist, when his views are not tempered by a genuine philosophical or theological alertness to things that lie beyond control and compel submission. The devotee of scientism, controlling reality, has the impression of creating as God does, and so without the true God, he tends to deify himself and to make the world his product.

Another remark on control is in place here. Control is not knowledge any more than throwing a toggle switch means that a man knows the principles of electrical engineering. Control as control can be included in the abstraction and reasoning about a context where it is involved, but of itself and taken purely, it is not self-revealing. Control requires prior knowledge of the subject, even in empiriological physics, and it is this knowledge that the philosopher of nature would like the positivist and naturalist to remember. The first experience is not an experiment, and the primary knowledge of man is not experimental. But the empiriological physicist who boosts his work to the philosophical level, gives the impression of forgetting about this prior knowledge and of seeing his specialized system as having a monopoly on all meaning.

EMPIRIOLOGICAL PHYSICS IS NOT STRICT SCIENCE

It is not surprising that empiriological physics, after three centuries, is still awaiting a satisfactory diagnosis of itself. It took long centuries until the identity of philosophy emerged through its historical achievements. It was a disaster that the spirit which waved on the empiriological spirit in the modern age should have had only contempt for those thousand preceding years of intellectual struggle and their hard-earned triumphs in tremendous issues.

Empiriological physics is emerging more and more into the clear. Like philosophy, it is taking time to develop and to identify itself for appraisal in terms besides generalities. Einstein and Heisenberg purified it more and more, so that it stands out a little more lucidly for what it is. Into their self-styled experimental physics, Newtonians were introducing a great deal of extraëxperimental contraband which contemporary systems have removed. The purer definition of empiriological physics is a victory for philosophy too. In the case of empiriological physics, as in everything that he studies, the true philosopher wants to know what it is. Empiriological physics stands on the modern horizon, more transparently and as it is, than it ever stood before. True philosophy is unafraid of the genuine advances in the empiriological domain. It welcomes relativity and quantum physics, and as the sequel will show ever so briefly, it finds in them more of a reflection of itself than it did in the somewhat pseudophysics of Galileo and Newton.

With an eye to the direction of empiriological physics, it is enlightening to rethink the realistic definition of science as a certain knowledge in terms of causes.

A thing is scientifically known in so far as we rationalize its existing nature, arriving, as it were, at the *what* and the *why* of it. There are two kinds of knowledge: (1) speculative knowledge which is sought and had for its own sake, and (2) practical knowledge which is wanted for the sake of action. Thus in psychology, the soul is studied with a view to knowing it, while a radio set may be studied in an electronics laboratory with a view to repairing it. The practical is a personal and, taken by itself, strictly subjective kind of knowledge, having for its aim doing or making in an individual case and therefore taking the form of prudence or art. The speculative deals primarily with what things are apart from action, universal to all of us and hence controlled by none.

That philosophy is a science only the skeptic can dispute. Taking its stand in experience, full, real, and objective, it strikes a covenant with the causes and reasons of things, as preceding pages have shown. But how does the matter stand with the empiriological approach, especially with empiriological physics which is of primary concern in connection with the science of nature and which provides the prototype of all empiriological methods? In view of the importance which modern man ascribes to his empiriological physics, a more elaborate discussion of its nature is in line with a defense of philosophical physics and with the spirit that genuine philosophy can profitably bring to our age.

Empiriological disciplines are busied about the measurement, correlation, and prediction of phenomena. The results of measurement, say the clocking of an object sliding down an inclined plane, will yield a law like the law of bodies falling in obedience to so-called gravity. A hypothetical background called a theory—like Newton's idea of universal gravitation—is then worked out in order to correlate a group of measurements. But a theory to be tested and validated must predict new phenomena. That is its primary reason for wearing the empiriological uniform, and it is thus more of a tool for discovery than a matter of proof. This whole orientation, moving from measured fact to theory and to the prediction of new mensurations, constitutes the empiriological method. But how can this procedure meet the classical rigor that a science must be certain, have a knowledge character, and attain to causes?

First of all, the conceptual apparatus of empiriological physics cannot be treated univocally. If theory is filtered out from law, hypothesis from the facts which the hypothesis is projected to predict, it is clear that theory has only a provisional character. The history of empiriological physics teems with the obituaries of discarded theories. Even in the two leading ideas of modern quantum and relativity mechanics, there is such a deep-down contradiction that one of them must eventually be discarded or, what is more likely, both of them must be surpassed. (Quantum theory holds that the space-time properties of a body have no meaning when taken together; relativity theory says that exact space-time correlations are the only meaningful statements that can be made.)

A theory is of value to empiriological physics only in so far as it is doubtful and questionable, unsettled and provocative. Since a theory aims to predict experiment, every experiment is a test of it. If a theory were the final word, there would be no reason for experiment since the outcome would be foreknown. In the words of Fabry, if empiriological physics ever devised a theory that could explain all phenomena, it would be a sign that physics had reached an impasse. Even something like the extremely well-verified atomic theory may be superseded. In fact, Einstein has already proposed a field theory to compete with it. A theory is timely rather than timeless, provisional rather than certain, dynamic rather than settled, questionable rather than apodictic.

It may also be asked how physical law follows in the wake of what strict science really means. Law, a generalization of measured fact, has a contact with the real. But our certitude with regard to physical law is only physical certitude, deriving from the order of nature rather than dictating this order in stern and unbreakable terms. Since law is indeed the locus where the empiriological physicist makes contact with the real, it keeps him from being swept away into the mathematical clouds and is his strongest claim to a scientific realism. But besides presupposing the order of nature to give sense to generalization, a law only discovers and describes facts. It does not explain them.

Secondly, a science must be knowledge. Now knowledge, it may be shown, is not a transeunt but an immanent relationship. The idea is immediately and, in a sense, immanently related to the thing known. The thing known has "been become" since any other approach would leave the knower outside the object and hence ignorant of it. The knower becomes the object rather than, to use a popular phrase, beats around the bushes outside of it.

But the empiriological spirit understands knowledge in a different way. The physicist measures something, but the relationship of the measure to the thing measured is again specified, to be experimentally meaningful, by another measurement; this is the reason for symbolic logic and semantics, the application of the empiriological method to thought. Knowledge is thus envisioned as a transeunt relationship. The corridor of the infinite regression must be faced if this series of measurements is to be consistently carried out.

The transeunt character of knowledge, as the empiriological spirit considers it, may be illustrated by the Lockean views that secondary qualities, like color and sound, are not objective but are the result of material phenomena, acting transeuntly and efficiently, on a psychological complex, indeed a physiological complex known as the human nervous system. Such a view takes no reckoning of the formal character which is demanded if knowledge is to remain in contact with the world as both real and really remaining itself, while "being become" by the knowing subject. Such a view, as Maritain says, destroys the intentional character of knowledge. Thereby, knowledge itself is destroyed. Naturalism has abandoned the term knowledge. Dewey speaks of "having"; Alexander of "enjoyment"; and Whitehead of "feeling."

A theory is not related to a fact after the fashion of an idea which is, in a genuine (intentional) way, the thing known. A theory is related to a fact transeuntly, if the discussion is had on the platform of modern physics. The empiriological method, as such, will not admit that the theory or theoretical entities *are* the familiar world in the way in which the idea *is* the thing known. Following his method exclusively, the empiriological physicist will argue that the familiar world is an illusion; he will attempt to account for the illusion by transeunt relationships. The familiar world does not remain what it is, valid, immediate, and objective —while "being become" by theories. It slips away physically into the theoretical entities themselves. In empiriological physics, cause and effect are equivalent; there is nothing in the familiar world which remains after the empiriological physicist has completed his task—remains, that is, after the fashion of the world known by an idea which does not destroy its object but becomes it, leaving it unaltered and objective.

Finally, the empiriological physicist does not interpret the world in terms of causes. There is no hierarchy in the world of pure empiriological physics, no difference between cause and effect. The whole reality of the cause appears in the effect. The two are equated.

Thus, as certitude, as knowledge, and as a quest for causes, the empiriological method when taken in its purity everywhere falls short of scientific rigor. Its strongest point of intersection with real knowledge is in the domain of law. But here too, the certitude is only physical, the knowledge empiriologically defined is not knowledge, and the factors which might be called cause and effect are rigidly identified so that there is no such hierarchy as a causal relationship.

What strict science there is among empiriological physicists is attained because they are men and because they are philosophers, not because they are pure empiriological physicists. The data of empiriological physics can be fitted into a truly scientific framework only by a philosopher, either by a professional one or by the empiriological physicist who like every man is ever thinking philosophically without knowing it. Since what there is of knowledge proper in empiriological physics is the fruit of philosophy, the genuine science of nature likewise has a right to interpret empiriological data. If there is a difference in interpretation, experience must decide between the rival views. How it does so is another story and belongs to later sections of this book.

PURE EMPIRIOLOGICAL PHYSICS TENDS TO SUBJECTIVITY

Man has tended to become very much self-centered in modern times for reasons that are theological and philosophical alike and have their counterparts in the Renaissance and the French and the Industrial Revolutions. An index of that subjectivity is scientism and the overwhelming commerce of the modern intellectual with the philosophy of method. Method has, reversing Kant's order, practically become a thing in itself, to be isolated, studied, and glorified for its own sake. Thus Northrop has argued that throughout the course of intellectual history matter may come and go; theories may revolutionize our conceptions of the universe from day to day; the constant through such changes of matter can be method. Such a sentiment would be echoed by the naturalists whose symposium, *Naturalism and the Human Spirit,* closes with J. H. Randall's plea for a faith in the empiriological method. Russell says that what may be transferred from one discipline to another is not results but method. Dewey dubs his philosophy instrumentalism which is nothing but empiriological method in philosophy. Bergson called empiriological physics "a logic spoiled." Modern philosophy began with a study of method, in the famous discourse of Descartes. Bacon entitled his leading idea a new organon. Method in modern times has become very much of a creature unto itself studied apart from matter. Kant used the phrase "pure reason," a kind of method without content.

But what is method in its character as a reality? Actually it turns out to be a being of the mind, an *ens rationis*, logical being only. It is in between the mind and the object, and yet it cannot be a real being as an interlocutor since the mind is aware of the object and not the method. Wedged in as a third thing between the mind and reality, it would not assist man in knowing. It would impede him. The method would be the object of knowledge, and the real object would never be known. Method must be transparent like a window and not opaque like a wall. It is therefore an *ens rationis* and reduces to logic. Logical empiricists like Carnap, Reichenbach, and Morris recognize this fact implicitly when they trace the grounds of empiriological physics to logic, where Russell had already carried the discussion. They want to turn philosophy into a set of rules rather than view it as an organism of content, and it is gospel with strict logical empiricists that the meaning of a statement is its method of verification. In his operationalism likewise, P. W. Bridgman draws meaning into an identity with method when he reduces the sense of a proposition to the set of operations that confirm it. Contemporary philosophy, as far as it emphasizes method, tends to acclaim the purely subjective, logical, formal, and non-real.

Whatever genuine philosophy may say about ideas, it shows that they are representative, patterned after the object. They are not bald beings of the mind. In fact, it may be disputed whether philosophy can lay claim to a special method. It proves the convertibility of being and truth—where truth is not something superadded to the object, like a can to the tomatoes, but something intrinsic to it, assuring the objectivity of our contact with being. If truth were superadded, we would always know only it and never the thing which it wrapped within it. Truth makes a purely logical addition to being and hence does not change be-ing's intrinsic and objective character. That is why by means of an *ens rationis*, the mind can know being as it is, relating it to it-self. Method and matter, in a realistic convergence, cannot be separated. When method is skimmed off as an entity for its own sake, empiriological physics becomes nothing but method or tech-nique and that, taken in all of its purity, is perhaps the chief originality of modern empiriological disciplines.

Evidence for the lack of ontal reference in empiriological physics, as such, can be drawn from the picture of the universe which it strokes. The secret of the empiriological method, as such, is its preference for control. But being can be controlled only in so far as it shrinks passively to human power, like pliable clay. If the entities studied by empiriological physics are the only ones deemed real and meaningful, then this material universe is one where pure passivity predominates. In the actual order, pure passivity is non-being; it is nothing. As Chapter 2 showed, it is prime matter. If then this passive view of things is ferried to its ultimate destiny, the universe fades away into a vacuum. Thus, empiriological physics in its formal method does not study the ontally real. It does not have objective reference when taken in all of its purest form. Whatever else he may be doing, one does not study the real when he decides that it is a vacuum.

This search after the passive is also evident in the notion of inertia, that every being at rest or in motion continues in such a state until it is acted upon by external forces. It is not proposed here to enter into a debate on whether a body, started in motion, would continue to move forever in a straight line unless disturbed from the outside. For one thing this idea has already been scrapped by the theory of relativity. There is also no wish at this point to discuss the relation of velocity and acceleration and whether the one is something natural to bodies and the second is impressed from without. The philosopher is interested in the ultimates, and the question here is only about the ultimate mean-ing of inertia.

Carried out to its farthest reaches, a universe of inertia would be a universe of passivity, taking its being and its motions entirely from outer transeunt agents. Even Kant admits that the only way of formulating this principle is to admit that every material change has an extrinsic cause. This means finally that there would be no intrinsic causality like that exercised by form. Prime matter alone would remain, and all distinction would be explained by motors only, acting from without like Mind in Anaxagoras or the Forms of Plato. The law of inertia states in its distilled form that all bodies are neutral or indifferent. They are at the complete mercy of outer forces to change their motion and direction, their structures and tensions, their quantity and quality, their densities and distances to each other. Probed far enough, inertia would rob bodies of all intrinsic reality that has been called nature. It would evacuate the universe.

The notion of inertia is another way of phrasing the empiriological preference for control. When Dewey affirms that "evidence is always extrinsic"[3] he is simply defining the prologue to the logic of empiriological physics. A thing is known, Dewey's analysis means, when we know what is outside of it. What it is is totally determined from without. In themselves, things become nothing. Reality once more reduces to a vacuum.

To show passivity in the empiriological world a third clue is the equivalence of cause and effect for a thoroughgoing empiriological method. It was the merit of Meyerson to have put this identity into pointed argument.[4] In the end, of course, like so many others who have perceived a partial truth, he carried his thesis to the extreme of including all human thought. Focused on empiriological physics, his work gives a valuable insight. The typical expression of the empiriological method is a mathematical equation, and this, of course, has interchangeable sides. As Leib-

---

[3] *Experience and Nature* (Chicago, 1925), p. 18.
[4] *Identité et realité* (Paris, 1912), *passim*.

niz put it in one of his phases, *causa aequat effectum.* Or, *effectus integer causam plenam vel ejus gemellum reproducere potest.*[5] The effect must be pure passivity. What is inert, the empiriological physicist will say, is sluggish; it is sluggish because indifferent. There is nothing in the cause which does not turn up in the effect. Empiriological method is grounded on the law of the conservation of momentum which is the general truth embodied in Newton's three laws and which even relativity mechanics retains. Max von Laue calls Einstein's $E = mc^2$ "the law of inertia."

When Newton coined the famous slogan, *hypotheses non fingo* and expressed his wish to avoid "unknown causes," he simply meant to accept no causes into his study that were not exactly equal to the effect. If there is any doubt about this point, reference should be made to the first of Newton's rules for philosophizing, as he called them: "We are to admit no more causes of natural things than such as are both true and sufficient to explain the appearances." In the ultimate, cause and effect become equal. Newton's apparent condemnation of hypotheses is but his way of defining the modern logic which is based only on economy in idea and principle.

The stark equating of cause and effect would tend to destroy the entitative character of the universe in the sense that nothing could ever *be* an effect, owning a character that sets it off from its causes and from other things around it. There would be an undifferentiated continuum, lacking in activity and in being. Nothing could ever produce anything else since there would be lacking a *preëxisting* subject, one that was more than pure passivity. All would be *ex nihilo.* The transeunt cause would be responsible for the total effect. If nothing acts out of a vacuum, there must be something more to the universe than pure passivity.

Empiriological physics, emptying the real as it does, is less ontology than it is logic. It is more method than matter.

---

[5] "The whole effect can reproduce the full cause or its exact equal," *Mathematische Schriften* (Halle, 1860), VI, 439.

PURE EMPIRIOLOGICAL PHYSICS LEADS TO NIHILISM

Empiriological physics has tended more and more toward unity as its history has developed. Our contemporary research is witnessing the latest steps of this forward drive. Radiation and mechanics, believed separated by classical systems, are now united in quantum mechanics. Einstein's theory combines the field and particle approaches to empiriological physics. It tends to unite electromagnetic and gravitational phenomena into one all-embracing theory that will describe the whole universe. As this march toward unity proceeds, there is a growing vagueness and generality of expression, a progressive diluting of content to obtain universality of form. Carrying this tendency to its ultimate fate by simply following present directions means that in the limit empiriological physics will wind up with an equation so vague that it will say nothing. This only confirms the views expressed above that empiriological physics tends to be pure method without matter, all frame and no picture, formalism without content, skin without the bones. The approach to being in empiriological physics is in terms of passivity, thinning out the act and the being of things until they vanish. Unity of method is being won at the expense of forsaking all content.

The ambition to make nothingness the ultimate can also be traced from what has been said about control which Dewey seems to take as the essence of empiriological method and in what has been said about making the world to man's image and likeness in the empiriological method as Kant welcomed it. By its theories, empiriological physics aims ultimately to deduce the whole range of human experience. The starting point for this deduction of all reality can only be the non-reality or nothingness if the deduction is to be radical and untempered. In its insistence on the primacy of control, empiriological physics would like to officiate at the creation of the universe, leading it *modo humano* out of nothingness and turning absolutely everything into its controls, uses, and forms. Empiriological physics is closer to Plato than to

Aristotle. Its world is a chaos, known by logical forms from out-side it, and the ambition of the pure empiriological physicist is to be a Platonic demiurge, making the world according to an ex-trinsic pattern, rather than discovering it as it is.

This tremendous productive ambition of empiriological physics was foreseen by Descartes who wanted it "to render us masters and possessors of nature."[6] How Francis Bacon, another promoter of the empiriological enterprise, wanted a science of works rather than of thoughts and how he lauded Knowledge as Power are well known. Descartes and Bacon were more than the pioneers of the empiriological method. They were its prophets.

Actually, it is what we do not control that is most important. Act and being man cannot make or break. He must take them as they are, obeying their laws and recognizing his dependence for knowledge and action on the eternity of their stable principles. These realities empiriological method simply cannot attain, and so scientism is hopeless as a teacher of what men should think, do, and hope to achieve. It is these ultimates that the philosopher ex-amines. He attains ultimates because outside being there is nothing, and being is what he studies.

EMPIRIOLOGICAL METHOD IMPLIES UNDEFINED TERMS

Kurt Gödel, the German logician, has established conclusively that the empiriological method must contain a certain number of undefined terms which he called "the undecidables." This is but a thesis, in the symbols of mathematical logic, of what philos-ophers have long labeled as a vicious circle in empiriological method when it attempts to verify its own self by using itself to do the verifying. Another way of putting this is that empiriolog-ical method is ever heterological, to use Grelling's language, a heterological expression being one that does not apply to its own self. Thus the word "sound" when spoken is a sound and is not

---

[6] *Oeuvres* (ed. Adam and Tannery, Paris, 1897–1913), VI, 61–62.

heterological; "silent" when spoken is not silent and hence does not apply to its own self in oral speech.

Recognizing that empiriological method is basically heterological and must always contain "undecidables," modern logicians in their attempt to ground empiriological knowledge have been concerned to reduce the undefined terms to a minimum and, if they fail in the project of elaborating a system that accords with the data of the working empiriological physicist, they abandon the project and start all over again with new terms. Such efforts have turned philosophy from a serious business into a mental sport. This is true especially in works inspired by David Hilbert and Rudolf Carnap, and to a great extent by Bertrand Russell. Carnap tried to construct the world from one undefined relation, that of similarity. Russell attempted to build the universe through undefined ideas called types. In a similar vein, the naturalists are aware that their first premise, the nature of empiriological method, is not rigidly established, and so they accept the method on faith.

Now to begin with what is not rigorously established or establishable is really to begin *ad libitum*. It is to sink the whole edifice of empiriological knowledge into the mud of mere whim. When naturalism counters, for instance, that the evidence of empiriological physics is validated by its public character, it still must be accepted on whim that publicity has something to do with validating and verifying. The only real reason why the conclusions of empiriological physics are public is because the empiriological physicist does not practice his method purely and simply. In the back of his mind, if not in the foreground, he has unconsciously held on to the sanities of being, unity, cause, and objectivity which the philosopher discusses and justifies. Left on his own, the empiriological physicist, *qua* empiriological, would become purely subjective.

But if the principles that save the empiriological physicist from lapsing into solipsism are really defended in philosophy, why, it will be asked, has the genuine philosopher in modern

times received so little public accord for his views? The reason is
that the empiriological physicist, while retaining the traditional
views of things as the support of his ideas, has placed all his accents on shallow phenomena. He has simply measured, and by
the concreteness of his measurements and their engineering
achievements he has appealed to the emotions. Ideas, abstracted
from matter, cannot as ideas stir the emotions, but images always
set them going. It is in the zone of images and sensations that the
empiriological physicist, as such, conducts his whole enterprise.
Readings can be taken with our eyes, atomic blasts can be heard
and felt. The reason why the empiriological physicist has received
more of a hearing than the genuine philosopher is that his ultimate criterion of truth, when he makes his physics his philosophy,
is an emotional one. Strange as it may sound to men like Dewey
who think they are living in a rough and tough world, the extremist of scientism is ultimately a sentimentalist in philosophy.
It is the case of the emotions of man running counter to the
higher faculties and crowding them out of their proper use. The
reason for the greater belief in modern empiriological physics is
that man has a physical as well as a rational nature, and the physical nature can deform his higher capabilities.

Measurement, without the self-evident relationship between
the measure and its object, likewise becomes a matter of caprice.
A yardstick is known to be a yard long ultimately because it is
seen to be so, not because it is measured by something outside itself. Such a process of measuring one thing by another *ad infinitum* would not offer a starting point unless the principle of
identity holds objectively and a thing can be eventually related
meaningfully to itself. If there is an infinite regression of standards, one can begin the study of the universe with an initial indifference that would convert the first premises of empiriological
physics into affairs of random selection, as from the rolling of
dice.

This thought can be given another turn. Opening the infinite
series of standards, where one is calibrated by another, would

lead to an indeterminacy. Thus the method of empiriological physics, like the picture of the world which it makes, points to a pure passivity. In fact, "the undecidable" is practically a synonym for "the indeterminate."

PHILOSOPHICAL PHYSICS KNOWS MOTION THROUGH BEING

Empiriological physics, to repeat, seeks to interpret reality only in terms of an outside frame of reference. Einstein and Heisenberg should never allow us to forget it. A frame of reference is but a yardstick or standard in terms of which values are assigned, just as the sun is a frame of reference for measuring the motion of the earth. But what is the frame of reference in the philosophic science of nature? What is to be the criterion for assessing when an explanation is sufficient and satisfactory?

For an answer to these questions, it may be remembered that being and its motion, as Chapter 1 indicated, are to be taken together. In the final analysis, this is still to be starkly maintained. But within that whole that is mobile being (*ens mobile simpliciter*), a real distinction may be made between the two terms, and it can be readily defended that the being apprehended by the intellect is clarified by the motion which the senses experience, and motion is in turn illuminated by being. In broader way, it could be argued that the effects in causal argument may be used to indicate the existence of a cause, and the cause in turn clarifies the effects when they are reconsidered. William James and Bertrand Russell, taking their cue from Ernst Mach, speak of thinking a thing "twice over." Here, changing being may be considered once as changing and once as being, and the two clarify each other. The principle of identity—being is—is not tautological. Reflecting on its meaning enables the metaphysician to draw out all his first principles without the middle term of a syllogism.

To say being *qua* being, for example, is not to be tautological. In the first case, being is materially considered and in the second case, formally. A similar situation confronts philosophical physics. The clash of being and motion helps the mind to abstract and thus to clarify both notions while insisting that in philosophical physics they are inseparable. These remarks may help to explain how the philosophical physicist can stay in his own territory and still make progress, rather than elope with the empiriological physicist to the second order of abstraction. Philosophy recognizes that a thing can be understood in terms of its own self. It may be its own frame of reference. And this is true no less in the first than in the third order of remotion from matter. To be its own frame of reference is what is meant when a thing is called self-evident or *per se notum*.

EMPIRIOLOGICAL PHYSICS IS METHOD ONLY

Indications that empiriological physics is a method only can be found in the words of the existentialist Martin Heidegger that the major advances in science have been in method or concept more than in matter. The two twin cornerstones of twentieth-century empiriological physics, the principle of indeterminism and the theory of relativity, both arose from the question as to what is observable. They were questions that one would expect from critical philosophy, and they emerged when empiriological physics became self-critical by seeking to work toward purer form.

Heisenberg and Einstein might just as well have asked what is passive or what is controllable. Their questions and their answers enable man to get a better hold on the universe, as later chapters will indicate.

Passivity is a principle of difference rather than of likeness. Only being is great enough to be shared. Traditional thought has always associated the fact of individuality with the principle of passivity in matter, insisting that species or form accounts for likeness. In James' language and to a certain extent in that of Santayana, the universe of empiriological physics is pluralistic, indifferent, amenable to man. There is no being in it and hence no dictation of reality prescribing rules of thought and norms of conduct. Only in a universe of being can there be objectivity, universality of conclusion, certitude, necessity, and immutability in knowledge.

Passivity indicates plurality from another angle also. It can be actuated, so long as it is passive, by a number of agents in a number of ways. It has no absolutely fixed and firm ground in the order of determined reality. Act is a principle of unity. Once passivity has been actualized, it can be thus and nothing else. What is, is. But so long as it is passivity, a number of fates could befall it. A pluralistic world is always an indifferent one.

From still another viewpoint, passivity betokens indifference, and pluralism. Only what is actual has tendencies since a reality cannot tend or act toward anything until it first actually exists. The passive is, as it were, lacking in what is termed a final cause. Mechanism is the consideration of reality entirely in terms of passivity. A machine has no intrinsic final cause because it has no inner tendencies as a machine. Its reality and its meaning come from outside it. The denial of the final cause, like the ignoring of the formal one, is accomplished only at the sacrifice of all the act and being of matter, with their reduction to a passive state that could neither initiate motion nor respond to it. Such a view transfers the reality of things to the controlling mind and thus exalts method into the importance reserved by the philosophical science of nature to the objective world. Method becomes the thing-in-itself. The world collapses into a chaos.

THE EMPIRIOLOGICAL PHYSICIST IS NOT A COMPLETE PHYSICIST

Man does not really learn about reality by studying how it is acted upon. It is only when, under the impact of an external stimulus, a reality acts from within that man knows something of itself and of its nature. When birds sing at dawn, there is something in the sound that does not wholly require the existence of outside inertial influences to generate it in the birds and to identify it in man. A tree has a reality from within itself. Iron never has the properties of copper; and we would never learn anything at all about the iron as such if we adverted only to the external forces slanting in upon the iron, without referring to the iron as distinct from these forces. We could never learn about iron by studying only the not-iron. Iron is something more than a name for a collection. It is really and truly contrasted by the mind with the forces acting upon it, otherwise it would pass unnoted. It is only when he closes the doors in his laboratory that the empiriological physicist equates iron to these outside forces. The intrusion of the empiriological physicist as a man into his life and learning as an empiriological physicist is so constant and connatural as to escape detection. It is as natural, in Meyerson's language, as breathing. Does method imply man's freedom to choose his approach to reality? In actual fact, man does not have the power beyond incidental vagaries of procedure to choose his own method of knowing anything. It is said that method is a constant in empiriological physics. But is not this very constancy, this freedom from the arbitrary, precisely owed to the fact that the matter determines the method rather than the method determines the matter—to the fact that reality is something more than the passive controllable stuff that empiriological method studies?

In other words, the empiriological physicist, though his rules do not tolerate it, clearly indicates that his logic is coerced by ontological considerations and that it is ontological and uncontrollable facts that guarantee the fixity of his method. A certain method is applied because the material, say the quantified aspects of the real which the empiriological physicist chooses to chronicle, requires it and is seen to do so. This means that there is a third reality which sees the relations between matter and method with the one dictating to the other. This reality is nothing but human intelligence, apprehending being and apprehending truth or method as only a logical addition to being, thinking a thing "twice over." If the empiriological physicist followed his metrical method to the letter, he would have to represent what is measured without representing it. He would have to measure only, rather than think of what is measured as a thing. To ignore a *being* that is measured is a rank impossibility, and fortunately the empiriological physicist ranges beyond the harsh limits which his methods impose. He is never a complete empiriological physicist. If he were, he would cease to be a man.

EMPIRIOLOGICAL PHYSICS IS PRIMARILY ART, NOT SCIENCE

But if it is decided that empiriological physics is not primarily science but more of a method unqualified, what is its positive meaning? To answer this query, it is important to rethink the logical and methodological character of empiriological physics, taken by itself. Empiriological physics tends to present the credentials of a practical type of logic. Logic is a liberal art which classifies thought with a view to putting it together in knowledge. Empiriological physics—and the empiriological disciplines generally, all of which view physics as their prototype—classifies things with a view to combination in the mechanical order.

From many points of view, this conclusion is impressed upon a critic. Empiriological physics goes wholly after the potential aspects of things. The reason for such an approach is to determine how matter will yield to human power. It is only the potential that we can control. What is known, however, in true speculation is certain and cannot be changed, and already it appears that empiriological physics, taken in all of its purity, does not have truly scientific knowledge for its object.

Human motor causality is largely a reshuffling of parts rather than the unaided production of new beings. Man did not make an atom bomb in the fullest sense. What he did was to dig out laws of interaction and combination in matter. He put nature together in new ways, adding nothing new to it since everything he employed was already in nature in the year 2000 B.C.; the idea alone is the twentieth century's. The bomb is a work of art, and to make it, man discovered in what respect nature was potential, and how, by his activity, he could control nature.

The indeterminate, the plural, the disorganized, and the passive are not directly knowable to man, and as Aquinas says, prime matter is the last reality recognized in our analysis of a thing. It is easy to see from what has already been said that empiriological physics, which descends toward prime matter more than toward anything else in the universe, is posterior to the philosophical physics. It strikes out toward what is last and least known in things, and what is known with respect to form; and hence it is not a prolegomenon to the philosophy of nature but, if anything, an epilogue.

Passivity is the locus of human motor causality. It is only art, or its analogue, that becomes important for its own sake. It is only the passive that man can command.

Art, it has been shown, has its principle outside it. This is the same as saying that the material, in art, *qua* art, is inert. Though in a practical case, art can never completely purify itself because it would require pure passivity as an actual medium, it remains the secret ambition of empiriological physics to view matter as pure art—eviscerated of all intrinsic character and indeterminately there for man to shape. When Protagoras utters his famous dictum, "man is the measure of all," a realist would agree with him in art *qua* art. Aquinas also states that art takes its measure from man and redounds to him.

But the world is not merely art to be controlled by man; it is a network of natures to be studied for what they are.

Art is thus a kind of controlled nature, and the element of control reveals the affinity of art with empiriological physics. Dewey was at one with realism when he wrote that "art is not nature, but is nature transformed . . ."[7] The more nature is harnessed in the laboratory the more material progress man can make in life. The purpose of empiriological physics, as its history shows, is to discover how and where nature is inert and how and where man can gain a hold on nature, turning it for his own ends. This purpose and that history show empiriological physics as fulfilled in engineering, making new devices for human use like refrigerators and airplanes and television sets, studying how things may

---

[7] *Art as Experience* (New York, 1934), p. 79.

be acted upon but never what they are. It is significant that the theoretical physics of one generation becomes the engineering rules of thumb in the next.

If the passive taken in itself has meaning only when there is something to be made, and if it appeals more to the artist than to the pure scientist, empiriological physics slopes toward the art of logic in the mechanical order where the prime purpose is not knowing but production. Samuel Alexander has detected this tendency and pointedly expressed it:

> Experiment is our control as to the material or empirical details. Logic controls us in the formal nature of this process, for it is concerned not directly with the empirical features of reality but with its categorial (*sic*) ones.[8]

Knowledge, to be objective, cannot interfere with the thing known. In empiriological physics, this interference is the rule. In such physics, whatever is meaningful is controllable.

Empiriological physics thus classifies material for putting things together. Logic, as an art, does not have knowing for its purpose, but use; it classifies thought for combination. Empiriological physics has a purpose that lies beyond itself, and that extraphysical territory is the area of human use.

Bergson argued that man tended to turn the real into geometrical solids in order to manipulate it. But this analysis, in both philosophical and empiriological physics, is misdirected. The model for the empiriological world is not solidity but the continuum, the flux and flow of Heraclitus which Dewey detects in modern empiricism and calls "the most revolutionary discovery yet made."

The empiriological physicist must envision matter as a Heraclitean continuum to get a hold on it. The indeterminate, the infinite, the purely passive, and even chaotic proportions which the empiriological world assumes under the seal of the empiriological method are only the synonyms for the inert and control-

---

[8] *Space, Time, Deity* (New York, 1920), II, 271.

lable cosmos that has been in the making from Galileo to Einstein and Heisenberg and Schroedinger.

An insight running from Aristotle through Aquinas and even to Whitehead affirms that the potential is the continuous and undifferentiated, while act confers identity on things making them different from each other. The element of difference between things involves a breach, the gap between being and not being this or that. When matter is viewed as a continuum, it is impossible to assign differences and to account for the original and intrinsic character of the various differing realities. All things fuse into the potential.

What is continuous is controllable. Empiriological physics wants to shift the universe into neutral to get a better command over it. What is act and what is being man does not control, but obeys. Thus Einstein, to achieve a better control on things, denies the difference between quantity and motion, space and time, matter and energy. Quantum physics shrinks away from treatment of discrete and individual particles, preferring to work with continuous aggregates. There has always been a temptation to idealism in the empiriological enterprise, to a doctrine of continuity between mind and its object that stands in contrast with the realist's notion of a break between inner and outer worlds. That tendency to idealism, the empirical spirit has never overcome. It is the signature of pure art.

By holding to continuity between knower and object, space and time, quantity and motion, and among the various particles in an aggregate, the empiriological physicist retreats from act and strokes out a more potential and controllable and neutral world. He wants a fluid world, water that will take the shape of any Protagorean vessel he prepares for it. Only he wants to give the water more than shape. He wants to invest it with everything that it owns.

But just as logic is never pure logic, so empiriological physics falls shy of its ambitions. There can never be a pure logic, for the reason that it would have nothing left to logicalize; there must always be the intuitive, the directly apprehended which will stand in the way of what modern logicians call "the formalization of logic" in its entirety. Neither can there be a pure empiriological physics. Empiriological physics can grow onward indefinitely and so can the mechanical aspects of civilization which it fertilizes. But matter, because it is not pure potentiality, will constantly rebel at being reduced to the empiriological categories and will break out to dictate their revisal. The theories of physics are schemes to help experiment gain a hold on the passivities of things. But since matter is never completely passive and potential, the theories will keep failing, and new ones will constantly be projected to take their places.

But if empiriological physics is directed toward the practical, how can its knowledge character, or lack of it, be explained? The answer is that every art must work with a medium. In sculpture, the medium is marble; in music, it is sound; in carving, it is wood. The theoretical side of empiriological physics studies this medium, as any artist must do, to exploit it to the fullest in the mechanical order. Empiriological physics is not pure at this point because the art is not pure. Thus no art can proceed without knowledge, whether it be the painting of a madonna, the making of a stained-glass window, or the cooking of a meal. But the knowledge is for the sake of the art.

Every art is a compromise between the general principles of the art which are known and used and the practical demands of an individual situation where the rules are applied. For matter is never wholly passive, obedient to the law of inertia, which every artist must somehow recognize, and which empiriological physics has devised a means of studying in an intense way and as applied, theoretically, to all matter. There is a point beyond which the typewriter, for instance, will not yield in obedience to inertia. If it were made purely passive and potential, a stenographer could not write on it. The real originality of the artist designing the typewriter consists in getting the most out of the potentialities with which he works without losing the reality of the typewriter in the process.

The necessity of relaxing its hopes for controlling nature at a single stroke and the need to bargain with its matter that makes any art a compromise has often split empiriological physics into what it calls a crisis. In the classical system, for instance, field physics was at odds with particle physics; matter would not obey the laws of energy; the luminiferous ether was so hotly debated that someone finally defined it as "the subject of the verb *to undulate*." These large oppositions of view simply reflected different ways of gaining a hold on matter which refused to ease itself into any equation that attended only to passivity. As in the case of a household artist, painting a kitchen chair, the atomism and the modified dynamism of the nineteenth century represented different stances and angles of swing and intensities of stroke upon a matter that would not wholly surrender to a single formula for its inertia.

Because matter can never be simplified into a pure passivity, empiriological physics, an art, will always oscillate between various theories, each of which yields it something of matter's secrets but none of which can tell all. Crises are normal to it. There are such conflicts even in the present between relativity mechanics and quantum theory, between spacelike intervals and timelike intervals in relativity itself, and in quantum mechanics between wave and particle approaches. There are deep differences, as the next chapter will show, between the first and second laws of thermodynamics, and between the statistical and macroscopic treatment of thermodynamical phenomena. Matter will always revolt at being treated too passively; nature will always revenge itself upon an art that becomes too conscious of its own power and its own purposes. The empiriological physicist must use now this theory, now that—whichever gives the best results, and as with every artist, we are not interested so much in how he proceeded in his work as in what he made.

Einstein's latest view (1949), which he calls the generalized theory of gravitation, is a bid to overcome the cleavage between gravitation and electromagnetism. It is a movement toward a unified field theory that would not only harmonize relativity theory with Maxwell's work in electricity but join relativity and quantum mechanics which have been at odds. Thus far Einstein has been unable to give physical meaning to his mathematics that would suggest experimental tests of his theory. But significantly he works out his deductions from an equation ($g_{ik} = s_{ik} + a_{ik}$) containing a symmetrical factor (s_{ik}) and an anti-symmetrical factor (a_{ik}). Once more a split remains to annoy the empiriological mind since electromagnetism is still somehow admitted to follow different and anti-symmetrical laws by comparison with the greater symmetry of gravitational phenomena.

In the conception of his work, the artist cannot consider pure passivity alone, or he would have nothing to make and no end to be attained and nothing to use for a material. To achieve his goals in a practical way, the artist selects the best combination of his matter's potentialities with the end that he has in view. It is on this point that the empiriological disciplines differ. Their method of knowing general rules is alike, but they all have a different subject matter and a different actuality which they wish it to possess. Thus biology differs from empiriological physics, and physics from chemistry, and empiriological psychology from empiriological sociology. It is this practical consideration of their matter and the ends they put upon it that divide the empiriological disciplines from each other, and it is this point in the practical order also, uniting the theoretical side of empiriological physics with its engineering aspects, that explains why the empiriological method does not misfire into nihilism.

From the knowledge viewpoint, nihilism would result from the empiriological method; but empiriological physics is not speculative knowledge primarily and absolutely; it is in the ambit of art, and every art is a compromise. This compromise forces empiriological physics incidentally and secondarily to be knowledge. There is a resistance to the physicist's sorties, just as it is wind resistance that keeps an aircraft flying. It is this contact with the actual and the objective—for no science is possible without them—that enables empiriological physics to participate in knowledge in a derivative sense, and that ought to be explored further elsewhere.

This resistance element that empiriological physics does not control but must ever concede, philosophical physics takes into account. It could be argued, in this fashion, that it is the things which empiriological physics does not know in its own method that give it whatever claims it has to be speculative knowledge. The realities which the empiriological physicist will not concede to be real and objective confer the only realism and objectivity that his efforts can boast. Speculative knowledge of the world is only in terms of nature, not of art; and the empiriological physicist, in a secondary sense, makes some oblique contact with nature which compels him even when he controls it, which yields its inertia only if he will take its act, and which rewards his obedience, making him come to terms.

It should also be pointed out again that since art is an imitation of nature rather than nature an imitation of art, the conclusions of empiriological physics cannot be transferred to the objective world without criticism by the philosophical physicist who has kept his roots in nature and therefore his branches in a realistic atmosphere.

EMPIRIOLOGICAL PHYSICS FREES MAN FROM NATURE

Freedom, as this concept is understood and defended in genuine philosophy, is always freedom for . . . freedom for God, freedom for self-development, freedom for religion. It is never freedom from . . . In the aim of empiriological disciplines, this relation is reversed. The purpose of empiriological physics is to free man from nature, to make him independent of hot and cold, hunger and material need. Modern travelers are free from the vagaries of nature which played havoc in a day when vehicles on land and sea were far less secure than now and when weather forecasting was hardly known. Man is no longer a slave to nature in the way of travel, farming, disease, and time-consuming tasks about his home. Empiriological method has rendered him freer from nature.

But such a freedom does not make sense unless it is supplemented by a doctrine which tells what freedom is for. Freedom from . . . is a mark of conquest and respects only those things which man can control. Freedom for . . . is the mark of obedience, law, and order. It respects that which controls man. Man is free only because he is controlled and created, having within himself a principle that requires his allegiance. Right is always founded on duty. Even in freedom from nature, man is never completely free because his art is never pure. He develops a trolley-car system which makes it easy to go to and from his work, but he must stand on the corner and wait for the streetcar to come by. Man is a master. But nature is not purely passive before his power.

Empiriological physics, when left to itself, tends to free man in a purely pagan way. From its premises, if they become philosophical dogmas, naturalism is the logical outgrowth. What keeps the various tendencies of man, individual and social being that he is, from getting out of stride is something outside the empiriological domain. The potentialities of things are what make them good instruments. What is outside the instrument, however, measures what it will be and what it will do. To be attracted to others for what they can do to us is the lowest kind of friendship. The highest type is benevolence, the love of like for like. There is something of this sort also that can be applied in our attitude toward matter. To regard matter only for its potencies, to think only of its uses, is selfish and subjective. To be attracted by what is actual is to be attracted by what makes man lift up his mind and heart to God. Here there is another way of setting empiriological physics off from philosophical physics and identifying its aims. Empiriological physics is geared to action; philosophy, even in the first order of abstraction, aims to know. The empiriological method, as a way of knowing, cannot bring man up to God. Since God is pure act, as metaphysics shows, nothing can be learned of Him by thinking of the purely passive. Empiriological physics has use for its purpose. Being is that which determines the use and the user. When we emphasize only potentiality, we have an indifferent universe.

The laws and theories of empiriological physics tend to show it only as an instrument, to use Dewey's term, without being able to give certain knowledge of the causes and reasons of things. Of what value is it for us to know the so-called law of gravity except to use it in our daily lives, for example in designing an hydraulic elevator or the wing structure of an aircraft? It is important to know that hydrogen and oxygen combine in such and such a proportion with a view to the manufacture of hydrogen peroxide or for the decomposition of water to obtain the elements for other uses.

Theories have for their purpose to predict. To gain a hold on things, a certain temporal sequence is necessary—a *continuous* passage from potentiality to actuality. The empiriological physicist, getting ahead of a thing and predicting its arrival, has the impression of presiding at its production.

Prediction in time is the analogue of deduction in thought.

The empiriological physicist cannot study this temporal sequence causally, and he has no wish to do so. His world is potential and what is potential as such (passive potency) cannot be a true motor cause. So the empiriological physicist studies temporal sequence descriptively. This is but another way of saying that he classifies, and Tennant was right when he pointed out that empiriological method does not really seek the order of nature but a certain logical type of organization and deducibility, "not a teleological reasonableness, but rather a quasi-logical rationality."[9] Simon[10] argues that there is a "resemblance" between antecedent and consequent in what he holds to be the notion of

---

[9] *Philosophy of Science* (Cambridge, 1932), p. 145.
[10] *Prévoir et savoir* (Montreal, 1944), p. 52.

causality in empiriological physics, and McWilliams[11] takes the empiriological concept of cause to be one of form rather than of efficiency. Is not the "resemblance" that of classification and the "form" chiefly that of the logical world?

Logic involves a description or classification of things. Philosophy is the study of their causes. To classify and describe is not to explain. To explain is to give causal reasons why a being is in this or that class and not simply to establish the fact of classification. Truly scientific knowledge can never be purely descriptive since it is only in terms of causes and reasons that science is science. Description is a logical device.

Functionality also is not a process of explanation. It is a process of classification or description, to test the classes that belong together.

The only reason why the empiriological physicist comes to concepts of true causes is because he is not a pure physicist. He is also a man, thinking like a man, and matter not being purely inert has likewise resisted him. He attains speculative knowledge because he goes beyond pure empiriological physics and because matter puts more than its passivities before him.

EMPIRIOLOGICAL PHYSICS CATALOGUES FOR THE ENGINEER

Description is something characteristically human. Like logic, it does not exist in either God or in the angels. Men like Kirchhoff, Pearson, and Mach held that the aim of empiriological physics was only to describe, and Husserl has elaborated a complete philosophy of description called phenomenology.

Description must go from part to part. It must presuppose its object to be like a machine and like the prototype of all machines which is the undifferentiated continuum. Description is stopped by the chasm between being and non-being, which is another way of saying that it cannot get at being from within. Like logical classification in the tree of Porphyry, description can never state

---

[11] *The Modern Schoolman,* XXIV (1947), 11–18.

what a thing is in terms of its own self. It does not bespeak self-evidence. Description is always in terms of outside genera and figures. It is formalistic and artistic. What is formalistic is what is logical, and classification in terms of parts bears a close kinship with mechanism. Description, art, formalism, classification, and mechanism are closely interlaced. It is only in terms of causes that being can be studied.

Empiriological physics deals with the description of events. It remains on the level of the reality described, the universe of quantity and its relations. Indeed, only quantity and the quantified cede to descriptive techniques.

In the empiriological field, functionality allows the scientist to describe what happens when something else happens. It is a way of classifying.

Induction, as the empiriological physicist conceives it, indicates the potential character of the being which he studies. Pure induction is the counting of things that are singular. As singular things, they are not intelligible, but as singulars they can be marshaled for human use. Counting the singulars is a way of classifying them. In empiriological physics, describing them, it is their use that is important.

Probability plans a tremendous role in the discussion of contemporary physical problems where large numbers of particles are involved and where precise individual measurements are not feasible. On the practical plane, probability is often satisfactory as mental state. It has often been said that probability is the guide of life. Whatever truth this maxim may have in the science of ethics, it can easily be seen that probability is a good guide in the field of production. It is lacking, however, in full scientific rigor as far as it falls short of certainty.

In philosophy, induction (abstraction) is a method of discovery, and deduction is a method of proof. It is by induction that the premises of demonstration are formulated, induction in the sense of abstraction. By deduction, the premises are properly combined so that a conclusion may be drawn. It is known by induction, for example, that man is a rational animal and also that what is rational is spiritual. Hence, it can be concluded that man has a spiritual character.

In empiriological physics, deduction is in the order of discovery. It is the purpose of a theory to predict experiment. Deduction is the organon, and if a theory can uncover and predict new individual facts, it is said to be validated. Induction is more a method of proof. The criterion of truth is the facts of experiment, inductively assembled. This only shows again that the highest activity of the empiriological physicist, his ideational background, which is called theory, is really subservient to another end besides scientific knowledge. It aims at discovery.

Discovery, not proof, is the goal of empiriological physics. From Georges Sorel, one may borrow the term *systematic* and some of its meaning. Empiriological physics makes a system or catalogue of facts for the engineers. It multiplies data by schemes that are not explanations and are not ultimate. The ultimate in the empiriological order is the practical and the factual of experience.

If discovery is the main target of the empiriological physicist, there are some important conclusions to be drawn, and empiriological physics, in its most characteristic feature, is removed from the field of philosophy where it has been conducting at least a cold war throughout the modern period.

Empiriological physics has to do not with the cognition of causes but with the discovery of fact. Discovery is a matter of experience in philosophy. It is the point of departure in philosophical physics rather than its highest goal. The empiriological physicist multiplies data, but such a multiplication of experience does not explain experience any more than merely counting eggs can ever reveal what is inside a single one of them.

But such a multiplication does provide the practical man with new ideas. As Max Scheler says, the destiny of empiriological physics is in what the Germans call *Technik* and what might be translated as applied art or engineering—adapting man to his environment. In the maxim of Auguste Comte, *savior pour prévoir afin de pouvoir*—"knowledge for prediction and prediction for power." Practice is learned only by experience. By multiplying experience, although we may not add immediately to speculative knowledge, new practical insights can and are being developed. Multiplying experience also multiplies data for the philosopher.

Empiriological physics, it was seen, tends to be a pure method, geared toward discovery. Attending only to the inert, it searches out the ways in which matter is passive for control. Speculative knowledge, in the proper sense, is secondary and comes into play because man is never a pure empiriological physicist and nature is never sheerly inert. Realistically assessed, empiriological physics tends, it would appear, to the temperate zone of art, controlling by classifying and classifying for control. Empiriological physics aims not so much to explore as to exploit, but the medium of matter with which it works prevents its art from ever being a pure art, guaranteeing thus the unlimited progress of empiriological physics while forever forcing its final hopes to crumble. But while showing the engineer how to get more for the investment of his efforts, empiriological physics also makes oblique reference to philosophy.

This remark serves to recall a statement from the beginning of the present chapter. Empiriological physics is a complicated business, and it is not likely to yield its definition in a terse and tidy formula. Though the foregoing developments attempted to follow it in its principal aim, it would be fatal to close the eyes to everything else. Since in the practice there can never be a pure art, the empiriological method tends to bulge out beyond its narrow limits and make contact with philosophy. There are thus several ways in which empiriological physics may be considered:

1. *Pure empiriological physics* is in the direction of art, as shown by its vision of matter as only passive and its method of study which is control. It aspires to formalize its subject, but the achievement always stops short of its goal. Empiriological physics in this light is always becoming (*in fieri*).

2. *Empiriological physics in a loose sense* is more modest in practice. It mingles common sense philosophy into its technical models, constructing what Simon calls "a cosmic image."[12] This looser form is the status that empiriological physics must always take in the concrete. Backed by common sense ontology, it is hence not devoid of certitude. Ohm's law is not a logical figment, and neither is the valence of nitrogen or the Carnot principle or Boyle's law.

3. *Empiriological physics in the line of philosophy* affords data to the philosophic science of nature that must be interpreted in the light of the full experience where philosophical physics ever takes its stand while empiriological physics branches off into experiment. In the early stages of empiriological physics, like the classifying of the stars or the clocking of falling bodies, the interference by experiment is not very prominent, if present at all; the stage is more one of observation within experience and its philosophical and empiriological physics are close together if not one. But when the experimental technique is pressed, empiriological physics begins to take its distinctive shape as a discipline of control. Even here, however, the philosophical physicist can appropriate the experimental data, supporting them not by a common sense ontology but by his certain speculative science and finding that they relate to his larger truths previously established. The consideration of data from empiriological physics is not the basis of philosophy. Passivity and potentiality are the last things known about bodies and presuppose a prior science if they are known at all. Knowledge should always go from the more familiar to the less if it is to be consecutive, as logic requires.

When empiriological physics comes to be evaluated, it is in the first sense that it is to be taken. A subject should be judged by what is principal in it, and the originality of empiriological physics is the approach to matter by controlling and classifying its

---

[12] *Op. cit.*, p. 104.

passivities. In the second and third senses, the primary aspect of empiriological physics is mixed with other ingredients, and the empiriological method, as such, must be isolated from the mixture to be assessed properly for itself.

In the second sense, the empiriological physicist as a man, without a formal philosophy, tempers his technical world view with whatever support it needs from common sense to keep it from shriveling into the vacuum which pure art would make out of objective reality.

In the third sense, philosophical and empiriological physics can cross-fertilize the world view of man, the whole. Though the experimenter, because of the metrical character of his work, cannot pronounce on the significance of what he is measuring in the line of mobile being, philosophical physics can take the data which empiriological physics uncovers and submit them to speculative appraisal. Or better still, the empiriological physicist should be equipped with a philosophical background to appreciate for himself the significance of those aspects of the whole of matter which he brings to experimental focus. Philosophy thus can bring experiment meaningfully back to experience and by integrating empiriology with speculative principles can give the findings of the laboratory a much more scientific character than they now have. In this sense, empiriology opens up a vast treasure of discoveries to be evaluated for the completion of empiriological physics, the enrichment of philosophical physics, and the integration and progress of human thought as fully human.

This truth is especially apt for the present age where the opinion is rife that the empiriological physicist alone is busied about what is truly knowable, while genuine philosophy, which is after all the highest science of nature, is often ranked with poetic fancy or is called, in the naturalist vocabulary, a supernaturalism. It is easier to throw bricks than to lay them in place for a home, and naturalism's home is far from orderly.

Probably no age is as rich in data as ours, and if the philosopher thrives on experience, in no age have the potentialities of philos-

ophy been as great. That profit has not been reaped from all
capital of material can be explained by the fact that the c
absorption in matter and overconfidence in the power of con
ling it have dulled the proper use of man's higher spiritual p
ers, which are directed to truths that he cannot control an
good that he has only to obey.

The theses here defended differ somewhat from the opinio
Maritain who gives to empiriological physics the status o
science distinct from philosophy; and they diverge also from
verdict of De Koninck and the Laval school, where empiriolog
physics is taken as a continuation at the dialectical level of
demonstrative science that is true philosophy. According to
latter view, empiriological physics would search out ultir
differences among things that demonstrative philosophy, bea
upon the larger and more universal truths, cannot strike.
piriological physics would thus read the fine print in the l
of nature.

This chapter has taken a different slope toward the natur
empiriological physics than does Maritain.[13] It has inflected
experimental side of physics, while Maritain has underscore
mathematical form and has envisaged perhaps the second sens
empiriological physics in the foregoing division. Though
gestive of classical intermediate sciences in its noetic aspect
perhaps only in the way in which an operative science is subc
nated to a speculative one,[14] knowledge is something secondar
empiriological physics taken purely. The only reason for its a
ogy to mixed or intermediate sciences might be the way it lu
physics and mathematics, extension and motion, and all the o
dualisms, into that mixed or continuous status to gain a be
hold on its matter. The continuous or potential is the controlla
and the more continuous the empiriological world and em
ological disciplines can be made the more control results. So

---

[13] Cf. *La philosophie de la nature* (Paris; Tequi [n.d.]); also, *Le
grés du savoir*, chs. 2, 4.

[14] Cf. *In Boethii de Trinitate*, q. 5, a. 1, ad 5.

analogy to intermediate sciences may be only an analogy and an historical accident besides. Far from rejecting Maritain, the analysis of this chapter would find him an ally on many points and fit his larger conclusions into the present context.

De Koninck's view,[15] which is also suggested by the independent and later development of Sofia Vanni Rovighi[16] in Italy, seems also closely akin to the conclusions which the preceding pages indicate. This is especially so, if dialectic is truly accepted as the attempt to know a thing by principles extraneous to its nature—an analogue of the empiriological ambition.

The difficulty is, however, that when empiriological physics is taken by itself, its logical structure and its ontological references are so radically opposed to those of the philosophical science of nature that one can scarcely be regarded as the continuation of the other. When the empiriological physicist, as such, goes after pure inertia, he can hardly do so in order to know it since it is not properly in the line of knowability for man. To put the thought in another way, the emphasis on control would seem to put the empiriological physicist in the company of art, of the regulative and operative, rather than the speculative and scientific. It is by that which is principal about a thing that it is to be judged, and everywhere within the strict limits of his method, the empiriological physicist has been found busied about the passive and potential only. In this light, the end of his method, taken purely, is not in speculative knowledge but in man, the artist.

Empiriological physics, as the progress of the sequel will show, can analogate philosophy. It can illustrate philosophy in a sense in which Aquinas used the word *inductio*. But it can hardly enunciate philosophy. Thus, philosophical physics can interpret the data of empiriological physics, refining the ore to exemplify

---

[15] *Culture,* IV (1941), 465–476.
[16] *Rivista di filosofia neo-scolastica,* XLI (1949), I, 77–90. Vanni Rovighi is, however, poles apart from De Koninck in the role assigned to the philosophy of nature, as opposed to metaphysical and empiriological disciplines.

its own certitudes and using what is descriptively organized as an aid in abstracting explanatory principles. In this fashion, empiriological physics is accepted (*finis operantis*) into the status of a naturalized citizen in philosophical physics. But to search out the passive would seem to install empiriological physics as primarily concerned (*finis operis*) with the operable and the productive which man approaches to alter and not to contemplate.

If the reasoning of this chapter is accepted, it leaves no grounds for the scandalous war that has racked the modern period, between laboratory and life, empiriological and philosophical physics, the matter of ancient learning and the method of the modern one. All men are philosophers by birth because they are thinkers, and in some inchoate form, they are also empiriological because they are makers. Between philosophical and empiriological physics there is no more conflict than between man, the thinker, and man, the maker, using both his thinking and his making in different ways to attain his supreme goal of happiness.

Suggested Readings

Aristotle, *Posterior Analytics* (*passim*).
Dewey, John, *How We Think* (Boston, 1933).

6

Motion, Dualism, and Modern Physics

MATTER DISCLOSES A PLURALITY OF SUBSTANCES

The question of whether nature is one or many is a favorite theme of philosophers. In a variety of form, it plays through the whole symphony of man's philosophical endeavors, leading him at times into the discordant notes of pluralism or monism and often to that delicate harmony of a realistic mean.

The extreme views in this controversy are alive today. William James, George Santayana, Bertrand Russell, Rudolf Carnap, Charles Morris, and in general the whole empiriological spirit slopes toward the view of pluralism. This doctrine involves the Humean reduction of substance to phenomena and the tendency to hold the infinite dividedness or the radical indetermination of all things in themselves.

Monism, typified in the ancient world by Parmenides and on the modern stage by Spinoza, Hegel, Marx, and F. H. Bradley, comes to light in the present-day systems of dialectical materialists, of Samuel Alexander, of Alfred North Whitehead (in a modified way), and of the theory of relativity when it elevates its space-time continuum into a philosophical altitude. For monism, everything is substantially one and at most only apparently different. If this reality is called God, the monism is called pantheism.

In this chapter, evidence will be adduced first in a familiar way and then a little more technically to show that atoms and molecules are all distinct substances and that the changes which they undergo are therefore substantial changes. But a preliminary issue is the problem of whether there are no substances whatever in the universe, resulting in a pluralistic cosmos; whether there is only one substance in nature, justifying monism; or whether there are, as a realism would hold, many substances in nature each charged with a unity of its own, making for a plural (as opposed to pluralistic) universe.

As the philosophical science of nature presses onward in its reflex purification of common-sense notions, it observes that the realities in the mobile world are, so to say, drawn in upon themselves; they are invested with a stamp, however frail it may sometimes appear, of isolation, exclusiveness, nucleation; things have a certain centricity (a datum which the atomic physicist also admits when he seeks and sees the centralizing tendencies of the nucleus in an atom and now, in the era of the meson, of the "nucleolus.") As Bergson put it, "matter has a tendency to constitute isolable systems . . ." [1] All these facts are crystal clear in that part of the mobile world which is living. Plants have an intussusceptive character; animal action is more immanent than the vegetative; at the summit of nature stands man, so centralized within himself that he can achieve a total reflection on his own being and determine his own actions through his own will. In the organic world, the hierarchy of being stands forcefully there for man to see. The original substantial character of each living thing is shown by its interiority to itself which we may call immanence.

The substantial nature evidenced in a man, an animal, a plant, is also realized, however feebly, on the level of inorganic or mineral matter.

This could be shown, according to one approach that looks promising, by comparing the thinker's experience of himself with the similar but lesser types of being whose operations are apparent

---

[1] *L'évolution créatrice* (Paris, 1918), p. 108.

in the outer world. According to this view, man understands the sensation of the animal and the vegetation of a plant much more intimately when, as justified by their operations which are seen as analogous to man's, he projects beneath these operations what sensation and vegetation mean in his own self-experience.

This understanding of the lower world in terms of ourselves rather than the reverse procedure, which evolutionary psychology has popularized, is suggested by the psychophysiologist, Kurt Goldstein. It could be extended easily to the inorganic world where there is found a feeble analogy to that substantial unity which man himself understands in his own being, and finds tapered off as he goes down the scale of reality. Certain existentialist approaches might be taking this heading.

But on the other hand, valid knowledge, it was established in Chapter 1, must begin with the general and move toward the more determinate, and a take-off from our subjectivity, an individual being, would involve the reversal of this direction. Hence, the approach suggested here seems inadequate and wears at most the character of a confirmatory argument.

But there is another avenue also open to show the plurality of substance in matter. What is meant by saying that in the objective world beings seem drawn in upon themselves, centers of action, nucleating identities? A first approximation to this answer might be given in Spinoza's maxim, *unumquodque in suo esse preserverari conatur*. Things in interaction resist one another. There is no mere Heraclitean flow. There is dynamism in nature, but at the same time, there is something somewhere that is definite in everything. There is a plurality of differences, or else things would be indistinguishable. No motion, and above all, no distinctions in motion could be and be discerned in a pure flow.

To deal rigorously with this problem, philosophical physics may well resort to the idea of inertia which is at the core of empiriological physics and should be clashed against the notion of nature. What is inert has its principle of motion outside of it, as the very converse of natural movement; what is inert is sluggish because it is indifferent, passive, actualized completely by outside agents. If inertia rules the real and nothing owns anything from within itself, there is an infinite regression in matter.

Aquinas censured the Pythagorean spirit for using principles "extraneous to the natural." Moreover, he argued, if a thing has a finite velocity, it cannot be moved completely from the outside. For if bodies did not put up resistances to these outer agents and did not bear a reality from within, by the same force that moves a thing it should be moved faster and faster until an infinite velocity has been attained.[2]

Now if there were no natures with their inner principles and if all things had their principles of motion outside them, anything that moved would move infinitely fast. The plain fact is that there are no infinite velocities in our universe and that, if (*per impossibile*) they did occur, they would be indeterminate and hence closed off from knowledge. If bodies differ in motion, as they do, then none is infinite. Far from being indeterminate, they are comparable and hence definite in themselves. In other words, granted that there is such a thing as inertia at all, it cannot be unlimited in this moving world of ours, and if it is limited, there are brakes. And these brakes are natures or substances.

It is said that there must be natures or substances, a plurality of them. For differences cannot be explained if there is only one so-called bottleneck to inertia. Opposites have diverse principles. To ground the fact of differences, there must be a manifold of these counteragents to inertia, a plurality of things moved from within. Aquinas depicts every nature in the strong language of a "prime mover" and declares as the study of being more clearly shows, that these prime movers on the finite scale are not moved inertially but by participation in the Prime Movership of God.

The empiriological physicist may counter that the resisting principles to inertial movement are inertial themselves and that

---

[2] *In de coelo et mundo*, Bk. III, chs. 3, 4, 7.

the world is a cosmic cascade of mere inertia where the fluid is simply seeking and finding its own level as time goes by. But this view is not satisfactory. For what is inert cannot be differentiated; one purely inert thing could never differ from another, and if there is only inertia in the world, there are no differences. If there are differences in inertia, there is no pure inertia; there are principles of difference within the inertia, an equivalence to saying form and matter. Since the inert as such is indeterminate and has no distinctions and since nature unfolds a plurality of differences, there must be a plurality of non-inertias, a plurality of substances, a plurality of natures. For substance is a nature existing.

A purely inert world would be actually nothing. Where there is one divergence from inertia, there would be only one being formed by the two opposites. Where there are two such divergences, there would be two differing citizens in the cosmos. If there is a plurality of being, there is a plurality of non-inertias.

This logic is enough to show plurality, but it may not convince the monist, holding that the mineral world is one substance, at least at its roots, while branching into a plurality of appearances or attributes. In Spinoza's language, the world is *natura naturata,* and for Alexander, it is a continuum in which individuals are nothing but "pieces" of space-time.

There are some pointed answers that can be given against the monism of the material world. This world, if it is radically one, would not be a mobile reality since it would have to move itself; there is nothing outside it in matter that could move it, and ontologism of course would lead to pantheism too. Hence, there could be no motion in a monism of matter.

Nothing could account for such a world in its temporal history. If it were one, it should be absolutely ordered, and yet there are disorders like earthquakes and tropical storms which clearly argue to a cosmos that is more than a single substance.

A monistic world should not produce the novelty which motion discloses. As a mover, it would have the actualization in the first place and would not, could not, confer it on itself what it already owned.

But there is another way of disproving monism. An acute accent should be laid upon the difference between the living and the lifeless which the philosophical science of nature, the study of mobile being taken simply, has a duty to discuss. Plants and animals, acting immanently, are more perfect than lower matter; they are more finalized with respect to themselves. The lifeless, lacking the immanence-conferring form of the living, has less of a unifying principle to muster its various differentiations into unity and marshal them to final good of their subject. From the amoeba to man, a living thing shows its own individuality by its motions, and is capable of achieving a remarkable unity amid functional and structural difference.

The living is greater than the lifeless, more directed to itself, more whole-making, more unifying of variety. A single tree is greater than the entire mineral universe, just as all the trees in the world could not act as immanently as a single moth.

Now of the unity amid variety in the inorganic world, there can be no doubt. The coursings of the stars, the cycles of the weather, the neutralization of storms and lightning and even meson showers, the pull of gravity that presumably keeps the crust of the earth from peeling off into space, in fact all the phenomena pondered by empiriological physics show the order, coordination, harmony, and general balance of the material world.

But if this material world were all one being, the perfection of it would have to be greater than that of a living thing. The nonliving world, single reality that it would be in a monism of matter, would be ordering itself, acting on itself, and integrating such variety into unity that the single mineral substance would be a being more perfect than the individual plant and even the animal. The single material nature would be more versatile than the life above it, if it could unite the whole manifold of the mineral world into a radical oneness. To state a corollary, this mineral unity would have to act, like every cosmic being, for its own intrinsic good, and its unifying achievement would be greater than that of life. So if the inorganic is less perfect than the living, as the previous logic revealed, then the material world cannot be one substance, and monism must be rejected.

The argument against pluralism showed that there are natural differences in the universe. The present assault against monism shows that these differences cannot simply be modes of a single substance and that there must be many substances in the material world. If then, nature is neither many nor one, it must at the same time be one and many, or since the oneness and the manifold affect the same things, it must be one-in-many. This is one of the meanings of matter-form.

It was said above that inorganic things are bent in upon themselves, self-centered, and nucleated. There is a real resistance by a thing to every movement which tugs at it. There is always a reaction to action, a stubborn opposition of things differentiated from each other, and this balking character in the mineral world shows itself whenever differences are to be changed. When hydrogen reacts with oygen to become water, it does not do so without putting up a resistance. It does not flee off, falling away like an infinitely long line of tenpins when the first one tumbles over. It stands fast. It tries to hold its own. If it did not resist becoming water, it could never become water at all. If there were no friction, a machine could never produce anything—automobiles could never run, a pen could never write; if there were no analogue to friction in the atom, the atom bomb could never have exploded. The thing that resists in an atom must be the very same thing that yields. Otherwise, there could never be any action at all.

One may well use empiriological physics as Aquinas applied it, by way of illustrating philosophical physics rather than by way of proof. In such a light, an example of the centricity of the atom can be seen in the present attempts to account for it. The orbital electrons are viewed as moving around the nucleus. The nucleus is composed of protons and neutrons, and their cohesion is presently believed associated with the meson, the supreme centralizing agency so far detected in mineral matter. But how can this centralization of the atom and its withdrawal toward itself be explained?

Such use of empiriological physics does not of course subscribe to an ultrarealism regarding the submicroscopic and insist that so-called "scientific objects" in Whitehead's language—such as atoms and their substructures—really exist in matter as they do in empiriological theory. But they have at least a basis in the real world. There is some analogy in matter, some real counterpart to the empiriological report on them. Otherwise, the triumphs of empiriological theory would be impossible. "Scientific objects" might be called constructs, partly real and partly logical, but Russell has given the construct an unfortunate meaning. It is safer to say that electrons, protons, atoms, and the like in some way analogate real things, and this applies not only to the foregoing mention of "scientific objects" but to the discussion that will soon get under way.

Material substance cannot be its own passivity, for then all would be prime matter moving, when moved by the lightest stroke, with an infinite velocity, and making the universe indeterminate. It is something more than potency, plurality, and quantity. It is acted upon through its potency, but it is not passivity and inertia alone. The world is not pluralistic.

Nor can material substance be its own activity. For then it would have its own perfection to begin with and motion toward the new would be impossible. It would be pure act. Hence the world is not monistic.

The same subject must ultimately be active and passive. If this were not so, then either the passivity and activity, running in parallel, would never be rooted in the same principle, and no action could occur; or the substance would be both passive and active simultaneously and under the same aspect—a contradiction. That is why Aristotle argued to the existence of nature as the subject of contraries and why, in his view, the active character of things seen by the monists and the passivity which the pluralists exalt are accounted for by avoiding the errors of both extremes.

THE ATOM IS A SUBSTANCE

It may be now be proposed that this fact of substance is realized at least on the level of the atom and the molecule. No one can deny that atoms of the various elements parade a dazzling heterogeneity. One can begin with hydrogen, the first element, and run the scale to the recently fabricated element, berkelium, the ninety-seventh, finding in the long stretch that no two elements have the same pattern of properties. Some are colorless, some are colored, and their colors, varying in wave length and wave amplitude, cover the whole visible spectrum and range beyond it at both ends. Some of the elements are gaseous, some liquid, some solid. They taste differently and smell differently. Each has a different weight, a different electrical and magnetic structure, different spectroscopic lines when suitably excited. Some are soft, some are hard, some cannot be felt, others would be injurious if we touched them. The same rainbow of difference shines at the level of the molecules, as every freshman chemist learns.

Now the point to be debated is this: Can a single type of subatomic substance account for these differences of atoms, or if there be a plurality of types of subatomic substances, can they in turn by a merely mechanical rearrangement explain this heterogeneity which the atoms of the various elements exhibit? This is the critical issue in the struggle between the dualism of matterform and the contemporary empiriological spirit. (The case of mechanism in chemical compounds will be discussed after settling the question of the atom.)

The first alternative can easily be dismissed. A single type of subatomic structure, rearranging and recombining in myriad ways to form the manifold of the mobile world would have to be as versatile, as adaptable, as pregnant to relations, and as immanent as life itself. There must therefore be a plurality of different *types* of substances. At this point, the issue becomes: Can these different subatomic types by their various recombinations give rise to the manifold of motions in the sense world? Though the answer is somewhat more difficult than in the preceding case, the philosophical physicist is compelled to decide in the negative.

The reason for such a decision would lie along this line: As we scale up the ladder of being from mineral, to plant, to animal, to the human level, there is noted a growing interiority and a dying away of that inertia which limits the spontaneity of a nature. Neutrons, protons, and electrons, together with the lesser known entity, the meson, are the building blocks of minerals and would lie at the base of the ladder. Looking again at mineral heterogeneity which experience discloses, if so few units could account for such a vast and varying number of immediate relations—for every relation must ultimately be rooted in the immediate—the periodic chart would be a story of subatomic particles more versatile and adaptable than life itself. These (four or so) particles would have to be capable of immanent operation, of the spontaneity, interiority, and originality displayed by plants, animals, and even man.

The material world which affects our senses (much less, as will later be shown, the subatomic particles which are even lower on the scale of mobile being than elements) is not capable of achieving the immanence of a living, many-talented thing. Immersed in inertia, activity and spontaneity are limited to a corresponding degree. Whether matter-form terminology be employed or not, the point cannot be denied that such entities as neutrons, protons, and electrons, few in number and poor in property, do not have sufficient reality, an adequate amplitude of substance, *being* which is intrinsic enough, to individuate so many attributes and relations as the elements reveal. Charles Hartshorne has rightly pointed out, for instance, that the superiority of a dog over a pillar is that the dog can relate itself in various ways to the pillar but that the pillar cannot do likewise to the dog.[3] As Aquinas remarks, the degree of actuality, of perfection, of interiority in a subject is measured by its ability to receive accidents.[4] The subatomic particles do not have such perfection, actuality, and interiority to account, of their own inner natures, for the heterogeneity of our experienced world.

A comparison of the mineral and living worlds spells out the verdict that the living is higher than the lifeless and cannot enjoy an immanence and versatility greater than that which turns up in the living domain. In full-dress terminology, the subatomic particles are much more "determined to one" capacity than living things, much more limited and localized, much fuller of inertia and passivity, much more specific and particular, ampler in potency and poorer in act. "Determination to one" is the opposite to originality, spontaneity, versatility, and immanence: "the less a thing is immersed in matter, the less it is finited," says Aquinas.[5]

Form in the inorganic world is so faint that a mineral is almost completely under the tyranny of inertia; hence, the success of the empiriological method in the region of the mineral, its lesser success in biology where form is greater and more exertive, and its shortcomings when it attempts to philosophize about man, the reflective self-determining creature, where form triumphs over matter or over inertia. Mineral matter is much more "determined to one" accident (or several) than it is capable of subsuming many. If all facts of difference could be reduced to a few rather simple subatomic substances—electron, proton, neutron—determined differently in forming atoms by the corresponding interiority and versatility of their own intrinsic powers, there would be a contradiction in nature. Effects would be beyond the com-

---

[3] *The Divine Relativity* (New Haven, 1948), p. 7.
[4] *De natura accidentis,* ch. 1.
[5] *De natura materiae,* ch. 1.

mand of their causes. The operations of subatomic particles, achieving such heterogeneity, would be richer than their impoverished principles.

On the ladder of being, it is found that the plant embodies the perfection of the mineral world; animals have the perfections of plants; and man has the perfection of all the world below him. Man has all the perfection of, say, a rose, but this perfection is not specifically and distinctively present, like a panel on the door. It is indeterminately present in the unity of man's being. In Aquinas' view of men by reference to lower creatures," they are less finited." Rose-ness is indeterminate in man because man's formal determination is of a higher nature. At the very peak of reality stands God, the exemplar of all things, and yet He is a simple substance. Now if all the facts of difference which experience reveals in the mobile world are to be reckoned from a few subatomic realities, recombining under their own mechanical power and in a purely mechanical way, they would be, as it were, the exemplars of all their possible determinations. They would have a fullness of being that would be as the fullness of man, containing all the perfections of the world below him. But such a richness cannot be conceded to the subatomic entities.

The stature of a being may be measured, to borrow a Kierkegaardian expression, by its ability to relate itself to itself. In this respect, man is the greatest of changing beings and a mineral is the lowest. A living thing is more operative of itself, and though still requiring potencies for all of its activity, is more capable of coming into direct contact with what is external to it without changing in its substance. The ability of a thing to relate itself to itself is the measure of its ability to assume relations to the outside without changing. The lower beings in nature depend on their accidents and have a feebler power, from the natural resources of their own substances, to assume relations to the outside without that loss of identity which matter-form dualism would claim to be the fate of subatomic particles within the atom.

The "determination to one" is but a paraphrased and realistic version of Spinoza's maxim, "every determination is a negation."

There is a determinate proportion between an agent and what this agent can produce. If the principle to be acted upon by the agent exceeds the proportion of the agent, no effect will follow; but when the passivity in the being to be acted upon is scaled downward by increasing and thus brought within the sphere of influence which the agent commands, then motion can eventuate. This is but a rephrasing of the principle of causality or sufficient reason.

The variety in the mineral world demands a variety of principle, while the subatomic principles actually grow not more varied but fewer in number than the mineral heterogeneities they are supposed to explain. And as the units become fewer in number, their depth of being would have to be greater to assume, without changing, so many relations as the macroscopic manifold would require. Is their being so deep, their reality so rich?

MODERN RESEARCH ARGUES TO HIERARCHY

To answer, it is enlightening to consider the Thomistic principle of continuation or hierarchy, compared with the latest developments of empiriological physics. The hierarchy in nature is arranged according to the degree of actuality owned by the various grades of being or in other words, starting from the higher entities and tapering downward, according to increase of passivity or inertia. As Aquinas so pointedly puts it, plants are more inert than animals and the atoms and molecules are more inert than plants:

And therefore in the elements the matter is least perfect, because only one form of one element is actuated at a time: and if sometimes the form of another element is virtually present, there is no abiding of the first thing but a change, as for example when the heat of fire acts on air inducing the quality of fire. In compounds, indeed, matter is more perfect: for here, with the one form conferring actuality to the compound there are present all the forms of the elements, virtually however and not essentially because each of these requires its own determinate quantity . . . ; hence since there is one substratum for the compound and one existence, its form is one. Some compounded substrata, however, are animated, and especially man whose form is not produced from matter predisposed by the quantity of the compound; hence it is fitting that in the animate world the essences of some forms should be without their full perfections; for this is the profoundest way in which animate things transcend simple compounds, namely by perfecting their matter through the acquisition of more than one form at a time, just as we see that in one way what is simple is resolved from compounds and in another way from prime matter in which, prior to the becoming as such, there is nothing actual of the form to be produced . . .[6]

The reality of hierarchy in the world of changing being is of so striking importance that another analysis may be cited:

And hence it is that the forms of elements which are the most material of all are characterized by active and passive qualities, say hot, cold, humid, dry, and so on as befits the disposition of the matter. But the forms of compounds, namely of inanimate bodies such as stones, metals, minerals, besides the powers and activities which they participate from the elements of which they are composed, have some other more noble powers and activities characterizing the forms specific to them . . . and thus in a constant ascension, the nobler the specific form, the more excellent the powers and operations proceeding from it; so far forth that the noblest form which is the rational soul has the intellectual power and operation, that not only transcend the power and action of elements but all corporeal power and action.[7]

Empiriological physics has disclosed data on particles below those of the element which provided the first step in the Thomistic hierarchy, a hierarchy that may be described in terms of matter-form, as Aquinas himself preferred in the foregoing passages, or described in the broader perspective of various degrees

---

[6] *De natura materiae,* ch. 4.
[7] *De occultis operibus naturae.*

of changing being. Descending beneath the surface of the atom, the empiriological physicist has sounded a further increase in the degree of inertia, a greater determination to one, or in the more picturesque way of putting it, a greater immersion in matter.

According to relativity mechanics, even energy is inert. A photon (light particle) at rest would be of zero mass; it must be kept in motion to preserve its being. A single atom or molecule is thermodynamically meaningless since heat depends on the agitation in an aggregate; a single particle is neither hot nor cold, according to empiriological physics. An electron by itself is also without significance; it is inertly defined by what is outside of it, say a proton. Such entities are poor in their being.

The free electrons which account for electric conductivity are "free" in different ways depending on the substance in which they float and in whose tyranny they are. That is why the conductivities of different substances differ. An electron, if empiriological physics be correct, has only two properties, mass and charge. In the same category is the proton. The neutron has only one property, weight, and like its fellow subatomic particles, it manages to enjoy a magnetic moment by its spin. A neutron in nature is limited and quite determined to one, like all the other fundamental particles. Its slot in nature is the nucleus whither it tends, never having enough interiority and independence to make a permanent abode elsewhere, for example amid the orbital electrons. The negative meson, first detected in cosmic ray showers, survives in independent status for only millionths of a second, and the neutral meson, believed now as the fundamental cohesive particle of the atom, has a lifetime that is almost incomparably shorter. Such entities are in matter's poorhouse.

Atoms, empiriological physics reports, can appear colored through a kind of resonance radiation: the wave length of the incident light which strikes the natural vibrating frequency of the outer electrons in the atom will be reflected, while the other wave lengths are absorbed. An electron is the cause of color, but color itself it cannot claim. It is impoverished. The neutron, proton, electron, and meson can be combined in so many different ways only because they are so dependent, impoverished, and inert, so determinable not of their own intrinsic powers but by forces acting from without.

An atom is much more respectable in its status. Oxygen cannot combine in as many ways as an electron combines into other systems, simply because oxygen is less inert and has more of its own, more independence, more nature. An atom is richer, less immersed in matter, greater in nature and in being; in the Thomistic terminology of hierarchy, the subatomic particles even more so than the elements are characterized by their enslaving localization to only one form at a time; they are more determined to one, more impoverished, "more finited"; they have less power and activity than even the elements; they are more inert.

What empiriological physics has done and what the following sections will attempt to deepen is to revise downward the hierarchy of being detected in experience, a hierarchy that begins with the material and mounts from the element to the compound to the plant to the animal, and finally to man. Empiriological physics has dug out a world below the elements. Such a world is weak in being and can no more account by its own power for the level above it than inertia added to inertia gives less inertia or the sum of passivities yields act.

EMPIRIOLOGICAL PHYSICS TENDS TO THE LOGICAL ORDER

In Chapter 5, it was seen that the difference between empiriological physics and philosophy may be projected against the difference between art and nature, the logical and ontological orders. A further pursuit of what this means will forge a powerful tool for the denial of mechanism in the atom.

In the ontological order, the so-called order of first intention, beings become richer and fuller as the scale is mounted, beginning with the quiddity of sensible things and stretching to the perfect simplicity of God. In the logical order, the richness of a thing, as the analytic of logic moves along, becomes less and less, intension decreases as comprehension increases. In the end, being has become so vague that it has virtually lost all content. Hegel, mistaking this impoverished being of logic for real being, denied the principle of non-contradiction and identified being with the naught. From the content angle, the procession in the ontological order is from the complex to the simple; in the logical order, it is from the simple to the complex. In Alexander's words, "Things are grouped extensionally into classes; intensionally they are connected by a common nature."[8]

Kant held, in his attempt to ground Newtonian physics, that ontology must give place to analysis, and Lachelier was keen enough to detect that empiriological method is essentially analytic and regressive. Empiriological physics as such seems to make this option for the analytical and logical sequence. Each part isolated, not being capable of immanence or nature, tends to have a distinctly compartmented function; united the parts form the whole as in the logical sequence. Theories, for instance, are judged not by their intension but by extension in their domain of application. Intension cannot be treated in empiriological physics as such; it is available only to abstraction.

To reinforce this view of the empiriological disciplines as categorical and summative, a typical modern textbook on biology may be consulted. The simplest forms of life are studied first, the one-celled amoeba or paramecium, then comes the study of the hydra, then perhaps the earthworm, then fishes, frogs, guinea pigs, and so on—until man is studied last, as though he were simply a more complicated form of the preceding structures. This order is dictated largely by the theory of evolution, and it moves from the simple to the complex. A similar direction is revealed in empiriological physics where, for instance, the world experienced by man is pictured as a more complicated form of particles and processes of submicroscopic dimensions. Even in Russell's latest language, for instance, and "event" is "a bundle of compresent qualities."[9]

---

[8] *Space, Time, Deity,* I, 176–177.
[9] *Human Knowledge* (New York, 1948), p. 83.

It is not surprising to find logic joining hands with mechanism; both are formal, both are art, both stress categorical parts rather than participated or entitative wholes. Reality, instead of ever being thought in the form of a whole, is perpetually treated as a sum. Empiriological physics stresses the differences between things and their dividedness, just as the logical categories do in their purely logical aspect. In the end, the universe becomes a pluralistic one for the physicist because he studies only differences, as J. B. S. Haldane, a Marxian scientist, has recently averred. The logical universe is likewise plural since the only unity studied is itself a category, the predicamental unity within the genus of quantity. Comte divides the sciences not according to the intensional hierarchy outlined in Chapter 1 but according to scope or extension. It is more than a coincidence that positivism should finally wed itself, as *logical positivism* shows by its name, to the science of logic. Logic is the favorite pastime in logical empiricism, and Dewey with his company of naturalists also makes capital of it. It is in logic that the final meaning of the empiriological method is today being sought, and typically enough, the critical issue in the search is the relation between intension and extension. Russell now founds the first in the psychology and the second in the logic of form.

Logic and the empiriological approach to reality have more than the name, logical positivism, to indicate their points of matching. Both logic and the empiriological method prescind from being as existing, as unitive, as substantial, natural, identical, immanent; they prescind from being as changing. It is by existence, as the metaphysician shows, that all realities are alike; it is by their categorical, essential, logical, inert implications that they differ. Empiriological physics has made its option for a plural, logical universe, and though perfectly legitimate as a means of gaining the control on matter which logic seeks on thought, such a universe should never be allowed to disguise itself as ontology.

Aquinas accused the Platonists of his day of neglecting the

world of nature. He charged them with a logical approach, declaring that "from many things which they, in the logical order, consider in universal form, they make facile conclusions." Platonism is categorical and mechanistic, having much in common with the modern empiriological approach. Like empiriological physics, Platonism fits its forms—obtained as in modern theory ahead of the sensations which they interpret—to the world that is not self-intelligible but transeuntly known. Russell's logical universe, capped by Frege's notion of "types" which are undefined terms that define other terms, is similar to Plato's. Emphasizing the logical construct Russell has coined a "supreme maxim for scientific philosophizing" which states: "Whenever possible, substitute constructions out of known entities for inferences to unknown entities." These ideas will be considered more specifically in Chapter 9.

Platonism, like Russell's logicalism, is not the science of changing being, and neither is logic or empiriological physics. In seeking to free empiriological physics of anthropomorphism, positivism has made the physics more than ever anthropomorphic because empiriological physics has thereby lost contact, *qua* empiriological physics, with objective changing being. The logical approach affords the empiriological researcher better control on the relation of method to matter which he conceives as art, and by a better control over method, he gets a better control over matter. It is art working on art. But it is not ontology.

Only a metacategorical, natural universe can be objective and non-anthropomorphic.

SUBATOMIC UNITS ARE LOGICALLY GENERAL

The protons, neutrons, and electrons are poor in their being like the entities of logic. They are extremely passive and determinable. They are general. They do not exist independently in nature but tend immediately to servitude elsewhere. Certainly, when passing from one atom to another they may be said to possess a minimal form, like an atom existing in nature that will later be part of man. But the point here is that the atom is not simply a subatomic machine shop. It is a substance, a nature existing, and the subatomic particles cannot, by simple summation, explain it because they are too poor and general to account for its riches and heterogeneity.

The subatomic particles have a meager independence and a paucity of property which makes the "determination to one" almost literal as a determination to one property only, and such entities cannot account for the variegated motions in the universe. In their own operation, the subatomic particles display an inert and almost total determination from without. An electron will not act except incidentally and by mere mechanical impact with another electron. The principle of like acting on like, a corollary of the principle of causality, which the science of being is competent to discuss, does not appear in the empiriological technique.

In friendship, for instance, the love of like for like is the very highest type, since each party is not interested in the other for what he can get; they are alike in the first place, and so in a sense, nothing is to be gotten by either. The love of concupiscence, on the other hand, is not a relation between two acts but more between potency and act. One party loves the other for what the second party can confer on him.

Mutatis mutandis, there is something of these relationships existing analogically in all material being because interiorly all creatures are alike, imitations of God. An electron will not seek another thing like it but will seek what can confer something on it. It will seek a proton, for example. Empiriologically speaking, it cannot be said to produce what is like itself (in the sense of *omne agens agit sibi simile*) namely, another being distinct from itself. An electron has such a feeble and univalent reality, almost unipropertied reality, that what it causes or produces is, as might be expected from the law of inertia, something unlike itself— hydrogen for instance, if it unites with a single proton. Nothing that is in hydrogen as such, no hydrogeneity that is, can be found in the electron as such. Empiriological physics has a preference for the categorical. Like, for the empiriological vision, never produces like in the original association of nature with the reproductive. An electron physically is in the hydrogen it "causes." That is why empiriological physics as such does not study causes, and another discipline is needed to explore the causal relations of empiriological entities.

The action of an electron—and the proton and neutron could be treated similarly—depends in slavish obedience on the conditions existing outside it. It will not act with another electron and, as far as empiriological physics has disclosed, with a neutron. It will not act except in a context that is eventually qualitative and formal. It will act, for instance, between the electrodes of an electroscope or between the iron, copper, or aluminum plates of a condenser or in an inductance coil of this or that material. Even in the free electrons which are credited with determining the conductivity of various metals, the number present depends upon the kind of material in question. An electron's action depends on a qualitative context to make its action possible at all, depends on a principle that gives being a degree of independence and intrinsicness as in atoms, on a principle that holds things together and makes them orderly, on a principle that resists inertia and is called nature. This simply means that if the electron acts in a multiplicity of ways there must be a multiplicity of different non-inertial factors in the world since the electron's nearly total inertia does not allow it to differentiate itself to account for the multiplicity.

These non-inertial factors may be called forms, and it should be insisted that the proton and neutron would bear the same analysis as the electron. Inertia cannot account for differences, and the deeper empiriological physics digs, the more inertia it uncovers; and the more and more inertia, the more and more the world becomes indifferent. Empiriological physics cannot arrest the non-inert, the informed, the natural. This is available only to the intelligence and is discerned and discussed in the philosophical science of nature.

The more independent, stable, versatile, and active reality of the atoms cannot be achieved by adding together passivities and inertias. Activity is not just a sum of passivities, any more than a sum of dependent beings will yield the independent.

THE NEUTRON IS POWERFUL BECAUSE POTENTIAL

It will be objected, of course, that the above arguments are in contradiction to facts. What about the tremendous power of the neutron? After all, this little entity, smashing into the uranium nucleus and splitting it, was responsible for the havoc at Hiroshima and Nagasaki. Does not the empiriological physicist boast that his triumphs over the nucleus have armed him with the basic power of the universe?

But however powerful it may be to the atomic engineer, the neutron is powerful only in the general and inertial sense comparable to the poverty found in the logical category. Its stature is not great enough to exist and operate in a natural stability; its action depends on the nucleus which it assaults; it behaves differently depending on the material which it bombards, just as an electron acts differently in a vacuum tube depending on the material and structure of the electrodes. The neutron's speed can and must be regulated in atom smashing, a fact that was one of the knotty problems in the Manhattan project and was untied by the development of a so-called moderator.

Relatively inert, the neutron, as the empiriological physicist discloses it, must be acted on from the outside; inert in its own actions, its work is strictly proportioned to the subject (determined to one) on which it operates. The only reason why the empiriological physicist can employ and direct the neutron in his services is because it is so general, undifferentiated, indeterminate, inert, and potential. If it were powerful of its own, he could not gain a hold on it, commanding it to fulfill his designs. The empiriological physics of today is more powerful than its nineteenth-century forebear because it has pierced to realities more inert, potential, and controllable by man. Empiriological physics moves toward prime matter more than to form, to what is passive, indeterminate, undisposed to independent existence.

The neutron, according to present views, is responsible for the existence of isotopes, elements with different masses but with the same chemical properties. The general logic that the subatomic particles, pointing as they do in the direction of prime matter, are much too inert to account for the stable, active, independent character of atoms, must naturally include isotopes as distinct substances also. Neon, for example, has three different isotopes. The same chemical properties are associated with three different masses, each differing solely by the number of neutrons in the nucleus. In one, there are ten neutrons, in another eleven, in the third twelve. That the neutron is long only on potency and inertia and is short on act is supported by evidence that it can alter only the massive or potentiality-principle within the atomic structure. It does not have sufficient intrinsic, qualitative, and natural endowments to change the more active, spontaneous, and original powers of the atom in question. In this connection, the proton seems a higher type of entity than the neutron, and in the latest advances of empiriological physics, there is evidence that despite the neutral character of the neutron, the proton is probably the stablest of the nuclear particles. When a proton is driven out of a nucleus, a radical change occurs in the chemical properties of the element. When the neutron goes, the change in an atom's policy is only minor.

RADIOACTIVITY DISPLAYS NATURE'S STABILITIES

Another objection might be launched from the viewpoint of radioactivity. Here apparently is an instability in nature itself, an argument against the thesis that "everything tends to preserve itself in being," a challenge to the idea that atoms are more independent and self-centered than subatomic particles, a preference in nature for chance . . . and indeterminism and inertia.

But the dualism of matter and form does not argue to a static stability in the world of atoms. On the contrary, it emphasizes and explains their motions. It is maintained only that the stability and independence of atoms is not comparable to that of the subatomic particles, and that instability added to instability cannot yield stability, any more than potency plus potency can equal more act.

But are we not off on the wrong mental track, since a team of horses, for instance, might pull a wagon up a hill where one alone would fail? Two of the same kind seem more powerful than one. If, however, you put the horses in the wagon, as the empiriological physicist puts his particles into atoms, the wagon would roll back down the hill rather than upward and would do so with a greater momentum when two horses were in it than when only one was taking the ride. The horses would be riding in the wagon mechanically and by way of art. Here, granted a plurality of natures, the question becomes what the subatomic particles can do by their natural power and whether they can form the wagons of atoms. And before considering radioactivity, the general principle should be repeated that stability cannot be gained by adding instabilities.

Now of the thirty-six isotopes of elements in the uranium, actinium, and thorium radioactive series, only five have a half life which is less than a second—a half life being defined as the time required for half the atoms present in a given aggregate to decay. But in a quiescent period, a radioactive atom persists stably and as a natural entity. Even in the case of Thorium-C′ which has a half life of a tenth of a microsecond (10^{-6} sec), the element is stable in its short span of independence, and no force, even the case of chemical combination, can accelerate or retard its half life.

Now this stability is a tremendous fact that cannot be brushed lightly away in the arguments against chance and a mechanistic universe. An electron, on the other hand—let us envision it as the beta particle emitted by a radioactive element—does not persist stably and independently. It immediately seeks the nearest substance that will take it in. On this point, the empiriological physicist might well argue that the electron has a drag that would indicate its desire to remain independent, a drag appearing for example in the phenomenon of "transit time." The counterargument would hold that the electron need not travel instantaneously to another substance when it is freed from an atom but simply that it immediately tends to do so. It does not thrive on freedom. The atoms tend more to independence.

The half-life period of radioactive elements, on the other hand, is independent of the environment. It persists even in compounds, lifeless as well as living, and for that reason radioactive elements have been used to trace and time the process of food assimilation even in man. Radioactive elements occur in nature, and their natural independence, even if their lives are fractions of seconds, is not duplicated by the neutron, proton, or electron which are defined, related, and determined practically in entirety by what lies outside of them.

SIMPLER FORMS ARE SOMEHOW IN COMPOUNDS

But the continuance of an element's radioactivity even when in combination with other elements and with the body of man poses the question of the manner in which elements are present in compounds and, if the atom is analogously a compound of subatomic particles, of the manner in which the particles are present within it. Aquinas declared that it was a matter of virtual presence and Scotus that it was a case of the formal-eminent status of the lower in the higher, like the presence of vegetation in man. Not wishing to labor a technicality but more to define and defend the general character of philosophical physics, virtual presence will be taken below in a wide sense, preserving the note of unity in compounds which Thomas stresses and at the same time doing justice to the diversity so ably emphasized by Scotus.

Virtual presence is a form of potential presence, but it is not a matter of raw potency, like the capacity of a tennis ball to be batted across the net. In a compound, the forms of the elements have actually vanished into a new unity, but the activities of these original forms, their virtue or their strength as the word originally meant, remains in some way since it has not been altogether nullified. Virtual presence may be said to imply a mixture of act potency, and its nature for that reason can only be explained through matter and form. The lower degrees of mobility in nature are always apparent in the higher, but in their more elevated form they are dominated by the higher reality in which they are, expressing its nature and coöperating in its actions. They are not expelled from existence in their adopted homes, but they are, as shown by the unity of the whole in which they reside, more indeterminately and subordinately present than when they existed in isolation.

In the wide sense of the word which has been adopted here, the most striking example of virtual presence that occurs in nature is the reality of man. His soul is a rational one, the form of his body. Yet it includes not only intelligence and will since it also is the source of sensitive and vegetative action as shown by man's unity. At the human level, sensation is thus present virtually, like vegetation—reliable psychology reports that there is no such thing as pure sensation in man; vegetation is also present virtually in animals; and the plants like the other living things are marked by the presence of the chemicals detected by the biochemist.

It is the office of that part of the philosophical science of nature which is called psychology to discuss the body-soul union and the way in which sensation is related to intellection. But if the conclusion of psychology is accepted that man is only virtually a creature of sensation, vegetation, and mineral matter, the solution of the present problem in the more general philosophy of nature becomes easier to exemplify. Sensation, at first glance, seems to be an actual and almost isolated part of man rather than a virtuality. If the rational soul, the greatest unifying element in nature, cannot transcend it any more than it does, it should not be surprising that compounds fail to obliterate the vestiges of the elements comprising them. Consistently, it should be expected that the ingredient elemental forms should be, in their new virtual presence within compounds, even more actually residual than the virtualities in man where the integrating force of form is greater. Compounds bear certain traces of the elemental forms in a greater or less degree, as sensation remains in the composite that is man.

The matter-form account does not declare that the subatomic particles melt into a homogeneous mass by their combination. If the atom is ever directly observed, it is quite likely that a certain granulated and differential structure will be disclosed. But this is true of living things from the amoeba to man and does not contravene the substantial unity of the composite. The unity may be looser in matter because the integrative force of the form is less than in animals and much less than in man. But a minimal form is still a form, and a virtual presence is still virtual even though the act might be stronger than the potency.

Rutherford showed in the early twentieth century that the atom is differentiated in structure, but this does not deny its formal unity. Nor does it establish that electrons, protons, and neutrons are absolutely the same inside the atom as out. Sensation *looks* about the same in the animal as in man, especially when attention is turned upon the appearance and structure of organs. But how a thing looks and how much it measures are not the standards for proving matter and form. Whitehead objected to reliance on "visual immediacy" and pleaded for attention to "causal efficacy." It is the operation, the action, the motion that counts; for it is motion that philosophical physics must explain. A human arm, seen for the first time while a man was wearing his coat, might give the appearance of being mechanically attached to the body. But its motion, apart from its static appearance which might just as well be the arm of a clothes' model in a window, discloses the unity of the arm with the whole man. It is not how the atom looks that counts or even how it is measured as impulses are measured in the human nerve. It is the motion that matters.

Radioactive elements retain their radioactivity when united in chemical compounds, but the other features of the element are transformed. In speaking of the presence of the element in the new substance, its radioactive features are not the only factors that matter. Melting point, specific gravity, magnetic properties, and other such identifying marks are not the same in radium as in a radium salt, showing that the element has undergone a substantial change. If the radioactivity remains, it can only be remembered that sensation remains in man but in its deeper aspects is found to be only virtually there.

THE LAW OF CONSERVATION ATTESTS TO NATURES

The discussion of radioactive decay leads into the more general discussion of thermodynamics, which will clarify in a more technical way what has been argued thus far about the relative increase of inertia as matter is smashed, and which will likewise lead toward a basic framework in which matter-form dualism can now be confirmed.

The first law of thermodynamics, an expression of nature's stability, states the principle of conservation of matter and energy, or, if one is a stickler, of matter-energy. The second law states the instability of nature: entropy is always increasing, unusable energy is constantly being produced, the universe is running downhill.

These two laws are rather radical in present-day empiriological physics, if they are not indeed the two most basic ideas in its world picture. From the days of Galileo and Descartes through Newton to Einstein and Heisenberg, empiriological physics requires two general facts to set up its equations. One is the quantities involved, the other their direction of movement. Empiriological physics is still true to Descartes' reduction of matter to quantity and local motion.

Now it is the first law of thermodynamics that has to do with the quantity in a given problem, and the second law with its direction. These two laws are something vital in empiriological physics. It may also be parenthetically remarked that the statistical treatment of thermodynamics, to be discussed in Chapter 8, has raised certain difficulties against these laws. However, in statistical thermodynamics, the averages are in accord with macroscopic thermodynamics, and so the laws of thermodynamics still remain something fundamental, if not the most fundamental ideas in empiriological physics, as descriptive.

The universe is the aggregate of the beings which make it up, and if the laws of thermodynamics apply to the universe as a whole, they must have their basis in the individual parts. The parts must be both conservative and entropic.

By recognizing such realities as natures, matter-form dualism argues to the existence of conservative principles amid the changes of mobile being. But empiriological physics alone, forced to a pluralistic view of things, can give no account of nature's conservatism. What is doing the conserving? There must be a multiplicity of conservative principles, for if only inertia reigned in nature, movement from the outside, then Aquinas' judgment may be here reinvoked that everything would be moving with an infinite velocity. The facts of difference and the denial of monism, argued in the opening pages of this chapter, pointed to a multiplicity of non-inertial beings, braking the inertia. The same argument may be reapplied, or simply restated, to establish in the material world a plurality of braking and conservative principles.

Atomic and subatomic units differ in their conservatism. An electron is not conservative in the way in which an atom, say, is conservative. An electron is much more inert and can therefore be influenced by many different contexts. It is true that atoms can combine with other atoms as every chemist knows, and they can do so rather easily. But the facility and readiness of combination is not on the same level with that found on the subatomic scale. Any element can be made radioactive by the addition or subtraction of relatively inert particles, like the neutron or proton, but not every element can be combined, say, with neon, silver, or zinc. What makes an element radioactive is therefore much more general in the sense in which generality has been previously defined, by reference to the logical categories, than what makes an element neon, silver, or zinc. The radioactivating particles are thus much less conservative than the realities of neon, zinc, or silver. Such particles more easily surrender themselves and are less and less self-centered, less and less moved from within and by natures.

What is more general is less and less conservative, where generality is again taken not in the ontological sense which applies to all being but in the logical sense where it applies to categories. What is more general is less and less capable of remaining itself and assuming outside relation, i.e., less capable of remaining itself and becoming something else. The abiding of the agent is realized in all action and to an eminent degree in that immanent form of action which is called knowledge. This is the highest type of action, cognition; it is most conservative because the subject remains itself and becomes other, as other.

Aquinas, it was shown, based one explanation of the hierarchy of being on the number of forms which a given thing can subsume at a time. Man can become all things in knowledge because he is so conservative. If the electron, neutron, proton, and meson can, while remaining themselves as separate substantial units, assume relations to all material things, indeed become all material things (and become them as other) they must have a degree of immanence like that of knowledge itself. Moreover, if their combinations are explored from the viewpoint of striving rather than of becoming, then as substantial units, existing only as an aggregate in the atom, their lack of "determination to one," their versatility, would be as the self-determination that is freedom itself. If they could interact dynamically and tendentially in so many ways of their own natures, then these natures would virtually have no determination from within in the sense of immanence rather than a tyrannical determination from without which increases progressively from the animal downward.

An electron is general not because it is so rich but because it is so poor in reality. A neutron is general not because it is so immanent but because it is so tremendously inert. A proton is so universal in its action not because of what it has but because of what it does not have. The philosophical science of nature can provide ultimate reasons for the fact of conservatism in nature. Empiriological physics can make no such claim. Conservatism and stability, like form, do not exist in nature as separate entities, and the empiriological physicist, as a man, would never know them unless he abstracted their meaning from his measurements. Philosophical physics finds that if conservatism and stability are abstracted from a nature, they must be principled not by a logical or Kantian *apriorism* but by a factor called form which they exemplify and which is knowable only by intellection never by number.

The empiriological physicist today has so much power through his atomic successes only because he has come to grips with entities much more potential and yielding than the ultimates in nineteenth-century experiment. They conserve less and yield more. Their act is little, their passivity much. The contemporary empiriological physicist thus grows not more versed in natures, what things have from within, but less. Though prime matter will never be isolated, thus opening an indefinite progress to the future of empiriological physics, the physicist is moving more and more in matter's direction than toward the reality of form. It is this latter road, not toward the potentialities of matter but its actualities—the principles and causes of motion—that the philosophical science of nature truly treads; just as matter and form are one in being, so empiriological physics and philosophical physics can settle their frequent blockade of each other if each decides and remembers what it is about. As Aquinas says, analysis goes from form to matter, and empiriological physics is, in Kant's language, dominantly analytic; Alexander's space-time naturalism is, he claims, "analytical to the death."

Stability, dependence, and conservatism are philosophical concepts. They cannot be measured by empiriological techniques. The conservatism on the level of the atom cannot be explained by inertia in the dominion of the subatomic particles, any more than we can explain what is positive by simply adding negations. If the inertial movements are the only forces in nature, then all is moving with a flux and a flow at an infinite velocity, and no differences or distinctions, no brakes, no conservatisms, could occur anywhere in nature and experience.

THE LAW OF ENTROPY ATTESTS TO NATURES

The second law of thermodynamics states the instability of nature. It does not say that energy is destroyed but that it is being transformed constantly into an unusable state. The clock of the universe, to borrow a Newtonian figure, not being self-wound, is running down, and since all movement depends upon a difference in energy levels, movement will no longer be possible when the sum total of the world's potential energy falls to the level of the amount of kinetic. There will be a heat death of the universe as we now know it. So at least is the most popular theory.

This second law of thermodynamics must also be considered in the line of the present discussion of matter and form. The whole universe is here considered as an unstable system. The sun, powerhouse of the material world, is gradually losing its power. The locomotive, steaming along the tracks, costs the universe an energy that once spent will never come again. The atom and the molecule, dimly and imperceptibly, discharge something of their being that makes them less atom and less molecule. The entropic cycle cannot be avoided by the living or the lifeless.

It remains now to examine whether the instability argued by this entropic process contravenes the dualism of the atom and favors pluralism and mechanism, as a satisfactory account. On closer view, it will be found that matter-form dualism is not only satisfactory but is necessary to account for the facts of thermodynamics. No matter what imperceptible changes may be taking place in an iron door knob, it still remains the iron that it was long before a prospector might have found, fifty years ago, the mine from which it came. But what would happen to an almost perfectly free electron in the same geometrical position with respect to the door? It would immediately seek a substantial home in which to reside. In its search, it might not remain itself for more than a few seconds by contrast to the enduring stability of the iron. Unlike even the short-lived thorium C′, which is almost stillborn into nature, it would immediately seek union with an element forming an ion or neutralizing an already ionized atom. It would lodge itself into a metal or in the air as a vehicle to conduct their electricity. It does not have the centricity, independence, and originality of the atoms of iron. The same is true of other fundamental particles.

Let the empiriological physicist counter that the atom is emitting radiation or even heat; but it still remains an atom. An electron could emit neither radiation nor heat. It simply does not have sufficient being to accomplish what the atom can do or to hold itself in a separate existence. It is much more inert than the atom, much more determined to its one task, having its charge and bearing a rather small mass. By a simple tripartite union with protons and neutrons, this little entity could not manufacture the atom. If there is pure energy with no carrier, and the electron is virtually thus, then when the electron acts transeuntly, there would be a discontinuity or leap in its combinations. If its mass is so small that it is practically energy alone, then it has nothing to surrender when it enters into combination and into system except to surrender its whole self. Its being is so inert as to be able to individuate not more than perhaps one accident or at most only a few. The discontinuity involved in its action of combination amounts to a virtual annihilation of the electron, since it has so little to surrender that the surrender of anything means the surrender of its whole electron-ness. This means that it cannot enter into combination unless it loses its nature, at least virtually, and this is exactly what matter-form says. The other fundamental particles could be treated similarly.

Interesting confirmatory evidence for all this might be culled from current quantum theory where a leap is associated with all forms of microscopic action and lies at the root of the Heisenberg principle. Matter-form dualism would expect that as beings become more and more impoverished and unable to hold on to their natures while acting toward the outside, this discrete character of action, which is dualistically described as a virtual annihilation of the agent, would become more and more apparent. But further probing of this point must be reserved to a more advanced and technical discussion than this broad introduction.

An atom, by comparison with the electron and other subatomic building blocks, is incomparably less inert. It is much more stable, more conservative, much more capable of acting without destroying its whole nature in the action. It may hold its own more when combined. It could be objected, of course, that the electron can act without losing its nature. The empiriological physicist might point up the phenomenon of resonance radiation, already mentioned, which explains the color of a substance by the fact that photons (light particles) for a certain wave length strike the natural frequency of the electrons vibrating in the outer orbit of the atom, and the corresponding color is emitted. But the electron has not obtained the vibrating frequency of its own nature. This frequency is determined by the type of atom in question, and hence atoms of different elements yield light of different colors. The electron is so general in the sense defined by reference to the categories, its being is so weak, unstable in independence, and inert in obedience to outside forces, that it cannot act apart from abject dictation coming from its environment. The relation of the electron to the emission of color, where the atom itself tunes the electrons to its own frequency, is but another sign of the virtual way in which simpler things are present in the compounded.

As a general entity, the electron—and what is said here applies also to the other fundamental particles—is largely determined by the context in which it is. Here lies the positive insight of so-called objective relativism, advocated by Samuel Alexander, Arthur E. Murphy, and more recently embraced by Charles Morris. In this view, oftentimes called contextualism or perspectivism, meaning and ultimately being are referred to a system and do not apply beyond it. Thus a penny may look oval when it is lying on the floor and viewed from an angle but would look circular to an observer directly overhead. Both views, the relativists say, are correct with reference to the viewpoints involved. They form a system, and individual entities within it take their reality and meaning from the whole. Now such a view would stand up if scientism reached its goal of proving all things inert and endowed with no reality from within, and objective relativism is much more successful as empiriological physics continues to approximate (never reaching) its ideal. The more inertia increases as the shafts of experimental physics descend into the subatomic wells the more relative beings become to their context. Objective relativism is correct in seeing that the more general is the more inert. Its failure is not on this point but rather in viewing all wholes, say atoms, as mere mechanical sums of their parts. Its failure is to neglect true conservatisms.

Now an atom is also subject to outside influences. It may be, it is, thermodynamically unstable, responding to the entropic cycle in its own way. But the atom has something much more of being and of nature in it. The point is not that the atom is stable and its components are not, but that more stability can not be obtained by adding lesser ones, more act cannot be obtained by juxtaposing potencies.

Even the radioactive elements of short biography are relatively stable by comparison with subatomic particles. This stability must be explained. This centricity and originality of the atom cannot be accounted for by only eccentric and inertial forces in the universe. Atoms occur in nature independently, and they live to a relatively ripe old age; isolated electrons immediately seek abode in some substance. The universe may be running downhill, but it is not doing so violently, inertially, and with an infinite velocity. There are conservative factors at work amid the "liberalizing" tendencies.

Theories have been proposed by men like Poincaré, for example, to avoid the concept, and hence the law, of entropy. But such theories must always recognize the factor of directionality in chemical and physical action. The law of conservation determines the quantities involved in work, and both sides of chemical and nuclear equations must be balanced for this reason. Entropy determines directionality, and was aptly dubbed by Bergson the most metaphysical of empirical laws. Entropic physicists establish that a reaction will always tend in such a direction that entropy will increase. If a non-entropic theory is substituted, the factors of instability and direction are not avoided but simply appear in a new dress. For present purposes then, where the only matter in question is the instability and imbalance that action tries to overcome, the non-entropic theories which are very much in the minority can be analyzed like the notion of entropy.

Thermodynamics informs us that the universe is running downhill. But there must be braking principles in the process. Otherwise, there is no reason why this downhill drive should not attain infinite speed and crush out all determination and distinction, even in appearances. The multiplicity of determinations is an index of a multiplicity of such resistive principles. The resistance movement of the atom cannot be accounted for except by its independent stature, incomparably greater than the corresponding reality on the subatomic level where the resistance is less because the inertia is greater. Inertia added to inertia can no more provide additional act, added instabilities give no more stabilities, than darkness added to darkness will yield light.

Empedocles advanced a cosmogony based on a law of love and a law of hate which he detected in the universe. This is like the two laws of thermodynamics discussed above. On the modern scene, Hegel and Marx view realities as containing their own dissolutions. D'Alembert attempted to found all mechanics on the notion of forces tending to move and forces tending to constrain. Newton's law of action and reaction, philosophically interpreted, presents the spectacle of a similar dualism. Santayana saw patterns in mobility and called them tropes. For Lalande, there is both "evolution" and "involution" in the cosmos. Alexander differentiated space and time in some fashion, or he could not have said "space-time continuum." Whitehead broke the world into units called "actual entities" which are essentially dynamic and creative, and yet he also insisted that there was discrimination and selectivity in their action, which he called "prehension." Spencer's world contained "an integration of matter and a concomitant dissipation of motion." Bergson painted a world charged with a vital impetus (*élan vital*) that in turn was characterized by associative (conservative) tendencies and dissociative (spending) tendencies. Holt stroked out a view of the world in terms of neutral entities differing in velocity. More recently L. L. Whyte has advanced a cosmology in which symmetry is in contrast with asymmetry. But it is only in terms of matter-form dualism that the contrary tendencies which all these men detected in the universe receive full justice.

THERMODYNAMICS CONFIRMS MATTER AND FORM

Two broad conclusions may now be stated from the discussion of thermodynamics: (1) only in terms of a nature existing, hence substance, as the subject of contraries, can that which is conservative be the very same thing that is entropic; the empiriological physicist would account for this opposition by a reduction to different principles, but basically there must be an identifying substrate in which both principles are rooted, otherwise there would be realities that obey the first law and escape the second, and vice versa; (2) only in traditional matter-form dualism can the bifurcated character of the atom be explained, its conservative principle flowing from its form and its divisive and destructive principle, from its matter. A subatomic particle instanced by an electron, does not have ample interiority and nature to unite so many contraries as are seen on the atomic level. The entropy and hence conservatism of the individual electron are thus meaningless. Both entropy and conservatism fall together, showing that the opposites must be rooted in a common principle of reality.

The subatomic particles almost contradict Spinoza's maxim. They do not relish freedom. They seek refuge in the quickest possible way, even when neutral, in the nearest substance that will harbor them. Or else they break down.

It is significant that modern thermodynamics so radiantly confirms the philosophical account of motion's principles. Thermodynamics marks a point where empiriological physics is more alive, than it usually can be, to motion and to motion in general and hence to the generalities which motion involves. Here indeed, where empiriological physics drives deepest into motion, it turns up with an account that is almost a restatement of matter-form dualism.

The latest advances in empiriological physics tend to suggest, at least by way of timely illustration, what matter-form dualism has long claimed as the true account of matter. According to the Heisenberg principle of indeterminism, all the factors necessary to understand a material being cannot be simultaneously known. Position and velocity cannot be exactly specified at the same time. If, as Russell says, one were exactly known, the error in the other would be infinite.

Position and velocity are bifurcated qualities. Though both properties of the composite, position stems more from quantity or matter and velocity more from form. One originates more in the inertial principle; the other is more varied and dynamic. The philosophical physicist insists that all factors necessary to specify a material being can be truly known in his approach to reality, because he has never mechanically dissected its unity, which is, as Aquinas says, the way an artifact is understood. The philosopher of nature transcends the bifurcated categorical contraries of matter and apprehends, if only as a limited mode of changing being and not in a genus-species way, that underlying nature which unites opposites and when existing is called first substance. Philosophical physics has insisted on what empiriological physics is now confirming by a type of empirical metaphor: that matter and form, taken separately, as their fate requires in the categorical approach of the empiriological physicist, are meaningless sport, and that mechanism, like that found in the categories of logic, delivers itself into discrete parts that never merge into an entitative unity.

The finer instruments become, or the smaller are the particles to be measured, the more importantly there looms the error in position and velocity. There is less of a unitive force, i.e., less of a nature to effect their union. Here the more and more a-natural, the more and more the inertial, has its say. Since error becomes appreciable in what is small, according to Heisenberg and his interpreters, what is small is not comparable to what is greater: an electron, for instance, is not comparable to the macroscopic world. In the limit, position and velocity for the empiriological physicist never get together, and the universe becomes plural. There is so little of being left in this quasi-logical universe of empiriological physics that the physicist is inclined, like Hegel, after impoverishing being of all of its attributes to deny that being is.

Following the empiriological physicist, the philosophical physicist is inclined to say that the subatomic entities are poorer in their reality than atoms. But if they exist at all, they are beings. However poor and dependent they may be, the limit of nothingness is never reached by dividing them. Dualism explains the union of position and velocity by its thesis that matter and form are immediately united.

In the subways beneath the atom, there is considerably more inert and hence less unitive nature than what is found at higher levels. Though plural, as Simon emphasizes, and potential, this nature is still a something that has both position and velocity, a something that exists but, so grossly inert and material, is almost too weak to "be become" by the knowledge act. As Aquinas realistically puts it, the knowability of a thing follows upon its immateriality. The subatomic entities are so steeped in matter that they are hardly cognizable. According to the empiriological physicist, they have no taste, smell, sound, color, or tangible properties. Yet this impoverished world has a mobile being, however feebly. If, for example, an electron did not have position and velocity and have them together, then no matter how many electronless, contentless positions and velocities were wedded together, the simultaneous appearance of position and velocity as noted on the higher levels of the real could never be achieved. By adding mere position and mere velocity together, one could no more get a *thing* that had position and velocity than he could reach a positive quantity by stringing together an infinite number of zeros.

An incursion into the account of structure sketched by the general theory of relativity reveals likewise the fact of bifurcated and contrary qualities in matter that must eventually be combined into a substrate called nature where nature in turn is dualistic. Relativity physics presents the spectacle of a space-time continuum, but it insists that the continuum is anisotropic and hence heterogeneous. Homogeneity must prevail in a continuum, and yet apparently in the Einstein-Minkowski picture of things, anistropy in space introduces the fact of discontinuity. Only in terms of an underlying nature whose bifurcated principles are immediately united can homogeneity and heterogeneity in Spencer's language, or continuum and anisotropy to keep Einstein's thoughts, be reconciled and applied under different aspects to the very same things.

The new generalized theory of gravitation advanced by Einstein is another testimony to the dualism in our world. It was previously shown that the fundamental equation contains a symmetrical part and an anti-symmetrical part, the first being an analogue to matter and the second to form. The generalized theory attempts to tie them together, as Aristotle did when he argued that the immediate union of matter and form constitute one being.

Aquinas felt that pre-Aristotelian cosmologists like Pythagoras with his duality of odd and even, Plato in his notion of great and small, and Anaximander who posited the condensation and rarefaction of an original indeterminate stuff as the basis of cosmic differentiation—all these were groping toward that basic principle of contrariety in nature which Aristotle discovered and branded matter and form. The very existence of these contrary principles in the philosophies before Aristotle simply showed, Aquinas felt, that shadow of truth which even false philosophies catch from the light of being. A similar estimate might hold of the rather Ionian atmosphere of contemporary thought. The facts and theories of empiriological physics bear a weak witness to the fundamental contrariety in nature which the Aristotelian does not ask to be formally adopted by the empiriological method but simply to be acknowledged as attained in another approach to reality that is called philosophy.

As a matter of fact, the amount of thought which the empiriological physicist lavishes on matter even with an eye toward its controllable aspects would be hardly possible unless there were scorched into his mind at least a weak analogue of what the mobile world really is. He tends, of course, to play down the real mobility of matter and to consider only the ghosts of motion. But the ghosts turn his physics into a haunted house, where theories are ever unsteadied by their provisional character, where crises are a normal state, and where there are always oppositions and questions, and new data that do not nestle neatly into the older forms of measurement.

OBJECTIONS TO MATTER-FORM ARE INADEQUATE

It now remains to examine some principal objections to matter-form dualism. If the planetary model of the atom is denied as being a mechanical aggregate, why not make the same statement about the solar system? Why is it acknowledged that the solar system is an aggregate but insisted that an atom is a substance? A house can also exist by virtue of its parts since it is not substantially one. Why cannot the same thing be said about the atom?

The answer ought to emphasize that, in the case of the solar system, bodies can exist independently within the system only because they own natures with such interiority, versatility, and originality that macroscopic reality, comprised of atoms and molecules, is seen to bear. Such atomic and molecular unities can and do have all the relations which experience discloses and experiment measures because their natures are great enough to enjoy a relative independence and to own many contraries. The subatomic units, mechanically systemized, decline to hold properties like those of atoms and molecules. They are much more passive and inert, more extrinsically determined and potential. As far as empiriological physics can disclose, their substances each individuate only one or two detectable properties. Atoms are different. They can be and can remain themselves while they assume relations, engage in motion, and possess qualities. They tend to exist independently; they are more conservative; they do not almost wholly abdicate their existence when they operate.

The example of a house could be treated in a similar fashion. The parts can remain themselves, combining only accidentally, simply because they have enough interiority of being to exist and operate independently. A house is not made of electrons, protons, mesons, and neutrons. It is made of bricks, wood, iron, and the silicon compounds which form glass. It has the unity of art.

As another objection, it is sometimes urged that crystallography shows a versatility of appearance on the part of a single element which would seem to show that the same chemical substance can assume a variety of relations without changing its nature. Carbon in coal and in a diamond is the same element, differing only in crystalline form, an example of what is called dimorphism. Other substances, like phosphorus, present an even greater variety of crystalline appearance and are called polymorphic.

But this does not explain away the fundamental inertias of the material universe, great on the level of the atom and greater in its component parts. Crystal structure and its variations depend basically on the geometrical shapes of the atoms in an aggregate and on their alignments to each other. Each substance has a small number of crystalline forms that it readily takes, and the patterns depend on the type of substance which it is. Thus, potassium under the same conditions crystallizes differently from silicon, and each is limited sharply as to the variety of patterns. It is the atoms which explain the crystals and limit their range of versatility. Patterns are specific to atoms, much like weight, specific gravity, and combustibility.

Most importantly, the standard for deciding the differences of nature is, to recall Whitehead, not how a thing looks but how it operates under the same external conditions as some other substance. Under the same conditions, carbon acts in one specific way, forming one type of crystal, and phosphorus another. Change the conditions, and another form of phosphorus will result. But the carbon will also show its own specific reaction to the change.

This standard is of the utmost importance in dealing with the changes of physical states induced by different thermodynamical conditions. Water in extremes of hot and cold no longer is liquid. It vaporizes or freezes, depending on the temperature. But subject other elements to the same extremes, and they will act differently, showing their differences in inner nature. Hydrogen, at the same temperature of the water vapor, will burn, aluminum would melt if the temperature were sufficiently intense, oxygen would more readily support combustion. The criterion to differentiate natures is not how they look to the eye or record their quantity on a visual instrument or even how they vary under varying conditions. It is their action and operation that count, and two different substances subjected to the same thermal extremes will be moved differently. They will also act differently when subjected to the same process of crystal growing. The principle determining the activity of the atom is within it.

Chemical compounds can be subjected to the same analysis as in the case of elements, and they yield the same evidence for matter and form. They will turn out to be substances because they show an inner principle of operation, called nature, which cannot be accounted for by the mechanical linkage of their component elements. In their limited modes of combination, atoms are not great enough to achieve such variety as the manifold of chemical compounds presents. In "testing" for the existence of substantial forms, distinct from the ingredients which they virtually contain and dominating them as rationality dominates man's sensory operations, the yardstick again must not be how a thing looks but how it is moved. Otherwise, water vapor might seem like hydrogen. It is combustibility, specific gravity, conductivity, magnetic permeability, and other such exhibitions of mobility rather than looks which enable the philosophical science of nature to discern and distinguish substances. In biology, the anatomist, impressed with the similarity in looks between man and the animal, when he studies their structures and measures mere quantity, is often tempted likewise to identify the two because he disregards the differences in their motions. Physiology ought to be more emphasized than it is.

THAT $E = mc^2$ DOES NOT REFUTE MATTER-FORM

A major difficulty in the reaffirming of the matter-form account of nature emerges from the so-called equivalence of matter and energy. This formula was developed by Einstein, reasoning from his theory that mass varies with motion. $E = mc^2$, where E represents energy, m mass, and c the velocity of light. According to this view, about two pounds of coal, completely turned into energy, could run the entire electric power industry in the United States, as of 1939, for two months.

This interesting principle lay largely unexplored and unexploited until 1939, when two German scientists, Hahn and Strassmann, bombarding the heavy element uranium with neutrons, discovered that they could produce barium, a much lighter element. It was quickly speculated by Lise Meitner that this uranium breakdown was accompanied by the extraction of tremendous amounts of energy, from the original raw material, and it was this idea that started the American experimentalists on the march to Hiroshima.

The relation between energy and mass measured by weight near the earth's surface can be discussed in round nuclear figures. In terms of standard atomic mass units where the oxygen atom is roughly 16, the mass of a proton is 1.00758 and that of the neutron is 1.00893. A helium nucleus contains two of each kind of particle, and calculating its weight from the component parts leads to an expected value of 4.03302. Surprisingly enough, the weight is actually 4.00280, a difference of about 0.030 mass units. Why does the helium nucleus weigh less than the sum of its component parts?

This is only a simple example. Phosphorus weighs 0.280 units less than the sum of the thirty-one particles comprising its nucleus, and the weight difference between the sixteen components of the oxygen nucleus inside and outside the atom is 0.1328. But what makes this difference in energy? Has matter been annihilated by the combination? Has mass been turned into energy? Has matter been converted into a property of matter? Can extended reality be reduced to the inextended?

A fuller explanation for all these puzzling events lies in the concept of "binding energy." This term is almost self-explanatory, the energy binding the parts of a nucleus together. It is obviously equal to the energy required to disrupt the nucleus, and since the bombarding energy just enough to cause the nuclear breakdown can be measured, the binding energy of every type of nucleus can be accurately computed. It turns out that Einstein's equation is satisfied by such calculation. The reason why the helium nucleus is lighter than the sum of its component parts is that 0.030 mass units have been converted into energy, when the parts are assembled. Some nuclei are more strongly bound within themselves than others. There are two types of nuclear reactions, those which absorb and those which release energy. Any nuclear reaction that results in particles more strongly bound inside their nuclei than those of the fissionable element will make energy available. The atom bomb exploits this principle.

The explanation of the Einsteinean formula requires attention to the way in which the empiriological physicist proceeds. In actual fact, empiriological physics measures reality without discerning its nature, and in a very genuine sense the equivalence of matter and energy was employed long before Einstein. A body on a high mountain weighs less than the same body at the surface of the earth since the pull of the earth decreases with remotion into outer space. Such a relation was known in Newtonian mechanics. Has an airplane at 30,000 feet of altitude lost some of the mass which it had on the runway?

Closer inspection shows that empiriological physics has always measured mass in terms of energy and energy in terms of mass. Mass is usually computed in terms of weight, and weight, no matter how we measure it, is reduced to the pull exerted by the earth. When a man steps on a scale, what is actually measured is the force of attraction which the earth exerts on his body. The spring has been properly calibrated to read, say, in terms of pounds and ounces, and what is actually measured is the amount by which the object weighed overcomes the resisting forces in the spring. It is true that empiriological physics now weighs particles by much more refined techniques, like the mass spectrograph which sends charged particles into a narrow beam through a magnetic or electrostatic field and by controlling the force of the field, thus deflecting the charged particles up or down, can register the amount of energy just necessary to overcome the pull of gravity. But such realities as pull, force, tension with its stress and strain, field—all are phenomena of energy rather than mass. Mass is thus measured by energy, and this is true of any measurement of inertia in general.

In kindred fashion, energy is measured by mass. The familiar unit of energy is the foot-pound, the work done in raising a pound of matter a distance of one foot. But matter is a mass concept. Distance involves extension, likewise a mass property. When the empiriological physicist measures current in an ammeter, he measures the amount of energy which overcomes the inertia (a mass property) in a mechanical instrument, say the apparatus of the deflection needle. In actual fact, both in the measurement of mass and in the register of energy, massive and energetic concepts play a part in all instruments, but the point here is that the dichotomy of mass and energy in classical physics was artificially made, and the more scrupulous empiriological physics of today has wisely corrected the situation.

It sounds like a vicious circle to measure mass in terms of energy and energy in terms of mass. Such a begging of the question is characteristic of pure empiriological method, left to its own devices, unsupplemented by the mind of the physicist thinking not only as an empiriological physicist but also as a man. Empiriological method therefore cannot solve the question of the equivalence of matter and energy. It has accepted a method which equates these realities from the beginning and forbids judgment, empirically, on their real character apart from the measures.

But the question of the real relation of matter and energy remains to vex the philosophical science of nature. Can matter be annihilated? It was said above that the helium nucleus weighs less when its parts are combined than the sum of the weights of its components outside their home. The difference is 0.030 mass units. But since the four particles must be held together by forces of attraction, it is apparent that the energy hitherto available for the pull toward the earth has now been turned to a new task. If this energy could be retrieved and directed downward toward the earth, it would show that nothing was really lost or gained in the process. Energy, with the modification to be made below, has at most been changed from one form to another, but in view of the commonplace conversions of energy from, say, mechanical to electrical or from kinematic to magnetic states, this conversion should not be startling. It is responsible for the lighting in our homes.

Although in a more correct formulation, Einstein's equation is really the problem of converting energy from one form to another rather than the conversion of mass to energy, taking mass as substance and energy as an accident, there may nevertheless be changes in the extension of the fission fragments by comparison with the original substance. But similar changes in extension or volume are commonplace events. The hydrogen and oxygen in water can occupy much less space than the same quantity of the component elements in a gaseous form when the pressure on the gas and liquid is the same.

Thus, the so-called conversion of mass into energy stands in no contradiction to previously known philosophical principles. The whole problem is the grossness of classical physics, the physics of Galileo, Newton, and even of Descartes. According to this view, matter is defined by mass, weight; in the Cartesian approach, by quantity. Any changes like those produced by uranium fission cannot fit into such a system. The quarrel of contemporary empiriological physics is really with its predecessors in the post-Cartesian world rather than with the philosophical science of nature.

Aquinas, for instance, does not define a natural body in terms of mass, quantity, or weight. He defines it in terms of its mobility and the dualism of principle which motion discloses. In an empiriological physics of quantity the Einstein equation appears as an atom bombshell. In the philosophical science of nature, a body is not defined in terms of mass, and there is thus no requirement that so-called mass be constant. Privation, form, and matter are involved in change, *prime* matter alone being constant. Since Einstein's contribution consists in displaying that energy also has inertia, it is obvious that the inertia in the fissionable material has not been lost (or gained) but appears in the massive and energetic properties of the products. The inertia in the results is balanced in an equation with the inertia of the raw materials, and so this aspect of relativity mechanics illustrates rather than refutes matter-form dualism by showing the constancy of prime matter amid the nuclear changes that philosophy insists are changes in the substantial forms of the atoms.

In reality, the whole concept of binding energy illustrates matter-form dualism. If it is true that the atom is a substantial unit composed of matter and form and not simply an aggregate of subatomic particles, it would not be expected that the particles would preserve in the composite nucleus the properties that they bear in isolation; they rather would be virtually present in the atom. The transformation of so-called massive property into binding energy (or vice versa) tends to show that there are profound changes in the subatomic particles themselves when they enter into atomic constitutions—changes that the philosophical science of nature calls substantial. Reflecting on present-day empiriological physics tends to require rather than refute matter-form dualism. The very same being that has inertia, more of a material property, also has activity, more of a formal property.

A dead fish weighs more than a living one. This might suggest the notion that certain energies of the compounded substantial being are consumed in the binding of part to part but, when decomposition occurs, are available for interaction with the earth to produce more "weight" than was previously present.

The so-called equivalence of mass and energy, far from contradicting the philosophical science of nature has simply made empiriological physics aware of the inadequacy of its older concepts and the danger of erecting a science on mere uninterrupted measurements. The Einstein equation has simply corrected certain of these measurements. What things are in their natures is known by intellection or abstraction, and this insight is the work of the philosophical physics to probe. As far as such a science is concerned, what could be more typical of matter-form dualism than to find in nature changes in the very being of things with a constancy of their so-called inertia?

But what is matter and what is energy? This is a logical sequence to the foregoing discussion.

A twofold answer must be given here, depending on the viewpoint assumed. For the empiriological physicist, mass and energy are two different ways of looking at the same thing since the physicist, precisely as such, cannot transcend his measurements to discuss the realities behind them. Their difference is purely logical in nature since mechanism does not entitle its adherents to pronounce on the nature of the stuff that is mechanized nor does dynamism on the nature of what is dynamized.

Truly philosophically considered, mass and energy are irrelevant questions. The philosophical student of matter speaks rather of substantial form and prime matter, or of accidental form and second matter. He would deny that energy itself is transformed but would hold that a natural agent, acting on another nature, evokes its potentialities into act when the apparent energy transformations occur.

This may be illustrated by an electric generator in which the electric current is induced into a loop of wire as it turns through a magnetic field and cuts the magnetic lines of force. The electric energy induced in the wire depends on the mechanical dimensions of the loop, the number of magnets present, the degree to which each is magnetized, the speed of revolution on the part of the loop, and its temperature. Electricity can thus be increased or decreased by mechanical, magnetic, kinematic, and thermal factors called "energies." Are these ingredient energies transformed into electric energies?

The empiriological physicist says, yes. But the philosophical physicist has a different answer. The causal agents through powers peculiar to *their* natures act upon the effect producing in it an act that depends upon *its own* natural potencies. Only thus can transformations, as they result in differences, be accounted for. Difference cannot be reduced to inertia, and the response of a body, which is said to be energy, transformed, is merely the actualization of the potencies original to its nature. Kinetic energy corresponds in general to the activities of things and potential energy, to their potentialities for reacting. Kinetic energy is exhibited differently, depending on the substance which is subjected to excitation, and the potential energy stored in it is also a mark of its inner nature and its capacities. If this explanation were not true, differences could not be explained, and the impossible universe moving with a violent and infinite speed would again be the alternative.

Every empiriological physicist, as far as he is a man, goes beyond his pointer readings to a knowledge, true or false, of what the being and the motion are that metrical numbers only represent, like a locust shell that has been shed. Since this transcendence of measurement is necessary to make even physically possible the operations of the empiriological physicist, he is absolutely compelled to adopt a philosophy that he cannot verify with his instruments. Even his differentiation of mass and energy or his identification of them is a philosophical judgment if he attributes its content to the real world.

Now it is on this metaexperimental ground that the philosophical physicist has as much right to be heard as the empiriological physicist who is always philosophizing. There is no more pure empiriological physics than there is pure art. Truly the genuine philosophical physics is at a higher reach into reality than the empiriological physicist and the debate is a metaempirical, philosophical one between the two. Philosophy is like being. It is impossible to avoid it, impossible to avoid knowing being and being a philosopher. In this light the contemporary mind formed and fed so largely by empiriological method must meet Aristotelian philosophy in its own territory. That it refuses to do so, dismissing this philosophy as a meaningless net of mere verbalism, is the fruit of sheer prejudice, and this judgment itself constitutes a metempirical philosophy.

Modern researches into the atomic wonderland have not contradicted the genuine philosophical science of nature but rather reinforced it. Instead of beginning the hierarchy of being now with the elements and then working up through compounds, plants, animals, and man, empiriological physics has unearthed realities in nature more potential and inert than the atom. In so doing, it has simply dug a new basement under an old mansion. And a better basement means a better structure upstairs.

Suggested Readings

Darwin, C. G., *New Conceptions of Matter* (New York, 1931).

Riezler, Kurt, *Physics and Reality* (New Haven, 1940).

Millikan, Robert Andrews, *Electrons (+ and −), Protons, Photons, Mesotrons, and Cosmic Rays,* rev. ed. (Chicago, 1947).

7

The Motor Cause and the Modern Mind

Thinking, especially with a scientific rigor, would have no permanent address in an indeterminate universe. When a car is in neutral, it can be pushed and pulled in any direction and at any speed, and if the universe were equally indifferent, man could make of it what he wishes.

Without extrinsic causes, the world would be indeterminate, and all science would drown in the flux. If a motor cause were not needed for every motion, a moving thing could pop up out of nowhere at any time and any place. A similar spree of chance would unsteady a non-final universe, where moving things were not angled to given ends and hence could do any kind of maneuvering when set in motion.

A genuine science has both the courage and also the courtesy to weigh any objections against its statements, and the doctrine of causality, introduced in Chapter 3, bears a comparison with its substitutes. This chapter will sift the more important ideas on the motor causes of nature, while final causality will be the burden of Chapter 8.

Broadly, the present chapter falls into three parts: a glance at the notion of causes introduced by Hume; a survey of opinions that make cause and effect too extrinsic to each other, too intrinsic, or equal; and a summary of opinions that would counteract mechanism, like Hegelianism on the one hand and emergent evolutionism on the other.

The first of these three parts is subdivided into an outline of Hume, a rejection of him, a sketch of his applications in empiriological physics, and a brief discussion of Kant, who was Hume's descendant.

The second large theme will show first that a motor cause is not absolutely extrinsic to the effect, nor absolutely intrinsic, but moves its effect by contact, which is a medium position between the extremes. But this contact is not an identity, as the law of action and reaction would have it, and entropy does not resolve the dilemma to which scientism is forced by the spirit of Newton's third law. Only nature and only a distinction of action and passion can account for innovation.

The final broad division of this chapter will discuss Hegel, Marxism, and emergent evolutionism, and show at last that dualism accounts for the truth in both modern dynamism and modern inertialism.

HUME VIEWED CAUSALITY AS SUCCESSION

Causality has been one of the big battlefields of modern thought. If empiriological physics as a science still survives the denial of motor causality, it is only because the haze of the battle has not yet cleared enough to let the corpses be counted. Hume rejected a motor cause as really influencing an effect and affirmed instead a causality that is simply temporal succession. One thing follows another as the light goes on after the throwing of a switch. But the switching is simply prior to the lighting, Hume would say; it does not influence it.

So far this idea to a mind meeting it for the first time seems as wrong as, in genuine science, it is naive. But it is a conclusion, rather than a starting point in Hume's philosophy, which is as a whole more critical than positive in nature and has won the plaudits of modern sensate man. Hume came upon the world through Cartesianism. In him was fulfilled the seed of skepticism which Descartes had planted and especially a denial of all natures and substances which are stabilities in the real world and the anchors of our certitude about it.

Instead of interacting natures and substances, the Humean world is speckled only by phenomena, appearances, brute sense data. Instead of grasping causes by intelligence, Hume stubbornly refused to go beyond sensations and took the simple successions of things which the senses present as the farthest fling of human knowledge.

In psychology, having fastened upon his universal denial of substance, Hume reduced mind to a series of mental states, not united intrinsically to each other but merely heaped together like flakes in a snow drift. According to Hume, the recurrence of a sequence like the moistening of the earth during a rain generates a mental association, or in a more modern terminology, grooves a reflex, which leads man to expect a moistening of the earth after the rainfalls in the future. But men are not aware, Hume goes on, that the rigor they ascribe to causality is only this rut in the mind. They dupe themselves into thinking that the rain causes the moistening whereas in reality, according to Hume, the two events have nothing more than a temporal regularity which our habits of association misread into a causal interplay. According to Humean views, the alarm clock would not awaken man in the morning; it goes off at one moment, and uninfluenced by it, man gets up in the next.

Hume's ideas are continued in John Stuart Mill, and the reader may verify the fact by a glance at Mill's canons of induction, especially the method of concomitant variations.

HUME CONTRADICTS REASON

But if causality is nothing but temporal sequence which leads the mind to associate two states so that the second member of the sequence will always be expected whenever the first occurs, man ought to say that every example of succession is causal. In point of fact, man does not say so or think so or act as if Hume were right. Shine a flashlight in a man's eye, in an example from Whitehead, and the man will not say that his blinking merely followed the light. He knows that the light made him blink. Thomas Reid refuted Hume with his classic example that night follows day and day the night, but no one says that one is the cause of the other. If Hume were right, this conclusion ought to have been reached and reached long ago since nothing is more regular and rutlike in the sense world than this procession of day and night.

Reason does not agree with Chanticleer that his crowing causes the sunrise. Why do men say that the engine pulls the caboose rather than the caboose pushes the engine? Because they clearly distinguish between successions that are merely temporal and those which are causal. By intelligence, they are able to examine the motions of nature, defining them and tracing out their relations until, with self-motion impossible, a mover is known to operate and to exist whenever and wherever motion occurs. Deny the power of intelligence and Hume is *almost* right—almost, it should be stressed, for the skepticism which follows upon the denial of intelligence would not allow a man to expound a philosophy, as Hume has done, and to discover and discuss such things as succession and association which are known by intelligence.

Hume's idea finds a counterpart in the modern reduction of causality to a functional relationship, under the powerful dynasty of Newton and Leibniz, fathers of the calculus. Functionality exists where one thing varies as another thing varies without the necessity of a causal intercourse between them (Chapter 1). That in less precise form is what Hume said two centuries ago and what Mill says in his method of concomitant variations.

But though valid at the empiriological level, functionality does not substitute for the necessity of causal knowledge. If functionality were adequate to a truly scientific system, one could say, to use Russell's language (though not his philosophy), "The barometer has ceased to have any effect upon the weather." For the barometer varies when the weather varies, and since barometric fluctuations forecast the weather and hence precede it, Hume, if not sheer functionality, ought to compel us to say that the barometer is the cause of the subsequent weather rather than just an index of what it will be.

EMPIRIOLOGICAL PHYSICS FINDS A PLACE FOR HUME

There is of course, something to be said for Hume in the territory of empiriological physics which, in its pure form, cannot mount outside the sense world and is descriptive, rather than causal and explanatory, in nature. Einstein, who admits the influence of Hume, purified empiriological physics in accordance with Hume's counsel.

The use of functions to express law in empiriological physics shows that Hume, if a dwarf in genuine philosophy, was a goad to the maturing empiriological methods.

Empiriological physics is more loyal to itself by ignoring causes. Causality is not mensurable, and when the empiriological extremist denies true causality, it is to be remembered that he is less prejudiced against causes than obsessed by measurement which alone has meaning in his precinct. For empiriological physics, causality obtains where events can be predicted in time, an analogue of Hume's doctrine on expectation. What is predictable is causal, for the empiriologist, and what is causal is predictable. This is not true causality, however adequate it may be in a merely descriptive enterprise.

True causality implies a break between cause and effect; the two are not identical because the effect is distinct from the cause. The hiatus puts causality in its genuine sense beyond the pale of empiriological physics which prospers best on a subject matter that is a continuum (and is treated by continuous functions).

For empiriological physics, then, the temporal continuum is fruitful as a substitute for causality since it eliminates the breaks in being, the hierarchies, natures, interiorities, and originalities in the objective world which experiment can neither detect nor manipulate. Hence, Hume was a stimulus to sheer empiriological physics by mooring it to "the observable," by furthering its views of the world as continuous, and by emphasizing the successive continuum which is time. But his skeptical sensism, if allowed to carry weight outside of the purest empiriological method, would break the back of all thinking.

KANT MADE CAUSALITY AN APRIORISM

Another rather unhappy warrior against the traditional notion of motor causality was Kant. In many respects, his notion of a cause is simply a plagiarism of Hume's. Where Hume reduced the causal relation to mere succession, so did Kant. Where Hume shrank the idea of cause to the association of mental states, Kant painted it as an *a priori* category. The chief difference between the two is that Hume held the association of so-called causal events to be a product of habit, while Kant, rejoining Leibniz, enthroned the idea of cause as *a priori,* hence innate.

As in the case of Hume, the burden of refuting Kant belongs to the metaphysics of knowledge. But though fatally inadequate in philosophy, Kant, an empiriological physicist himself, paved the way, as Hume did, for the greater purity in empiriological methods. Such consciousness of itself has given empiriological physics a mastery over matter in proportion as it has retreated from the realities that can be probed and proved only in a speculative science of nature.

But Kant had the effect of saying that because the empiriological physicist cannot recognize causality, therefore causality cannot be recognized at all. It is as though a carpenter should decide that there are no other tools but his own type. Kant thus seared into the modern mind the impression that ontological realities are simply anthropomorphisms, projected by man's mind, and that the real world is that of the empiriological disciplines. He helped to isolate empiriological from philosophical physics, but he inflated the first into a true science and deflated the second so that it could not survive.

From at least one viewpoint, there is today a general alarm in the empiriological physics that tried to get along on Humean and

Kantian premises, turning them into a philosophy. Quantum mechanics has urged upon the empiriological physicist that there is no such thing as the determined regularity and sequence in nature which Hume and Kant took blissfully for granted; the uncertainty principle declares that the universe is not ordered but random, if many of its interpreters are to be believed. Relativity theory, by denying that absolute motion and absolute time and absolute space can be detected and by suggesting reversibility in the temporal order, would likewise have to challenge the dogma of Hume and Kant.

But it is a matter of historical fact that Hume and Kant removed causality from philosophy and persuaded scientism to confine itself to a purely descriptive analysis of temporal order instead of searching after causes.

A CAUSE IS NOT ABSOLUTELY EXTRINSIC

Hume shades off into another problem. Motor causality implies a contact between the mover and the moved. It also requires a relation between them that is not simply equalitarian. A discussion of these two principles will lead into a more precise knowledge of what a mover is and does. It will show how philosophical —not empiriological—physics yields the only true science of motion.

By definition, the Humean notion of a cause denies a causal influx into the effect while sound reason affirms it. Now if Hume is right and if the parade of events is simply a matter of serial order with no causal interlocks, every moment gives birth to events that are rankly spontaneous and irrelational. If posterior events are undetermined from the causal viewpoint, then every event is a creature of chance and even an order in time would be impossible. Uncaused by a prior reality, every event would simply burst out of nothingness in an unpredictable fashion, self-caused and self-moved and abandoned to itself.

Forced to its logical doom, the Humean philosophy which wants only prediction out of empiriological physics melts away the axis of predictability by constructing a universe where all is self-motion and chance, hence unpredictable. The indeterminists in the empiriological physics of today have realized this philosophical conclusion in the concrete. All thinking would suffocate if there were no other atmosphere than this.

A realistic analysis of motion (Chapter 3) has shown that self-motion is impossible. In the foregoing remarks, there is a kind of confirmatory argument for this truth in the fact that the radical self-motion, a way of defining chance and the logical exodus of Humeanism, would devastate all thinking about the material world by reducing that world to an utter disorder. Somehow, the modern mind in its acceptance of Hume has been holding a candle that turns out to be a firecracker, and the explosions are beginning to be heard. If this self-motion, the issue of Hume's thought, is impossible because it would deny order and plow the world into chaos, there is additional proof that whatever is moved is moved by another. Order requires it, and order exists.

The cause exerts an influence upon the effect, and influx which means an inflow ought to be taken in a stricter sense than is sometimes accorded it. Self-motion having been rejected by the rigor of traditional scientific reasoning and by the absurdities of following Hume, there must be an outside motor for every movement and something more than an extrinsic juxtaposition between them. To put it crudely, it is not enough for a mover merely to touch the surface of the mobile, as though a tree could be felled by tapping its bark or as though a piano key would move downward by a light touch rather than by pressure. Such a picture of causality would be one of juxtaposition, and the Humean impasse shows that juxtaposition is not enough.

Motion implies a type of inner penetration by the motor into its subject. The whole mobile being, rather than merely its outer skin, is set in motion by the motor cause which must somehow spill over into the inner reality of what it moves.

This does not mean, of course, that motion involves physical compenetration, the presence of two bodies in the same place

(Chapter 12). What it does mean is that there is something more than a mere extrinsic presence of a motor when a thing is moved. The motor contributes something to the effect. There is thus ruled out the famous Leibnizian view that *A*, a mover, and *B*, the mobile, act without an interflow and by the preëstablished harmony of the universe. Much more realistic was Aquinas when he wrote: "The mover and the mobile are together" (*Motus et movens sunt simul*). Leibniz, like Hume, would make *A* extrinsic to *B*, for his monadic units of the world have no windows or doors and not even keyholes to relate them to each other. His philosophy, like that of Hume, leads to functionality rather than causality as an approach to nature. Leibniz' view denies the originality of creatures and prompts a pantheistic view of the universe.

A CAUSE IS NOT ABSOLUTELY INTRINSIC

So far, it has been said that the mover contributes something intrinsically to the mobile rather than stands off, extrinsically, to witness a motion that it did not produce. But this view raises a question about the other extreme: Does the motor contribute something of its own being to the effect, imparting an electron for instance, if it is an atom moving through a positive field, or a photon if it is a source of radiation?

In this context, there arises another key figure in modern thought, Descartes, and his curious doctrine of cosmic change. For Descartes, local motion is the sole kind of movement in the universe, and such motion together with quantity which is taken as the essence of matter forms the only real dualism in the Cartesian system of physics. When modern empiriological physics explains the smashing of atoms by the motion of its component parts (quantities) to other regions of the universe and when Einstein reduces matter to mere space-time (quantity-local movement), there is evidence that Descartes is not dead, but, like Hume, more alive than ever. Whitehead also makes the cause too intrinsic to the effect in his "causal efficacy."

Nothing really occurs in the universe, Cartesian physics says, except rearrangements, so that motion becomes not the product of a motor outside the mobile but a merely physical transfer of parts. When motion is completed, the part of the mover that accomplished the motion is physically inside the thing moved.

Though differing in temperament, Descartes and Hume are very much alike in their outlook on nature, and their linkage affords a deeper view of the empiriological mentality, especially how it parts company with philosophy. Where Descartes reduced structure to quantity, Hume saw only phenomena. And quantity and phenomena, taken alone, mean basically the same thing—an indeterminate and featureless universe with neither substance nor causes. Cartesian physics denied final causality, as the next chapter will show, and Hume carried on by rejecting even motor causes.

If all cosmic motion is of the local type, a shift of position rather than an affecting of things, there is no relation between mover and moved like that which experience and reason demand. In Cartesianism, the motor would not be outside the mobile as an extrinsic cause. A physical change like those, for example, in a radioactive series would be simply a migration of particles from the nucleus. Radium, when it emits an alpha particle, becomes radon.

But is an ejection of such a particle the cause or effect of the radioactivity? Empiriological physics equates cause and effect and calls their whole pattern of action spontaneous. Moved and mover become physically the same thing. There is a preference for the chance universe which Hume's system also inspires. The actual transfer of parts as an account of motion, where moved and mover are the same, turns nature into a chaos of self-moving and hence utterly spontaneous things. Such a view cannot differentiate between cause and effect. It must reduce empiriological physics, in its strict sense, to the problem of describing successions, which is exactly what Hume would want it to be. The meanings of Descartes, the rationalist, and Hume, the sensist, meet in the contemporary view of nature and have been married after several centuries of courtship.

The physical identity of the motor and the mobile which Cartesianism ultimately requires is as mistaken as their physical isolation from each other which Humean premises suggest. One makes the mover too extrinsic, and the other too intrinsic, with respect to the moved. If they eventually intersect, where extremes meet, it is only because true causality alone can account for order, and without such a causality the world plunges into a chaos, a self-moving and chance universe which is the issue of Hume and Descartes alike.

CAUSES MOVE BY CONTACT

From what has thus far been said on the relation of the mover to the moved, the following conclusion can be authorized; the mover and moved can neither be absolutely distant or absolutely identified with each other. There is a middle course which is called movement by contact. Moved and mover are together but not the same, different but not distant. Motion requires an extrinsic mover, but this mover, because it affects the thing moved, must somehow be united with it without that physical transfer of itself that Descartes' physics demands. The motor must remain itself, extrinsic to the moving thing, even during the motion which it is causing. The agent does not destroy itself by acting; the patient does not absorb the agent, like a sponge taking in water. The agent remains even after the process, and as the next chapter will argue, it exists even more fully and perfectly in this aftertime than if it had not acted.

Though the realistic mean, of movement by contact, can be guaranteed by the rejection of the two extremes, a positive analogy might be helpful. The point at issue can be illustrated by the nature of knowledge which is not something preternatural in the universe but the highest form of action. Knowledge cannot change the subject, like food that is digested or like acid poured on a metal. It involves that the subject, remaining itself, become the object in that intentional way which psychology more fully depicts. Knowledge, be it repeated, is simply the highest type of action, and the becoming of other as other which it implies is weakly whispered even on the inorganic level since action, like being, is not equivocal. There is of course a great danger of forcing the analogy too far. But somehow it does serve to suggest that the motor and the moving thing can, in a sense, be one and together without the absurdities of the Cartesian and Humean universe of modern thought.

The Neoplatonic idea of emanation yields another analogy that helps to hint at the important unity between mover and moved. Motor causality is a communication of form, where the agent, without destroying itself, confers something of its own inner being upon the subject moved. This is the only way in which the gain of a new form can be explained, if the mobile reality cannot account for its own form by moving itself. The poet leaves something of himself in his poetry. A good leader impresses something of his own mettle upon his subordinates. Floods leave their watermarks, and forest fires their trail of destruction. The motor communicates something to the moved. It is one with it, moving every part of it that moves and somehow showing that it penetrates to interiority in the effect.

The philosophical science of nature must leave the further development of this subject to the science of being which shows how an effect can participate in its cause without being physically and Cartesianly identified with it. In the metaphysical account, immanence and trancendence, the intrinsic penetration of an effect by a cause that yet remains extrinsic to it are reconciled in a way that leads to neither pluralism nor monism.

EMPIRIOLOGICAL PHYSICS EQUATES CAUSE AND EFFECT

Motion has two poles which have forced philosophy to distinguish between action and passion and have given rise to delicate problems in both traditional and modern thought. What the agent does is characterized by Aristotle as action. It is a kind of making, a doing of something *to* something else. The yielding in the subject acted upon is called passion or patience, which both indicate passivity and reception. Passion is the receipt of something *from* something else.

But if the motor and moved are one, how can action and passion be called different? So impressed with this intimacy between the agent and patient, Suarez held that action is formally in the patient. But this would tend to deny the extrinsic character of the extrinsic cause and lead to a mobile universe of self-motion. It is realism to affirm with Aristotle and Aquinas that action is in the agent and passion is in the patient but that they somehow communicate in the unity of motion—a dim analogy to the unity between subject and object in knowledge. Proof of all this can be made even more pointed if it is prefaced by the empiriological solution of the problem which emphasizes even more the need for the answer of Aristotle.

In a wide way, action and passion in their traditional meanings are mated by the pair, action and reaction, in the modern empiriological vocabulary. A more minute account of this parallelism would have to show that reaction, in its Aristotelian sense, is not the same as passion but involves a type of rebound from the patient into the original agent itself, with the patient being itself an agent when actualized. An axe that cuts is also dulled in the process. The modern view puts the reaction into the effect and makes it akin to what Aristotle meant by passion. In the following broad discussion, passion and reaction can temporarily be taken as the same, and reaction, in its Aristotelian sense, will be by-passed. Action will mean what happens in the cause and passion or reaction what happens in the effect. For after showing that the cause is neither completely transcendent to the effect as Humeanism would say or completely immanent as Cartesian physics says, the following discussion will use a more empiriological backdrop to show that they are not equal.

The equivalence of action and reaction was stated actually by

Galileo (in his parallelogram law) and formulated by Newton into one of his three principles that classical physics turned into its charter. Action and reaction are equal, says the Galilean-Newtonian methodology, where equality is taken of course in its mathematical sense. Ernst Mach brings out the full force of this equivalence:

> A body that presses or pulls another body is, according to Newton, pressed or pulled in exactly the same degree by that other body. Pressure and counter-pressure, force and counter-force, are always equal to each other.[1]

The law of equivalence here can be described as the principle of conservation of momentum.

This equating of action and reaction is perhaps the central peak of seventeenth-century method from which the whole of modern empiriological physics has descended. When Newton was abandoned, his basic principle remained as the aim of empiriological research and as the norm for deciding when a statement is meaningful. What acts and what reacts and the manner of measuring each, true enough, no longer loom the same today as on the horizons of Galileo and Newton. But relativity and quantum mechanics are still bent on equating things, with all else deemed indeterminate and unmeaning. Equalities or equations form the only language that the strict empiriological physicist will bother to learn.

In the effect, Newton's third law amplifies his first one, which is the well-known law of inertia. Convoyed to its ultimate destiny, this law, as these pages have frequently inferred, requires empiriological method to view all reality as completely determined from the outside. It implies the equivalence of cause and effect which the law of action and reaction simply files into pointed form.

It has already been shown in the discussion of Descartes and Hume that the modern idea of cause tends to equate mover and

---

[1] *The Science of Mechanics,* 3d ed. (Chicago, 1902), p. 199.

moved and to make for a world of self-motion. Descartes' quantitative world easily submits to the mathematics of equality. Hume's world is the continuum. Alexander, in the progeny of Hume, could write: "Causality is thus the relation of continuity between one substance and another . . ."[2] This notion of continuity, drawn from Hume, means identity or equivalence and rejoins the Cartesian effort. Descartes and Hume plowed the philosophical soil that modern empiriological physics has planted.

THE CAUSE-EFFECT EQUATION FAILS TO EXPLAIN NOVELTY

The equivalence of action and reaction is loaded with vast problems that empiriological physics must pass unanswered or, if they are to be faced at all, appeal for their solutions to the philosophical science of nature. If this equivalence holds, then how can there be any motion at all? The Galilean-Newtonian equivalence, which empiriological physics still adopts as the test of meaning and determinacy, implies the well-known case of an irresistible force meeting up with an immovable object. From such a clash, no motion could result.

Suppose a horse were attempting to pull a wagon up a hill (action) but that the opposing forces (reaction) were just sufficient to balance out the pull on the horse. The wagon and the horse would never move.

This is of course, a familiar freshman difficulty, and empiriological physics answers it by holding that the reaction is the motion. But this is really not an answer. For if the motion, as a reaction, is equated to the motor forces, there is no difference between them, and without that element of difference, the mover is the same as the moved; no effect has occurred at all. On the premises of empiriological physics which denies everything but quantity and local motion, this ought to be a static universe, with empiriological method prospering in the logical order only by ignoring the data of experience which discloses cosmic motion

---

[2] *Space, Time, and Deity,* I, 281.

at every turn. There is no true hierarchy in formal logic and there is none on the flatlands of empiriological methods.

Another way of expressing that important fact of difference between the motor and the moved, a difference that the law of action and reaction sweeps to equivalence, is the element of novelty which motions breeds. Motion delivers to the universe something more than was there before. There is no static tug of war between the acting and reacting things of experience. As Aquinas says, "every new reality needs an innovating principle." There is progress in nature, states that characterize its today that were not in existence yesterday.

This element of novelty cannot be wholly explained by equating action and reaction or by equating anything else. The propulsive forces in nature, what Boodin calls the plus factors, somehow win out over the contrary powers which tend to cancel them. In human life, for instance, if each man gave back to the world only what he got out of it, there would be no progress in philosophy, science, politics, economics, industry, farming, in fact, in the whole of individual and social life. Progress depends on man's giving to the world more than he finds when he comes into it. If an incipient mover in nature were immediately stalemated by forces opposing it, nothing would ever occur. There is something more in nature than a mere mathematical balance.

ENTROPY FAILS TO EXPLAIN CAUSATION

Empiriological physics, of course, would attempt to explain motion as the result of entropy, pounding the universe on to death by tending to balance kinetic and potential energies or, more precisely, by a slow exhaustion of usable energy: some day the temperature of the universe will be so uniform, its motions so balanced among themselves, that the thermal equality of all bodies and hence their motions would forbid further exchange of energy.

The inadequacies of this law, as a philosophical conclusion, will be examined in the following chapter on finality and chance.

But for present purposes, it may simply be stated that if all bodies are subject to the law of entropy and there are no canceling antientropic forces even in the mineral world, the equalization of energies and the cessation of motion should be accomplished with an infinite speed and in an instant.

Entropy still leaves the novel element in experience unaccounted for. It leaves unrepealed the law of action and reaction by which the constant and finite character of energy is established and entropy is made meaningful. For entropy would have no meaning in an infinite universe or, if the supply of energy in the world were not constant but augmented by new creations.

Entropy alone would imply the downhill infinity of the universe, but the infinity of the universe would imply the unmeaning of entropy. So with entropy ruled out as a means of explaining the fertility of matter and with the law of action and reaction ruled in as basic to the idea of entropy at the empiriological level, the element of novelty in motion still remains empiriologically unexplained and on empiriological premises even impossible.

Because the universe is in constant motion, it is moving unceasingly from a potential to an actual state. There is a hierarchy between potency and act which cannot be explained by an equality sign and becomes in fact a focal point for showing that action and passion are really different. A pile of potencies is no more actual than the weakest of them. There must be more to act than there is to potency in order to avoid the embarrassment of the equational universe of empiriological physics and to account for the fact that there is something new in the universe today that yesterday was not here.

NATURE IS AN INNOVATING PRINCIPLE

To understand all this, it is imperative to return to the concept of nature which is the only subject of philosophical physics. Nature is an intrinsic source and principle in things, unexplained by, because unequated to, the transeunt forces and inertial factors acting from without. Every nature bears something original within its bosom. As a source and principle, it is a kind of spontaneity; it is fertile, as the original etymological notion of nature even suggests. It is not a featureless puff of inertia. Aquinas, it may be repeated, referred to any nature as a prime mover, and it is nature, as a source and principle rather than as a hollow inertia, that again melts away the icy formalism of empiriological physics and illuminates experience like the sun.

Nature spills out over the constraining forces that would dam it up. Movement is not the result of equality but of the originality of the nature that moves and the nature that is moved. Truly enough, a nature acts when acted upon and only to that extent. Its motions all trace their origins to an absolute Prime Mover. But when it acts, in that chain of movers where it is a link, it acts in an original way. It is an inner principle of original tendencies. Spontaneity that it is, it explains why motion is not forever fettered by cancelling forces and why reactions in matter are different from the actions which touch them off. It requires a discussion of final causality to round out this science of cosmic reaction. Hence the present theme must be interrupted until the following chapter.

This outline has established the difference between mover and moved, action and, in the wide sense, passion, action and reaction, cause and effect. Movement always involves a spontaneity, or it would be stopped by the veto of an equalitarian universe. Things that are moved transform the motion that they receive before passing it along to another recipient, and they thus give the transmitted motion something of their own originality. They do not simply pipe on a mathematical equivalence. Form is a principle of motion. If this principle were itself only pure motion, the motion which it imparts would not bear its own specific seal but would be general or indifferentiated, the continuum of Heraclitus and Hume and Descartes. The recipient also received according to its own mode of being, as salt and pepper present different colors when illuminated by the same light.

Making a distinction between action and passion, action and

reaction, can be cast into the general difference between what a thing has from within itself and what it has from the outside. Both internal and external causal influences are at work in mobile beings. But in their relations to each other the intrinsic does not explain the extrinsic, for in that case matter would be perfectly immanent. Neither does the extrinsic explain the intrinsic for in that case matter would be perfectly passive and wholly plural. In the middle lies the dualism of differentiating cause and effect.

ACTION IS DIFFERENT FROM PASSION

Moreover, action and passion involve a difference in directionality within a movement. Action is an initiative, while passion is first and, in the strict philosophical sense, a receipt. And reaction, in the proper sense, is owed to the initiative of the receiver as an agent with its own nature. Action and passion are opposed like selling and buying, teaching and learning. Giving is not just a special kind of getting in the material world. Resistance is not the same as yielding.

Equating action and reaction or even action and passion would beckon on the self-moving universe of Descartes and Hume. If mover and moved were the same, self-motion and chance would ground our world.

If action and reaction (passion) were equal, then every nature could act on its own self. But nature is the cause and source of actions, not their end. Progress requires that things tend outside themselves. The equivalence of action and passion, of the extrinsic and the intrinsic, would yield complete self-motion where the end and agent are identified and where chance and degeneration would replace the progressive grounds of a universe that is progressing in fact.

Man of course can think about himself and determine himself. By this total reflection and by freedom, he makes himself in some way the subject and object, agent and patient of his own actions, weakly imitating that complete immanence which is found only in God. But the world below man progressively falls away from this apex of immanence because the cleavage between action and passion becomes proportionately greater from man downward.

Furthermore, in the efficient order, the cause is always greater than the effect, though progress is made possible by final causality as the next chapter will show. Action is thus always higher than passion, at the level of motor causality. Otherwise, the greater would come from the less; or, in the event that action and passion were identified, there would be no sufficient reason why anything at all should follow from their union.

Motion cannot be the result of the mere algebraic sum of forces from without. If these forces are constant, they would tend to be indifferent to motion rather than to produce it, since the moved thing would give back exactly what it received. There would be an irresistible force versus an immovable object. The moving hand could never even write, let alone having writ, move on.

HEGEL DOES NOT LEAD TO TRUE HIERARCHY

There have been and there still are very definite reactions against the equalitarian account of motion which would really strangle the universe into a standstill.

The most striking example of this attempt to reconstruct a hierarchy of being is found in Hegel, who had the dubious honor of going astray on his fundamental principle but reasoning with a most acute logic thereafter. Hegel parted company with the algebraic constructions of Descartes and Kant by insisting that the universe is pure becoming. In this respect, a new Heraclitus was arising to oppose Parmenides, reborn into the static flesh of the empiriological enterprise. Though extremely critical of Heraclitus, Aristotle stood more with him in his *Physics* than he did with Parmenides and Plato. Hence, Hegelianism, with its emphasis on process, was a healthy thing by way of reaction toward a moderate and dualistic dynamism like that of Aristotle. But it lost its health by catching the same fatal germs that Aristotle diagnosed in Heraclitus. Hegel not only saw process in the world; he saw nothing else.

To explain the dynamism of the universe, Hegel introduced the so-called dialectical triad. Whatever exists (thesis) calls its opposite into being (antithesis), and from the star-crossed tension between these foes, a third and higher thing is born (synthesis) which includes both of its elements by transcending them. If there is slavery in the social order, for instance, there must be a master; for otherwise slavery would be unmeaning. From the friction between these two classes, there arises a new man bearing something of the master and something of the slave within him but surpassing both in his higher unity. This famous master-slave dialectic is only one example of the fundamental mold of all cosmic process. There is a growth and a progress and a fertility about the Hegelian universe which is choked off by the equalitarian premises of empiriological physics.

But the price of progress in the Hegelian scheme is too great for realism to pay. It is pegged by denying the principle of non-contradiction. Instead of discerning the truth that a thing excludes its opposite, Hegel declared that a thing implied it. Instead of accepting the principle of non-contradiction which he had to use in order to think and to write, Hegel rejected it, equating being and non-being in a way that is even more serious than the empiriological equation of cause and effect. Though aware that a mere inertialism could not explain the real, Hegel affirmed that a thing is wholly determined from within and from without simultaneously—another concerto on the meeting of contradictories.

Yet there is a fertility about the universe that may be salvaged from the broader meanings of Hegel, and this mobility stands in contrast to the static death which scientism portrays. Hegel did not equate the effect, the synthesis, with the causes conspiring to produce it. Like Aristotle, he was aware that the effect is no mere mechanical sum of its causal elements. But Aristotle would vehemently disagree with the character of the opposition that Hegel sees in matter. He would say that the basic principles of motion are not contradictories but contraries and that action and passion, which analogate in the accidental order of operation, the matter-form dualism in the order of substance, are likewise contrary rather than contradictory in character.

MARXIAN DYNAMISM IS IMPOSSIBLE

Marx and Engels took over the dialectical method of Hegel and poured material cement into its molds. They felt that the Hegelian contradictories, as principles of nature, enabled them to do away with the need for an extrinsic Prime Mover.

Hegel had always insisted on the Absolute. It exteriorized itself to start cosmic motion, he said, and the same motion is but a mirror of the tendencies in mobile beings to return to this Absolute as their ends. Hegel had inherited through Fichte the pantheistic view of nature which Spinoza had proposed, and far from accepting the purposeless, mechanical, and deistic universe which the scientism of his time was constructing, he went to the other extreme of absorbing the world into God.

This theocentric orientation of Hegelianism Marx and Engels flatly rejected. In accepting the dialectic of contradictories, they could, they felt, explain motion without recourse to a Prime Mover. Motion, they presumed, was the explosion of matter, set off by the inner tensions of its contradictory structures. It was viewed as lightning which results when two clouds collide or as the dynamism in a magnet because of its positive and negative poles. Obsessed likewise with the meeting of opposites, Lenin called the principle of identity, *A is A,* "an intolerable vacuity."

Matter according to Communism is self-moved and hence self-explanatory.

Marx and Engels were not deep enough to discern that a thing which contradicted itself would result not in a mobile universe but would be precisely "an intolerable vacuity." Contradictories like a circle that is not a circle, a rose that is not a rose, an electron that is not an electron do not fertilize the universe by an intrinsic cross-pollination. They simply cancel each other out, leaving the zero of a vacuum rather than a moving world.

The Marxist arguments that matter is constituted of two contradictory principles turn out to be spurious when they are reasoned out. There is opposition in the universe truly enough. But one thing does not contain its contradictory at the same time as it is what it is. The opposition, which the Marxians emphasize, comes from outside the thing in question, like floor boards resisting weight or like contrary winds blowing into the sails. Negative electric particles are outside the positive ones; the two charges do not contain each other.

The Marxian oppositions in matter would tend to balance out each other, as in the equational universe of strict empiriological physics. The oppositions would not promote motion but rest and even vacuity.

EMERGENT EVOLUTION DENIES CAUSE-EFFECT EQUALITY

Another view of nature which in a way repeats scientism and in a way forsakes it is the emergent evolutionism of men like Santayana, Alexander, Whitehead, Bergson, Lloyd Morgan, MacDougall, Smuts, and Sellars. These men, despite differences of intellectual temperament and philosophical premises, all agree in rejecting the mechanical profile of matter and in holding to the spontaneous and even chancelike character of its development. They tend, overtly or not, to vitalize matter as in the case of Bergson's vital elan which affects not only organisms but the entire universe. They view the production of novelty as one of matter's essential characteristics that does not require further explanation. What is called chance is, in general, not a rarity but the law or rather lawlessness that matter follows.

Motion thus becomes unpredictable. It is uncaused by extrinsic agencies and is but the natural outbreak of matter itself. Pressed to explain what moves matter to act in the way it does, the typical emergent evolutionist would answer that it is matter itself. Such is its nature. Matter requires no extrinsic mover. This is counter to orthodox empiriological physics and to strict empiriological method. But in a way, it is ultraempiriological since it forces the Cartesian and Humean premises until the self-motion of matter, already deduced in theory, is actually wrung out of them.

Emergent evolutionism is also accepted more or less by contemporary naturalism, floating today largely on the current which Dewey has stirred and accepting as gospel truth the fact of a thoroughgoing cosmic evolution. Such a group speaks of an "organic imbalance," produced by the developing tensions in matter, and naturalism as a philosophy is designed principally to help man counteract that disturbance by getting into stride with his environment. The naturalists of today adopt a dynamism wholly at variance with the empiriological method which they otherwise claim as the sole tool of knowledge and which in fact decrees not a moving but a static world.

Emergent evolutionism—and the phases of naturalism which imply it—requires the impossible premise of self-motion and stands condemned before the bar of reason for thus making matter potential and non-potential, actual and not-actual, under the same aspect. Most of its adherents are loose thinkers, drenched with Darwinism, prone to mistake mere theory for settled fact, misty with a sentimental faith about the dignity and future of man, and inclined to settle for descriptions of the world rather than causal inquests. The principle of non-contradiction which they apply in thinking, writing, living, and teaching they fail to recognize as perishing in their philosophies of self-motion.

DUALISM HARMONIZES MODERN OPPOSITIONS

But with all the criticism leveled at strict empiricism, when it poses as philosophy, and at emergent evolutionism, which exalts chance, there is something to be said for both of them. They lie at the extreme ends of a spectrum whose only full and reasonable light is in the brightness at the center. Philosophers, biased toward the empiriological method, are right in their insistence that the cause determines the effect, the motor the moved, the agent the patient, but they make this determination so complete that cause and effect become synonyms. Emergent evolutionism is right in its thick accent on the spontaneity of nature and on the inequalities in motion that make for a universe, prospering and progressive. The error lies in twisting motion so far out of the equalitarian forms of classical determinism that the universe buckles into the self-motion of chance.

The full report on reality lies between these views with nature seen as an interior principle, and hence emerging source, while at the same time moved only by extrinsic agents and only as long as these agents act. Realism can live again in philosophy only when and if men, forsaking the limits of sensation which grasps only one thing at a time, recognize their intelligence which they use in practice to deny itself in theory. Until then, philosophy will oscillate between the extremisms that only a dualistic science can reconcile by transcending.

Motion is in many ways the leading problem in contemporary philosophy. Empiriological method tends to ignore it, and the philosophies of emergence incline to deny that there is anything else. Heraclitus is once again at odds with Parmenides, and a re-thinking of Aristotle would help men to arbitrate the dispute.

Now as in the time of Aristotle and whenever there is motion, form and matter are its principles, and their union requires an extrinsic motor which is called an efficient cause.

Suggested Readings

de Finance, Joseph, *Être et agir* (Paris, 1945).

Garrigou-Lagrange, Reginald, *God, His Existence and Nature*, transl. B. Rose (London, 1934), Vol. I.

8

Progress and Purpose

FINALITY ORGANIZES MOTION

In a genuine sense, this is a progressive, open, and expanding universe.

But progress without purpose, openness without order, and expansion that is merely mechanical would forge a world that was static, closed, and utterly exploded. If there is order in nature there is a final cause, and if there is a final cause there is order.

Although not always able to tidy the order into measured law, man can rest assured that a nature could never produce anything in its motions unless their order toward an end were fundamental. If a moving thing did not tend to this end rather than that there would be no reason why one effect should flow from given action rather than another. This would be a vacant world —indifferent, indeterminate, immobile, and chancelike.

The assault upon the mobile world lost a basic explanatory weapon when it rearmed itself in the seventeenth century without the steel of final causality. It is the reality of ends that alone explains the regularity, progress, and hierarchy in the cosmos, and without these goals beyond the natures that seek them, all the secrets of things become locked in their own limits and there is no reason for motion toward the outside. Sufficient unto itself, a moving becomes self-explanatory if it has no final cause, and as self-explanatory it becomes actual and non-actual, potential and non-potential, under the same aspect. Undetermined by an end, it can do anything when set in motion, and chance once again stampedes the universe.

A universe without finality would not provide the progressive and evolutionary march in which modern man has fixed his faith. It would be just the opposite, and one of the aims of this chapter will be to show why.

There are three overall parts to the chapter. The first argues to the progressive character of the universe; the second is an outline of tendencies that should deny progress; and the third is an evaluation of such trends and a defense of the realism of progress and of purposes.

In particular, the first large bundle of argument shows that finality explains progress without divinizing it.

The second broad division outlines modern views on chance, from the philosophical premises which construct a chance world to the inertial and indeterminate universe actually brushed out by empiriological physics. Getting down to cases, it is then shown that statistics is used in classical physics and for more complicated reasons in quantum physics. Getting down to details of cases, arguments for so-called indeterminism are instanced from thermodynamics, statistically examined.

The remainder of the chapter weighs the arguments just set forth. First it is shown that randomness is not the same as chance and that statistics in general and the Heisenberg principle in particular require rather than reject order. It is then argued that true chance is real, while empiriological physics emphasizes a chance that is methodological. Then the cases from thermodynamics are examined, and it is shown why empiriological physics tends to such indeterminism as these cases argue. The law of entropy is then examined in a more general fashion, first criticized for being extreme and then shown to have a counterpart in nature. The last theme restates the differences between philosophical and empiriological physics in their attitudes toward nature and chance.

FINALITY MAKES FOR PROGRESS

In the discussion of the efficient cause, there was a question about the true direction in motion. Does progress imply that there is more to the effect than to the cause?

Bradley hammered at this difficulty until he concluded with the Eleatics that motion can be only an illusion. Truly, if there is more perfection and greater progress in the finite world because of motion, the greater and the more might seem at first sight to come from the less, since the motion starts with potency and is completed by act.

An answer, of course, might be to deny all motion except that of the Prime Mover, but this solution would march with Malebranche on the road to ontologism which snatches all originality from creatures. And if creatures are not original, pantheism must be the logical conclusion. Evidently ontologism is not correct.

In the philosophical science of nature, there is indeed an ascension to a Prime Mover as a necessity demanded by reason whenever and wherever it finds motion and for every moment that the motion lasts. But when a creature is moved by God, its own originality is not thereby denied or impeded. God does not move things contrary to their natures. He moves them naturally. And since the seeds of progress are also in nature, the question still remains how there is apparently more in the universe after a motion than there was when it began.

This higher rung which things naturally attain from a lower one can be clarified by final causality. In the efficient order, it would seem as though progress in a finite world would make the effect greater than the cause. In the final order, balance is restored. The goal sought is greater than the thing going after it to the extent that the end completes and fulfills the nature of the seeker.

The final cause draws the agent onward and outward. Aquinas rightly termed it the cause of causes since it explains why the motor acts to effect this or that union of matter and form. The realistic cosmos is dominated by finality, which is an attracting cause and not one of merely mechanical pushes and pulls by agents on the same level with the objects they affect. Things are not sealed off in themselves but are angled to definite ends outside. Nature is the seat of these tensions toward a beyond, mak-

Date Due

13 1961	FEB 2 6 '62	
6	SEP 2 7 '62	
CT 2 7 1961		
T 3 0 1961		
1 6 1961		
OV 1 7		
OV 2 1		
OV 2 7		
OV 2 8		
V 2 9		
C 4		
EC 7		
EC 1 1		
C 1 2		
EC 1 3		
EC 1 4		
1 5		
N 1 3 '62	Sue Muckerman	
2 0 '62		
2 9 '62	S. Mere Lee	
1 2 '62	Ruth Benz	

ing progress not a riddle but the normal issue of natural motion.

The efficient cause cannot wholly explain progress, and it was a logical conclusion, with nature robbed of thrusts toward outside goals, to decide that the universe is not progressing but running down as the law of entropy states. Mechanism in general resembles the Aristotelian doctrine of material and motor causes without the complement of finality and form.

In the realistic universe, natures are charged with inner tendencies; finality and betterment and striving are in the heart of them. The original and goalward dispositions upset the static balance that a mechanical universe would have to be, and this tipping of the scale by natural tendencies to ends enables cosmic progress to be unreeled. A nature is endowed not only with a passivity to be moved but with a pattern to be realized. It is not only pushed from the rear but poised for action, drawn forward by something that is causally in front of it, something greater than it, something that is not itself in motion but is motion's goal. All these truths are mustered by the metaphysician into his proof of a Supreme Designer.

Natures seek what is good. Prodded into action, they do what is best for them, which is another way of saying that they do what is natural to their being. A piece of iron will resist efforts to move it, in order to conserve itself. Paper will bleach near strong heat because such a motion accords with its nature and is best for it. Natures do what they should do, what they must do, what is good and natural for them to do. Having fulfilled their appointed ends, they are greater, stabler, better for having had their potencies reduced to act. Natural act is better than natural potency.

GOD IS THE GOAL OF NATURE'S MOTIONS

Some contemporary systems, in the watery footsteps of Hegel, think that God is not the finalizing goal of the process but the effected product.

Whitehead felt a gust of the final causality in the world. His actual entities select their mutual organizations by what are called "prehensions" or "feelings." He envisioned the realities of the world as seeking "satisfaction." But God is not the goal of cosmic motion. God, in his "consequent nature," is the product.

In Alexander, God is a "nisus," ever the next highest stage in evolution to the one that is presently realized.

Hartshorne calls God "the self-surpassing surpasser of all" and holds Divine being to be affected, and hence effected in some way, by the processes in the world.

But all of these systems are inadequate, though laudably concerned about a grave and neglected problem in philosophy. God must exist as the goal of the process, and is not the result of it. If He were not the ultimate actually existing Being toward which creation strives, then motion would tend to nothing and the principle of sufficient reason would again be violated. From an even more swaying viewpoint, God is the Designer of the world, and if He did not exist independently of cosmic processes, He would be fashioning a world that in turn brings Him into existence. He would be designing before He existed.

At the other extreme, some philosophers, including scholastics like Marc de Munnynck, have held that the order of the universe cannot be a premise in proving God's existence but rather a conclusion that can only be established in the light of God's Providence. But the principle of finality does not have to await the study of theodicy before it can be stated and established. The tendencies of moving things to certain ends are simply other ways of defining their natures. The ultimate probing of ends and of tendencies to ends points to a Supreme Designer, just as the pursuit of motor causality leads to the reality of a Prime Mover.

The philosophy of nature is a preamble to metaphysics. It is not an appendix.

MODERN PREMISES CONCLUDE TO CHANCE WORLD

A world without finality would not be progressive. It would not even move.

The modern mind has abandoned a study of nature in terms

of final causality, and it has quite logically settled into the view that basically the universe is governed by chance and by chance alone. This course was charted out when Descartes' physics put to sea denying true final causes. He persuaded the study of nature to look within bodies rather than outside of them for the full story of their causes and reasons, as scientifically known.

Without a final cause, matter becomes aimless. With all its mysteries wrapped inside it, matter becomes self-moved. Shorn of its native tendencies to ends, a thing becomes indeterminate, a creature of the inertial forces impinging on it and of them alone. With no intentional thrust to an outside goal, it becomes legitimate to study matter by simply looking inside it and breaking it up. Chance, spontaneity, indeterminism, and atomism are good descriptions of present-day accounts of the world in empiriological physics, and they owe their origins in great measure to Descartes.

By way of preface to the scope of chance in modern thinking, it should be pointed out that a study which seems only to measure cannot possibly grasp tendencies to ends. It deals only with the quantified or plural aspect of things. It lacks depth perception into the dynamism which tendencies toward ends involve—a dynamism that is the result of such tendencies and also their revelation.

The quantitative approach which empiriological physics has chosen to pursue ignores all but the plural, whereas a nature in the world of motion has interiority or unity and acts toward a unified goal, toward one goal rather than another. A triangle has no tendencies, and neither does a number like 1 or π. Neither does inertia have tendencies. It is indeterminate, awaiting determination from the outside.

Finally, a tendency to a given end cannot be controlled. It is altered only by altering the nature which bears it, and hence a discipline that seeks to explore nature by control and to control nature for man must necessarily allow tendencies to pass unnoticed.

This experimental approach is, of course, the proper thing in its proper place. But like anything that gets out of place, it is wrong.

INERTIALISM SUGGESTS CHANCE

In Chapter 3 it was seen that inertialism must breed a chance universe since even an infinite series of inertial movers could never generate a true cause of motion. In such a setting, motion, when it occurs, must be considered as uncaused or as chance in origin. It has also been argued in Chapter 7 that as causation is defined in empiriological physics, since there is no causal influx into the effect, and since there is only a Humean succession in the world of motion, the posterior stage of a moving thing is independent of the prior one. Anything can follow anything else. It arises independently and fortuitously.

Chance is a rare deviation from the order established by final causality (Chapter 3). It is not an absolute disorder, for in such a case it would be nothing. It is a disorder resulting when two causal sequences intersect. Chance thus originates from outside the nature which it affects and which has somehow become embroiled in another causal series outside its own. This origin of chance, as extrinsic to the nature which is impeded by it, provides another way of relating chance to the principle of inertia. If all things are completely determined by transeunt forces from outside them, then this is a completely chance universe. Bradley detected this when he wrote of a completely chance event:

> It would have to stand without a relation, or rather with all its relations outside. But, since a thing must be determined by the relations in which it stands, the absolutely contingent would thus be utterly determined from the outside. And so, by consequence, chance would involve complete internal dissipation.[1]

By a similar line of reasoning it could be shown that whatever is "utterly determined from the outside" would be "absolutely contingent."

---

[1] *Appearance and Reality* (London, 1893), p. 392.

From another angle, it could be shown that since the cause of chance is not unified but plural, a world of utter pluralism would be chance, and chance would involve an utter pluralism.

A chance event Aristotle called an *automaton,* meaning "by nature vain" and the parent of our English word *automatic,* meaning self-operating or self-caused. Either word is an apt term for describing chance. The principle of finality affirms that nature does nothing in vain, and so the a-final or the vain is outside of nature and is chance. This meaning is matched by the modern English word *automatic.* In the last chapter, it was seen that scientism constructs a universe which can be pictured in terms either of self-motion or of complete inertia, where the entire reality of a thing comes from outside it. Chance is something extrinsic to a natural agent. It is spontaneous, self-moved, beyond nature, automatic. An automaton is another word for a machine, and a mechanical world would be one of utter chance.

From many directions then, it is logical for the empiriological physicist to coast from his premises to the easy conclusion that this is entirely a chance universe. Dewey, a proponent of the empiriological method, shows this in a more obvious form by bringing the indifferentism of empiriological physics along with him into the moral order. He stoutly rejects the notion of "fixed ends" in genuine philosophy. His universe is one of means only, a cosmic kit of tools, where an end is nothing but a means that an agent sets up locally as an aim for a project that socio-biological factors force upon him. Ends are called "ends in view," and they are different from means, only because of this temporary ambition of the moral agent solving a particular problem. They are logically different from means. For the philosophy of genuine and objective ends has been thoroughly extinguished in the dark world of naturalism.

An indifferent and featureless world would, of course, be more controllable because devoid of tendencies, and control is what naturalism glorifies. But to control is to get at the lowest level of things and not at what they are apart from man.

EMPIRIOLOGICAL PHYSICS EMPHASIZES THE STATISTICAL

Dewey's error was to lift into a higher and philosophical realm methods that are designed only for the lower levels where in the strict sense knowing things as they are is neither an aim nor a possibility. A chance world was germinating in empiriological physics from the time that Galileo emphasized inertia and Descartes, plurality and quantity. That this indeterminism has matured in empiriological physics can be seen from the frequent allusions to chance in the microscopic world and to the purely statistical character imputed to physical law.

Chance had its say even in the classical arena, and the work of men like Laplace, Bernoulli, Boltzmann, and Maxwell led finally to a statistical approach to molecular movement according to the kinetic-molecular theory of chemistry. Statistics is in general a way of measuring large quantities of individuals which single measurements would make too complicated. If, for example, white and black beans are thoroughly mixed in an urn and then withdrawn one by one, the statistician can conclude after the first hundred beans are drawn and their colors compared what the proportion of the white and black beans will be after the whole urnful has been sorted.

Statistics may be considered here as a movement from the part to the whole. Knowing the percentage of one factor to another in the part and knowing that the whole is homogeneous, it can be concluded that the two factors occur in the whole by the same ratio. For instance, in tossing a coin at random, the chances are 1 in 2 that heads will occur. It is so simple that it does not even require any paper work to show that if a coin were tossed at random 10,000 times, the number of cases of heads will tend to be 5,000. Statistics gives an accurate picture of the whole, often called collection, aggregate, or ensemble, represented by the 10,000 throws.

But this accuracy cannot be transferred to the individuals which comprise the whole. For example, after tails appears on the first throw, it is not certain that the next throw will be heads. The chance of heads is still 1 in 2. Even after two or three or n throws of tails, the probability of heads on the next toss remains $1/2$. In a statistical aggregate, the fate of an individual can only be described in terms of probability. Here too, however, it is the interpretation of the figures rather than the mathematics which is inaccurate. The probability is expressed in numerical form (like the $1/2$ above), and to that extent, it is precisely known.

Statistics differs from other mathematical sciences less by its form than by its subject matter which is probability, but when it is called a science of probabilities, it is oftentimes thought that everything about it is only probable. Where no distinction is made between matter and form, confusion is bound to occur about such a relation of mathematics to a physical subject matter. Already it is easy to see how the use of statistics often prompts the verdict that there is only probability in nature and in knowledge.

In the foregoing examples, the accent was laid on statistics as developed inductively, moving from the part to the whole as all induction does. But there is another approach, perhaps the more common one in empiriological physics, which begins with knowledge not of the part but of the whole, working deductively downward to the average character of the individual part. Knowing, for instance, the pressure exerted by a gas on its chamber walls and that the parts are homogeneously distributed through the whole, the average energy of the individual particle can be carefully computed. Here again, statistics is exact in its account of the average, which is its subject matter. Moreover, it can state in numerical form the probability that any particle chosen at random will have this average energy, but it cannot guarantee that a particle randomly chosen will actually represent the average.

In a practical way, statistics was applied to problems in empiriological physics and chemistry in the classical period of the nineteenth century—problems such as the average velocity of particles in a gas chamber, how far on the average a particle will travel before colliding with another one (mean free path), and the number of particles striking a chamber wall. Another famous field for the application of statistics is the flow of heat.

Radioactivity was likewise discovered in the classical system to be a statistical process. To give the framework, the half life of an element is defined as the time required for half of the atoms present in a given aggregate to decay. Radon, for instance, has a half life of 3.825 days, which means that no matter when an observation is begun on this element half of the atoms initially present will have decayed 3.825 days later.

Statistics does not say which of the atoms in an aggregate will actually decay. Suppose for instance that the decay went on until finally two atoms of radon remained. The empiriological physicist is sure that within 3.825 days after he begins his observation of the pair one of the atoms will disintegrate, but he does not know which one it will be. Hence as in all statistical problems, he must refrain from pronouncing on the fate of individuals.

The philosophical physicist should like to ask, for instance, what the empiriological method can say about the lone radon atom of an original pair, and the empiriological physicist is powerless to reply. For all he knows, the radon atom might last a thousand years or decay in the next microsecond. He cannot forecast the fate of the individuals. He considers the behavior of a single radon atom as indeterminate.

QUANTUM MECHANICS TENDS TO INDETERMINISM

Classical physics used statistics because it was too complex an operation to determine the initial condition of, say, every molecule in a liter of gas. It is simply too difficult to investigate singly the tremendous number of particles which an appreciable quantity of gas contains.

Quantum physics has other reasons for introducing statistics. According to Heisenberg, the measurement of individual particles is not only complex. It is impossible. In trying to measure the position of a particle, Heisenberg shows, its velocity is always disturbed, and in trying to measure its velocity, there is an interference with its position.

Empiriological physics, standing at this impasse, has relaxed its nineteenth-century ambitions. It has decided to settle for a probable knowledge of position and velocity, and from a given probability of these two characters in an initial measurement, it infers their probability at any later time of interest. Empiriological physics concludes that there is an indetermination in nature itself, and that its attack upon matter must stop short with probable values in its premises and with corresponding probabilities in the outcome of its predictions.

But Heisenberg did not pioneer this expansion of statistical physics in the contemporary world. Max Planck had shown early in the twentieth century that energy was not emitted continuously like an electromagnetic wave of light but spurted out in discrete and unpredictable packets which came to be called quanta. Enough has been said in previous chapters to indicate that empiriological physics cannot handle what is discrete but prefers to knead its subject matter into a continuum. From Planck's theory on, small energies like those involved in ordinary radiation or in microscopic processes have not been treated at the individual level but as a statistical aggregate. Quantum physics, stymied by discrete and "indeterminate" individuals, retrieves its accuracy through a statistical whole which is a form of the continuum and which yields a knowledge not of individuals but simply of averages.

After the wave theory of matter was advanced by Louis de Broglie to continue the quantum idea, Schroedinger devised a system of equations which combined the wave and particle aspects of matter and put matter and energy together into a single system of quantum "statistical" mechanics. On Schroedinger's reasoning, a wave becomes a mathematical curve, representing by its amplitudes that vary with time the probabilities of finding a matter or energy particle (in a single-particle system), whose initial position and velocity were known with probability. For instance, at the peak of such a mathematical curve or wave, the probability of finding the particle in a given position would be high and, at the trough, would be low.

Schroedinger's mathematics are thus said to describe probability amplitudes. It is not so much a real wave that varies in height but probability ratios. Planck, Heisenberg, de Broglie, Born, and Schroedinger are responsible for bringing statistics into a domain that classical physics expected, at least theoretically, to conquer by ordinary non-statistical mechanics.

Such developments have favored the belief that all the laws in nature are statistical in character and that, in the deeply subterranean jungles of experienced events, chance and chaos reign supreme. Individual particles and energies which Victorian researchers dreamed of measuring in exact terms have been surrendered by present-day methods to the realm of the indeterminate.

In their fervor over the new quantum systems, some empiriological physicists began to talk about free will in atoms, vitalism in nature, daily miracles in a universe once believed so rigidly ordered as to exclude even Divine intervention. Far from leaning tower of nineteenth-century studies which had hoped to reduce the universe to the precision of a single, all-embracing law, quantum physicists incline to say that nothing can ever be certain any more. Efforts to account for the uniformity of nature have been replaced by the denial that nature is uniform.

It is a long distance back to teleology and to the concept of nature as an ordered cause and principle. But it is a straight road over which contemporary thought come. Without finality, the cosmos becomes a chaos, a decision abetted by Descartes in his denial of true teleology in physics and by Galileo in his preference to study only inertia.

THERMODYNAMICS IS ALLEGEDLY INDETERMINISTIC

The laws of thermodynamics lurk in the background of the empiriological universe, and the view of scientism that the universe is only a statistical aggregate is reinforced by the statistical treatment of entropy which Schroedinger has called the prototype of statistical law.

Treated on the macroscopic plane, the law of entropy does not vary but applies with the rigor that its authors saw in it. Yet in the microscopic world, the determinism weakens. There, according to the empiriological report, a random series of events is discovered.

For instance, when electrons flow in a vacuum tube from the cathode (negative plate) to the anode (positive plate), they carry out their migration in great numbers, too great sometimes to be absorbed by the anode as fast as they arrive in its vicinity. There is, after a time at least, a disordered flow of electrons. Their surplus numbers form a kind of cloud where electrons move in somewhat random fashion, unable to be attracted to the positive plate in the straight-line path that the first few of them were able to follow. In this somewhat random cloud, occasional electrons will be found moving not to the anode but back to the cathode, apparently contrary to what entropy would require. In a random aggregate of electrons, is it not possible that by the laws of mathematical probability all of them might at some future moment flow back to the cathode, reversing the normal direction of current flow? If an occasional electron can move backward to the cathode, it is apparently possible for all of them to do so.

This reasoning of empiriological method can be dressed up in other examples where there is no electric force to attract or repel the particles, and where the idea of randomness emerges more lucidly. But a further discussion ought to be prefaced by a mention of the three contemporary systems for dealing with the movements of large masses of particles on a statistical basis. These systems differ from each other not so much in general method as in the initial assumptions which they make about their materials. They start with different "mechanical" models of their aggregates which all illustrate the crucial notion of randomness.

1. The Boltzmann system, which is the culmination of classical

statistics, assumes that all particles in a collection have average values and that the value of the whole is equal to their sum. Each molecule in a gas, for example, is assumed to possess average energies obtained when dividing the total energy by the number of particles present.

2. The Einstein-Bose statistics of quantum mechanics would assume that each particle can occupy all the positions in a given volume with equal likelihood. It therefore assumes that random distributions of the whole are equally probable, rather than starting with assumptions about the parts. The Einstein-Bose system applies to nuclei and atoms having an even number of particles and to photons.

3. The Fermi-Dirac system, also quantum mechanical, assumes that all the particles occupy different positions. Where the Einstein-Bose system holds that all the particles may have the same energies, the Fermi-Dirac approach makes the energies of all the particles different. It applies to nuclei and atoms having an odd number of particles and to protons, neutrons, and electrons.

All three systems work with averages: the Boltzmann system assuming that a particle is in an average state with respect to the system as a whole; the Einstein-Bose system holding that a whole is the average of many different possibilities of wholes; and the Fermi-Dirac system assuming that a whole is the average of differences. Classical physics treated a whole as an average because initial knowledge was difficult and the computational machinery complex. Quantum mechanics introduces the further factor that, in addition to being difficult and complex, the study of individual particles permits only average values to be assigned to them by their nature. They are indeterminate.

It will be noted from the foregoing outline that the three statistical systems, apart from their different presuppositions of a physical nature, all make a postulate of randomness. The Boltzmann system holds that there is a random distribution of parts in a gaseous aggregate; the Einstein-Bose system holds that there is a random distribution of wholes; and the Fermi-Dirac system declares that there is an equal repartition of differences. The empiriological physicist always insists on this random character of his subject matter if he is to apply statistical techniques, and because such methods work so well, he is often led to believe that nature at her subatomic roots is a random thing.

But why is it, empiriological physics is queried, that such random activity does not show up in macroscopic experience? And the answer is advanced that such a random behavior on a larger scale is actually possible but that the odds are so great against macroscopic disorders that they are next to impossible.

To close this parenthesis on the three systems and to return to an example which is even more eloquent that the swarm in the electron cloud, let us assume the molecules in an ordinary gas to be in random motion. With this premise of randomness, the empiriological physicist feels empowered to conclude that given a long enough time, the particles in, say, a cubical chamber might at some future moment all be directed to one side of the chamber, leaving zero pressure on the other five sides. Such a state of affairs would be called a disorder if it ever happened, and the empiriological physicist admits that the mathematical chances for its occurrence are very slim. But he still thinks that he must allow for it.

To take a third example of how statistical mechanics has affected the older acceptance of the uniformity of nature, heat is the random movement of molecules according to the empiriological report. It is a disordered movement, and the more and more energy is converted into heat the greater and greater becomes the disorder and randomness in the universe; the more the universe makes the statisticians' dream come closer to the truly random whole.

Now if the movements in boiling water are simply molecules in random agitation, their randomness might at some moment point them all in the same direction, say toward the center of the volume. When and if this ever happens, water would tend to freeze on fire instead of boiling.

In a similar way, the molecules in a desk are in random motion, and if random, might permit the desk some day to rise from the floor when all its molecules happen to be vectored upward. In the case of both the water and the desk, the odds are almost infinitely against the variation of their normal behaviors. But so long as their basic movements are random in character, the freezing of the water or the ascension of the desk must be deemed at least mathematically possible.

The treatment of thermodynamics by statistical techniques thus leads to results at variance with the law of entropy. This law, for many an empiriological physicist, no longer states the direction of energy flow with the rigor of classical thermodynamics. The law is most frequently viewed now, at least in theory, as stating only probable direction.

In a sense, a very important one, statistical mechanics eliminates the notion of heat from thermodynamics and tends to eliminate thermodynamics itself. There is no heat in a single atom. Heat results from the random movement in an aggregate and it is not a property of single particles.

But there is another way in which statistical mechanics recovers the idea of heat if not the formal laws of thermodynamics. Heat is defined as a disordered motion of particles, and disorder is the law of the atomic underworld, statistically explored.

The law of entropy states that all exchanges of energy involve a certain loss of heat which is no longer usable to do work. The quantity of heat thus increases with every cosmic process. But heat is a disorder, and where the Aristotelian universe was angled to order, the modern universe is said to be rampaging toward the opposite. Entropy or disorder, the empiriological physicist says, is always on the increase. The universe, he goes on, is becoming more random and hence moving from a less probable state to a more probable one.

RANDOMNESS IS NOT A CHANCE

It is possible now to evaluate the notions of chance which have been sketched. In tempering the extreme views which the devotees of scientism adopt, recourse might be had to the proofs earlier set down that finality is operative in nature but that mere measurement cannot come to a full and formal appreciation of its reality and force. It could also be shown that the empiriological physicist, as such, cannot possibly speak of order and disorder, chance and antichance, because such factors are recognized not by yardsticks and chronometers in the realm of quantity but by insight into motion. This would all be sufficient to turn back the indeterminism by which the empiriological physicist challenges the philosophical science of nature.

But the approach of philosophical physics can be toughened by pitting some of the modern views on chance against it, using reality to arbitrate the dispute and to show the strong points in the contemporary views and also the weaknesses.

It is important to note at the very beginning that chance is an equivocal word and that philosophical and empiriological physics are talking about two quite different things. Chance, in its physical and real implications, can be defined only in terms of final causality. It involves motion and in this setting was seen to be an aberration from a motion's natural destiny. Chance on the modern scene is not primarily of motion but of quantity, and removed from the world of tendency and teleology it is not properly chance at all.

This might be made clear by distinguishing chance from randomness. A random distribution of units forming a collection means that the whole is homogeneous and is a form of order where the parts are scattered equally throughout the aggregate. Such an aggregate is mathematically treated. The order which it reflects is defined by reference to a mathematical system, and mathematics, unconcerned with final causes, does not deal with chance.

True chance, on the other hand, is something physical. If the random collection is set in motion, then it is subject to the element of chance. Its random character, its homogeneity, might be disturbed by an extrinsic causal series, and the disturbance of the random order would be a chance event. A dice game can be studied mathematically. The statistician can predict how many sixes will occur in, say, 2000 random throws. But he supposes the random order which chance, the disorder factor, might disturb. What is random follows law, as the concept of an average can show; what is chance is lawless, unpredictable. What is random has a type of order; what is chance is disordered.

STATISTICS IMPLIES DETERMINISM

It is obvious that a statistical whole composed of elements that are apparently disordered is in reality an ordered whole, like the ratio of heads to tails over a great many throws of the coin. But such a whole is nothing but the sum of its parts, and if the whole is ordered, the parts must likewise be ordered in ways perhaps that man is unable to follow and record. If the units forming a collection were utter chaos, following the laws or rather the lawlessness of chance, no order like averages, radioactive half life, and thermal equilibrium would occur in the whole. Scientism, mistaking its own ignorance for nature's blunders, prides itself on apparent proofs that nature is disordered, but the existence of evident law in an aggregate argues that the parts comprising the whole are law-abiding too.

Order does not depend for its existence on our ability to measure it. To acknowledge as order only what man can measure with quantity and vary with instruments is anthropomorphic in the extreme. In fact, order as such has nothing to do with quantity; it is woven from the tendencies of natures to their ends and cannot be detected where reality is approached as something indeterminate and inert. If the small particles, believed in empiriological physics to be governed by chance, had no tendencies of their own and hence no order to ends, they would be wholly indeterminate, not only unable to act but unable even to exist. The occurrence of order in the statistical whole is a confirmatory argument for the order that the particles must obey individually to operate at all and even to exist in the world of mobile things.

This general rejection of a universe as governed only by chance applies alike to the classical and the quantum applications of statistics.

In regard to quantum methods, the wave equations of Schroedinger start with the probability of positions and energies and predict the ordered variation of that probability as time goes on and the positions and energies change. The probability in the premises is connected with the probability in the conclusions by order and by law. The difficulty in quantum physics is not the connections of the present with the future, which is order, but the inability to get exact knowledge of the present as leverage for prediction.

THE HEISENBERG PRINCIPLE IMPLIES ORDER

The Heisenberg principle sharpens this conclusion. In scientism, the principle tends to transfer a difficulty in measurement to a disorder in nature, leading to the verdict that nature is indeterminate. To drum home the truth that the uncertainty relation represents a subjective or logical indetermination, meaning of course an inaccuracy in measurement, and to show that it does not mean a disorder in nature, the philosophical physicist may propose the following argument:

A standard must be chosen with respect to which the indeterminism is said to exist. If it is said that a thing is disordered, there must be an order as a standard for deciding that there is disorder. Now this standard must be either subjective or objective. If the standard is subjective, so is the indeterminism which it defines, and this is what the philosophical science of nature would hold, a subjective and logical indeterminism as the issue of the Heisenberg principle. On the other hand, if the standard is objective, then all is not indeterminate in the world. At least this standard of order, with respect to which disorder is defined, is determinate and law-abiding.

Bergson and Bradley could be applied here in their agreement that "chance" is not disorder but order of a different type from the one expected. This "relative chance," as both Bergson and Bradley term it, is what the empiriological physicist, in classical or quantum garb, really means by disorders, and "chance" is thus objectively an order of a different type from the one that is of interest in a problem. The definition of "chance" in quantum physics rests on a prior definition of order and is real or not, depending on whether the norm of order is real or not.

TRUE CHANCE IS REAL

Chance, as Francis Bacon said, reflects man's ignorance more than nature's aberrations. And that ignorance, removable completely only by a knowledge of all possible fact and its combinations, which can also be called facts, cannot be overcome. With Chapter 4 for a background, it can now be stated that fact is as infinite as prime matter, i.e., potentially or privatively infinite. This can be shown, to take a telling example, by the divisibility of matter *ad infinitum,* and the tendencies of empiriological physics to pursue this infinite road by dividing matter, subdividing the divisions and then the subdivisions, without end. Each pace along the road of dividing matter yields a new fact that is somehow capable of altering the mobile world and of being experienced by man. But though man, in principle, can know the basic character of a nature at a single glance, he can never know all possible fact except through the impossible task of traversing the infinite series. Hence, the growth of knowledge cannot overcome true chance, a disorder arising from the crisscross of causal series.

Man's knowledge is of universals. He can never know all there is to know about individuals. God has such knowledge, and for Him nothing happens by chance. To this extent, Bacon is right. But man lives in a mobile world where individuals are in motion, and though knowing the general features of the individuals that move and knowing even their species, man can have a certain knowledge only of law; his knowledge does not exhaust all possible fact—let alone its combinations—which can be multiplied as much as individuals can be divided, hence multiplied indefinitely.

Ignorance in matters of physical chance, which is what Aristotle described, may be called negative ignorance, as opposed to the privative type. If a book cannot speak, it might be called dumb in a negative sense since speech is not owed to the nature of a book. But for a man to lack speech is privative dumbness, the lack of a perfection that man ought to have. It is in the sense of this contrast that ignorance in cases of true physical chance may be called negative.

But ignorance of molecular movement, for example, because it is difficult to measure individual particles, is a privative ignorance. It is possible to remove it but extremely hard to do so. Removing it is theoretically but not practically possible. Since the smallest atom is at least 1800 times as large as an electron which would be used in an electron microscope to "see" it, a single electron would not appreciably disturb a hydrogen atom or molecule, and it is theoretically possible to chart the course of any molecule presently said to move in random fashion because exact measurement of its path is so difficult. But it is not theoretically possible to overcome our negative ignorance in cases of true chance. Empiriological physics, by its concept of randomness, stresses a new and negative type of ignorance overlaid upon the natural and privative type which true chance involves. Randomness is methodological chance, but true chance is real.

EMPIRIOLOGY RIGHTLY TENDS TOWARD THE CHANCELIKE

Empiriological physicists are usually concerned with theories as tools to predict their experiments, and they should not, the good ones insist on this, impute an ontal value to theoretical constructions. Do not try to picture reality, they enjoin their students; accept as fact only the laboratory data which theories predict.

If scientism followed this counsel more carefully, it ought to conclude that the supposition of random partition which lies at the bedrock of its statistical superstructures does not imply that reality is really a jungle.

There is, however, a realistic backdrop for the empiriological belief in the randomness of microscopic events, which increases the more matter is divided. Simon has sketched the idea that the more an atom is divided the more parts there are and the more likelihood there is of interferences among causal series.[2] Besides, the more plural the world becomes, the more inert it is, and the more inert or extrinsic to itself, the more chancelike, according to the reasoning which Bradley suggested earlier in this chapter.

Moreover, the success of empiriological physics in exploiting the universe by taking its atomic rhythms as random tends anew to confirm rather than deny an Aristotelian version of what empiriological method is about. A random distribution is continuous and homogeneous and indeterminate, and the mineral world which is so little under the dominion of form and hence so much under the sway of matter tends to approximate this the more matter is broken up.

It was a thesis in Chapter 6 that the more matter is sundered, into subatomic particles for example, the more the inertial factor increases and the less form the units have. Empiriological physics, it was said, tends more and more to prime matter. But if atoms, and subatomic particles even more so, are almost random, almost inert, almost indeterminate, the *almost* is too important to neglect since the structures and substructures of atoms still have a minimal form necessary to keep them in existence as mobile beings when in a free state. The philosophical physicist can explain the success of the empiriological itinerary when it assumes that microscopic particles and their movements are random and indeter-

---

[2] *Prévoir et savoir,* pp. 60–61.

minate. That is almost what such realities and such events truly are. Their form is poor and their final cause is weak. That is why they are so controllable.

They are logically general.

THE ALLEGED EXAMPLES OF DISORDER INVOLVE ORDER

But there is still enough form and finality left, wherever an entity like an electron or a meson exists even momentarily in isolation, to make for the order that obtains between tendency and end; otherwise, there would be the indeterminacy and chaos of prime matter. This minimum of form, attracted by its end, insures that the boiling of a kettle on fire which normally takes place will continue to occur when external conditions are the same. It could guarantee the stenographer that her desk will not suddenly leap up at her when she is writing a letter.

Perfect randomness can exist only in mathematics with its equalities but not in nature with its hierarchies, nature where there is something more than quantity and its distribution, namely, motion and its laws. Each molecule of water in the kettle and each cellulose molecule in the desk is endowed with definite tendencies, and the sorting of the tendencies into the one that a motion actualizes in preference to the others is the work of the end. The motors, responsible for the motions of things, are likewise governed by final causes. The tendencies are weak it is true, and the ends are feeble, as evidenced by the control man clamps upon the mineral world. But there are still tendencies and still ends. Changing them means changing the thing that they affect.

An electron in the example of the vacuum tube will not turn backward to the cathode unless something changes it, and it will then respond by seeking the end which is natural to it under the changed circumstances. An electron is not self-moved or chance-like. When a cloud of electrons collects around the anode to which they were originally directed, it has the effect of generating a negative plate because the electrons are negative in charge. This negative cloud thus acts to repel electrons and to drive them backward toward the cathode from which they came.

Is it possible for all the molecules in a gas to line up some day in a direction toward one side only of a cubical container, exerting zero pressure on the other five walls? No, not unless an external motor coerces them from their three-directional movement into a one-directional path. If a zig is changed to a zag, there must be a cause for the change, and there must likewise be a final cause to explain why the particle took this direction rather than another.

Whatever is moved is moved by an external mover. Whatever changes motion is changed from the outside. Obeying final causes, the molecules are not spontaneous and self-moved entities, capable of picking and choosing the tendencies that they will favor in response to a causal impact. If they are in random motion, random in the mathematical sense of being homogeneous in partition and tridirectional in their paths, they will always so remain until they are changed from the outside and follow their final causes in the new set of circumstances. Once in zigzag motion, they will continue in it, unless external conditions change.

Will the desk take off from the floor and hit the stenographer in the face as it moves upward? It will do this only if an external agent moves it thus, changing the present tridirectional motions of the molecules into a direction entirely upward; and the molecules, obeying their final causes, will respond to the mover. In other words, where conditions in matter are the same the results will be alike also.

NATURE HAS A COUNTERPART TO RANDOMNESS

Where final causality is outlawed and matter is viewed as self-directed, anything can happen, and the empiriological physicist, who ignores causes and prefers descriptions, is justified in his conclusions about the disorder in things and their basic unpredictability. If Descartes is right, so are the indeterminists. If

Hume prevails and things arise spontaneously without a causal dependence on something preceding, then any motion or change in motion can occur at any time or any place. It is causality that makes for order, and causal knowledge that makes for certitude.

But if there is sufficient form in even the frailest mobile entity to save it from the chaos which a purely passive universe would become, and if there is a sufficient end to assure that any movement must be somehow ordered and directed to a goal, empiriological physics must forge its passport to make its way into a philosophical science of nature with such doctrines as the indeterminists propose.

The empiriological physicist, if he only recognized his aim to control nature rather than to contemplate it, is so close to being right that he mistakes his proximity to a truth as the final and whole science about the material world. There is something in nature corresponding to his enthusiasm. It is primordial matter, indeterminate, purely passive, inert, chaotic, indifferent, and chancelike. And the more the empiriological physicist descends through the lower stories of matter the closer he gets to this primordial substrate which the philosophical physicist joins in recognizing to be real. There is so much room for philosophical physics in the world which experiment explores that there is a whole skyscraper above that basement where empiriological physics works so well.

ENTROPY WOULD FORBID MOTION

The law of entropy states the directionality of movement in the universe. If there is any substitute for final causality in contemporary thought, this law fills the bill. Bergson called it the most metaphysical of physical laws because it plots the course which the universe is traveling. It views the world as tumbling from less disorder to more disorder, from a less probable state to a more probable one, from thermal differences to thermal homogeneity.

But if motion is determined only by the condition that entropy increase, there are some serious difficulties that must be faced.

If entropy tells the whole story of movement, the universe would be tending to destruction rather than perfection. Entropy is the opposite of evolution, and if the two theories exist side by side, it is only because the empiriological physicist has not worried too much about consistency of concept so long as he is able to control and predict matter's activities.

Cosmic evolution and entropy truly exclude each other. The one implies a tendency to order, differentiation, and life; the other bespeaks disorder, degeneration, and death. One of these theories must be cast off if empiriological physics is to become at peace with itself. Once again, Aristotle's dualism of matter and form rises up to reconcile the opposition between entropy and cosmic progress.

But there is more to be said about entropy besides its variance with the evolutionary temper inside scientism. If cosmic motion is governed by entropy, movement is not from potency to act as in realism, but from act to potency. Act would seek to potentialize itself, order to disorganize itself, on entropic premises.

Such a view is not only inadequate as a definition of motion. It would flag motion to a complete stop. The perfect does not tend toward the imperfect but to the more perfect. A thing moves in order to acquire what it does not possess, and it would not move if all that it could seek it already owned. A cow seeks food, something that it does not have and to which it is in potency. It does not seek to be a plant since it is already a vegetative creature in so far as it is an animal. It does not seek to be a plant but to eat one. Act does not seek potency; potency seeks act. Causality on entropic premises would always be a degeneration. If empiriological physics is a science of nature, it has the world shifted into reverse, the difference between logic and ontology.

NATURE HAS A COUNTERPART TO ENTROPY

Though denying that entropy alone can account for the direction of cosmic motion, replacing final causality, the philosophy of nature is alert to the fact that there is something like entropy in a universe that is finite. It would be strange indeed if empiriological physics, with all of its dealings in matter, did not have a dim and at least indirect grasp of truths in the speculative science of nature.

All things seek equilibrium. Unfortunately, the study of place must be reserved until Chapter 10, and it must here be taken with only promissory proof, that a body moving locally tends to its natural place and natural rest as the term of its local motion. Such an equilibrium in place, which things seek by local motion and where they tend to remain resisting outer disturbances, is viewed as disorder by the empiriological physicist. He defines equilibrium as randomness.

But in philosophical physics, as will be shown, this equilibrium in place which a nature seeks is the perfection of the moving thing. The nature asserts itself from within by preserving its identity as, say, a molecule of oxygen, against contrary forces acting from the outside. A progressively realized equilibrium would be expected if Aristotle is in general correct.

Defining order in terms of a group of particles in their interrelations rather than in terms of a nature and the fulfillment of its tendencies, the empiriological physicist inclines to conclude that equilibrium is disorder or randomness, without thinking that the individuals that make up the balance have been perfected from within by reaching a place where they can better retain their identities.

The empiriological physicist, to borrow a term from Boutroux, attains to a "mechanical equivalent" of the order which the philosophy of nature sees as the end of motion. The purpose of local movement is not disorder but the equilibrium of a moving thing with its environment. This balance is order for the nature which enjoys it since the nature can better survive and express itself. But the balance is randomness when the aggregate is viewed as a whole, without regard to the individual and intrinsic natures which only the philosophy of nature can explore.

CONTROL IS ART, NOT A SCIENCE OF NATURE

Chance, or more appropriately randomness, plays a tremendous role in empiriological physics. The empiriological physicist uses mathematics as his tool and tends to reduce nature to sheer quantity. But quantity prescinds from motion, and that is why evolution, cosmic and biological alike, is so alien to the strict equalitarian universe of experimentalism. Unable to account for origins and purposes mathematically, empiriological method goes to the concept of chance in the form of an evolutionary theory to explain the beginnings of things and to chance in the form of entropy to explain their ends. Fertility and progress, which are of nature, become impossible where sheer quantity is involved, and are attributed to disorder, since whatever is orderly must be mathematical.

Fertility and progress, the reasons which prompt empiriological method to posit chance as the ultimate are the very issues that receive a rational and realistic treatment in the philosophical science of nature, nature that is an inner principle and a source of motion. Without a philosophical science of nature, gazing on motion at its own level and not as quantity, the really big questions that fret the mind will forever remain unanswered.

All of this criticism does not deny the efficacy of empiriological physics. It only restricts the empiriological method by showing that motion, the most obvious and most important fact of direct experience, really eludes it and will continue to elude it forever. If chance is defined as the result of factors extrinsic to a given nature, it draws up alongside art, and if empiriological physics is primarily an art, it would be logical to seek a world of chance as its ideal subject matter. Both chance and art are extrinsic to nature in origin.

It ought to be expected that a discipline like empiriological physics which views matter as inert and as extrinsically determined should have hit upon chance as its foundations. The random, the indeterminate, the undifferentiated, the inert, is the controllable, and a complete control of nature would require that nature be perfectly extrinsic to itself, that natural tendencies and natural ends be repudiated, that chance be introduced as the only natural substitute for final causality, and that this chaotic world should be a nothingness so man could fashion it, creator-like, according to his own image and likeness.

The empiriological physicist may well ignore final causality to gain control of nature, and this necessarily results in putting chance at the roots of things. Once more the difference between the intrinsic and the extrinsic, finality and chance, philosophical and empiriological physics, tends to suggest the familiar distinction between art and nature. That distinction is like a master switch which beams a powerful light into many of the otherwise darkened rooms in modern methods. Philosophy does not intend to move the furniture which it sees there. It only wants to appraise it.

Suggested Readings

Aquinas, Thomas, *Summa contra gentiles,* Bk. III, chs. 1–24.
von Mises, Robert, *Probability, Statistics, and Truth* (New York, 1932).

9

Mathematics and the Infinite

NUMBER IS DEFINED BY CORRESPONDENCE

Aristotle frequently pointed out that the philosophy of nature ought to stay clear of the realm of pure mathematics. Unlike a vast contemporary aspiration, Aristotle did not erect a special method as the filter for all knowledge and insist that whatever failed to get through the meshes was not validly known. The feats of a method in one field do not mean that it is valid everywhere, any more than the worth of a razor in shaving a man attests to its excellence as a carpenter's plane. Aristotle kept his sciences distinct, and when in his philosophical physics he discussed mathematical reality, it was always applied mathematics that he had in view. In the twilight zone between mathematical and physical daylight Aristotle discerned the so-called intermediate sciences where such studies as perspective, the rainbow, and even astronomy are located. Because the applied mathematician pronounces on physical reality, philosophical physics has a right to debate with him.

But the theory of number does not directly touch the world of motion. It is pure mathematics. It belongs to the second order of abstraction which the philosophical science of nature does not scale. Yet there are two reasons why it should be discussed in these pages. One is that the mathematical theory of one age often seeps down into practice later on, and in an age which makes no distinction between its various disciplines and their methods, the discussion of mathematics puts empiriological physics itself into the forum. The second reason which invites treatment of modern number theory here is to ask if the actually infinite is mathematically possible. If it is, then it might be realized in the physical world. The case against actual infinity cannot rest when the philosophical physicist simply shows that it is not a fact. He must show that it is impossible. He must answer the objections from the gallery of modern mathematics. By an insight into Cantor's notion of transfinite numbers, Russell's logicalism, Hilbert's formalism, and Brouwer's intuitionism, the notion of potential infinity defended in philosophical physics will be toughened, like a soldier gaining strength and experience with each test. As Aquinas says, the solving of a doubt is the confirming of a truth.

Number, according to Aristotle, is multitude, organized and identified and measured by unity. Multitude is plurality, simple and pure and hence disorganized. Unknowable in itself like prime matter or potency, it is known only when measured by unity. To reduce it to unity is to number it, and our material world can accordingly be organized into units. On the Supreme Court bench there are nine of those units of quantity which we call men, enabling the mind to abstract the concept of nine. Adding or subtracting a unit varies the species of the number, so that there is a gap between the numbers. There is not just an infinite series of fractions which the imagination devises to mend the break.

But the contemporary account of number is much different. The key to it is the notion of correspondence which might be illustrated by the following example: Imagine two barrels of beans, the one filled with white ones and the other with red ones. As the first white bean W_1 is drawn from the one barrel, let the first red bean R_1 be taken from the other. W_2 may then be drawn together with R_2, and W_3 can be matched by R_3, and so on indefinitely. To each and every white bean there corresponds one and only one red one, and vice versa, a relation of mutual matching that the following scheme can represent:

$$W_1 \quad W_2 \quad W_3 \quad W_4 \quad W_5 \quad W_6 \quad W_7 \quad W_8 \quad W_9 \, \ldots \, W_n$$
$$\updownarrow \quad \updownarrow \quad \updownarrow \quad \updownarrow \quad \updownarrow \quad \updownarrow \quad \updownarrow \quad \updownarrow \quad \updownarrow \qquad \updownarrow$$
$$R_1 \quad R_2 \quad R_3 \quad R_4 \quad R_5 \quad R_6 \quad R_7 \quad R_8 \quad R_9 \, \ldots \, R_n$$

It should be noted that in the relation between the aggregates, called sets, of W's and the aggregates or sets of R's, a member of one set is matched by only one member of another. Thus R_7 cannot correspond to W_7 and then be used again to match, say W_{1289}. One member of one set corresponds to only one member of the other, and vice versa.

The relation of equivalence is technically termed biunique (biunivocal) correspondence. But how far can this correspondence be carried on between the aggregate or set of W's and the aggregate or set of R's?

The general answer of modern number theory can be given by another example: To each and every point on a line there corresponds a real number, just as to each and every one of the twelve major subdivisions of a foot rule there corresponds one and only one inch, 1, 2, 3, . . . , 12. Now let the line be subdivided just as the scale of inches is splintered into fractions. To each and every subdividing point on the line there corresponds a number different from the first but still a real number, just as fractions of an inch are still numbers. Moreover, declares modern number theory, since the number of points on a straight line is infinite, this correspondence of points with the number sequence can be carried out infinitely. If the decimal system is used, smaller and smaller decimal fractions are attained with each subdivision on the line. Whether the line be long or short, it contains an infinite number of decimals because on its continuous extension there is an infinite number of points. Any straight and unbroken line, for instance, represents a set to which all the real numbers correspond.

NUMBERS ARE FORMED FROM INFINITE DECIMALS

Real number is used in contrast to an imaginary number like $\sqrt{-1}$ which cannot, to put it roughly, be reduced to countable quantities. Real numbers in turn may be transcendental like or e (the base of the natural logarithm), or they may be algebraic.

Algebraic numbers are subdivided into rational numbers, like integers and ordinary fractions, and irrational numbers like $\sqrt{2}$, $\sqrt{3}$, $\sqrt[3]{7}$. All of these real numbers can be put into correspondence with the points on a line. On a continuous line the points are everywhere dense, meaning that between any two points there is another one. The line is continuous, and the quantities that it represents are often called the continuum of real numbers.

The principles involved here can be illustrated by Dedekind's classic theory of defining irrationals. Through a straight line representing the continuum of real numbers, let another line be drawn (Fig. 1). This line will divide the number continuum into two classes so that all those numbers greater than the number at

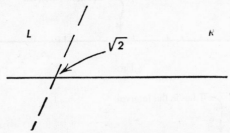

Fig. 1.   The Dedekind Cut.

the point of intersection will lie to the right of this point, and all those less than the number will lie to the left. Let us say we are looking for $\sqrt{2}$, which can be reduced to a long fraction beginning with 1.414 . . . but which cannot be rationalized by arithmetical means. The quantity, $\sqrt{2}$, may be found by drawing a line through the number continuum, separating it into two classes of numbers (Fig. 1), one whose squares are less than two and the other whose squares are more than two. The two classes mark out a "cut" in the number continuum, and the "cut" here defines $\sqrt{2}$.

Thus far no general definition has been given of number. Such a definition involves a more precise picture of the continuum and a more generalized concept than the Dedekind "cut" which defined the irrationals.

Let us return to our straight line representing the number continuum and divide it off into units at the points corresponding to whole numbers, as shown in Fig. 2, where we want, say, to define the transcendental number π. In this figure, the interval between

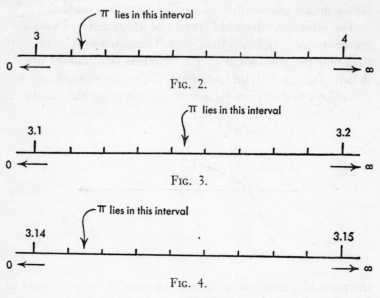

π lies in this interval

3   4

0 ←   → ∞

Fig. 2.

π lies in this interval

3.1   3.2

0 ←   → ∞

Fig. 3.

π lies in this interval

3.14   3.15

0 ←   → ∞

Fig. 4.

3 and 4 is divided into ten subintervals, and in the second of these is the fraction, 0.14, greater than the quantity represented by the first interval but less than the whole quantity represented by the second. Now let us (Fig. 3) divide this second interval into ten subintervals, corresponding to the ten 1/10's of the original 1/10 from 0.1 to 0.2 in Fig. 2. These units in Fig. 3 thus correspond to 1/100 of the interval between 3 and 4. In Fig. 3, the 0.14 of the 3.14 takes us to the fourth interval but π is greater than 3.14. It is 3.141 . . . , so the space between 0.14 and 0.15 must again be subdivided into ten units (Fig. 4). So we go on dividing and subdividing and subdividing again.

Each successive digit after the decimal point of 3.1416 . . . is given in terms corresponding to $1/10^n$ of the distance between 3 and 4. Thus the first digit 1 corresponds to 1/10 of that distance, the second digit 4 corresponds to 1/100 of that distance and the third digit which is 1 again (3.1416) corresponds to 1/1000 of that distance. Like a folding cup, growing smaller the more it is opened, each section comes closer to the exact interval between 3 and 4 where π is "nested." In the limit this interval would diminish to a point, and though knowing this point to be on the linear continuum, we are unable to establish exactly where.

This sequence might stop as in the case of 1.1000. . . . It might keep on going as in the case of irrationals like the transcendental number π or algebraic irrationals like $\sqrt{2}$. Such numbers as these two examples involve infinite decimals. Cantor defined irrationals as an infinite sequence of rationals, arriving at algebraic theory for what Dedekind, with his "cuts" had represented geometrically.

Yet a more elegant definition of number can be given by considering all numbers to be made up of infinite decimals. In a decimal like 2.9999999999 . . . , it will be seen that there is a certain ordered sequence which is eventually reached and repeated. Such a repetitive series is called an infinite periodic decimal. Sometimes, on the other hand, there is no order in the sequence, no matter how far decimals might be carried out. Such infinite decimals are called non-periodic since they do not repeat. Infinite periodic decimals are rational numbers. Infinite non-periodic decimals are irrationals.

Number in general is an infinite decimal.

CANTOR DEFINED A TRANSFINITE NUMBER

In this broad outline of the theory of number the concept of infinity has already appeared and may now be explored for its own sake. Since Cantor's ideas on the subject are now considered classical, his theory of transfinite numbers will be sketched. Transfinitude is the same thing as mathematical infinity and is in fact a better name since it does not involve the confusion with philosophy where the word *infinity,* as shown by the division of its senses in the Chapter 4, has many meanings.

Until the nineteenth century, it had been the common opinions of mathematicians and philosophers alike that there is no greatest cardinal number. As Leibniz said, the idea of a greatest number involved a contradiction—an infinite number that was definite would by that very definite character be finite. The number sequence was considered perpetually open and enlargeable.

But what if a point of view is taken that is outside the series and a number is defined that is not obtained by prolonging, say, the series of whole numbers but stands at a different level? Georg Cantor took such a leap outside the series that is strung out by counting, when he defined the transfinite number written here α_0 (alpha-zero, instead of Cantor's Hebrew notation aleph-zero). This number is the number of all finite numbers, or in a more technical language, the number of all denumerable sets, with denumerability to be described below as a phenomenon of correspondence. However, α_0 is not a number in the ordinary sense like $1, 2, 3, \ldots, n, \ldots$. It is a number in which these are, so to speak, the objects numbered. It is the number of a number. All odd and even integers have α_0 for their cardinal number; the same is true of all prime numbers—a number divisible only by itself and one like $1, 2, 3, 5, 7, 11, 13, 17, 19, 23$, etc. The number of odd numbers or the number of primes, for example, is equal to the number of even numbers. All are equal to α_0.

Cantor goes much further than the simple definition of α_0, as a theoretical backdrop. It is well known that integers are denumerable, i.e., capable of being enumerated in an orderly way so that there are no gaps in the series such as would occur in setting down the succession from 1 to 1,000,000, omitting the number 4. Invoking the tool of biunique correspondence between sets, Cantor shows that the set of rational numbers—all ordinary fractions—is denumerable. All the fractions can be put into one to one correspondence with the integers, like the red beans put into correspondence with the white ones. The display of how the rationals can be denumerated will open the door to the conclusion that there are numbers higher than α_0, and that there is a whole hierarchy of infinities. The rationals can be denumerated if a formula is found for deriving them.

Let us take the whole number 4 and (a) break it down into all possible pairs of integers x and y which form it as their sum, then (b) arrange all the x's and y's, taking each pair separately into fractions x/y and y/x, with the fractions to be written in the order of their increasing magnitude. For instance, (a) four is equal to $3 + 1$, $2 + 2$; and (b) the possible fractions are 1/3, 3/1, 2/2, taking each pair separately; this should be written 1/3, 2/2, and 3/1 to preserve the order of increasing magnitude. Six for example can (a) be broken down into $3 + 3$, $5 + 1$, $4 + 2$; and (b) the corresponding fractions of each pair taken separately are 1/5, 2/4, 3/3, 4/2, and 5/1. Each of the so-called natural integers can thus give rise to a class of fractions:

1.	0/1
2.	1/1
3.	1/2, 2/1
4.	1/3, 2/2, 3/1
5.	1/4, 2/3, 3/2, 4/1
6.	1/5, 2/4, 3/3, 4/2, 5/1

Now let all the classes be set down successively from 1 to 5/1, and instead of stopping at 6, let the series be continued indefinitely. Certain fractions like 2/4 and 4/2 can be reduced to 1/2 and 2/1 which have already occurred in the class of 3, and such reducible fractions can be eliminated, counting the fraction only the first time it appears. The resulting set can be put into correspondence with the integers.

0/1	1/1	1/2	2/1	1/3	3/1	1/4	2/3 ...
↕	↕	↕	↕	↕	↕	↕	↕
1	2	3	4	5	6	7	8 ...

Now all fractions will eventually occur in this procession, and duplicates can be eliminated by counting a ratio only the first time it appears. True enough, the fractions are not in the order of increasing magnitude, except within the classes; 1/3, in the sequence above is smaller than 2/1, its predecessor, and 1/4 in turn is smaller than 3/1. The enumeration of the millionth class would give a fraction 1/999,999, smaller than any of its predecessors. But the order of magnitude makes no difference in this sequence. The enumeration is not of ordinals but of cardinals, and Cantorians are interested not in the magnitude of individual fractions but solely and simply in devising a way for deriving *all* fractions, regardless of their order. To each and every fraction, set down according to these genial rules, there corresponds one and only one integer, exactly as in the correspondence of the white and red beans. If the integers are denumerable, so therefore are the fractions. In other words, all rational numbers are denumerable.

Cantorians hold that all algebraic numbers, rationals and irrationals alike, are denumerable. The rules for this deduction are too complex to be discussed here, but in broad principle, they correspond amply enough with the foregoing procedure to allow the conclusion to be asserted without proof that algebraic numbers are denumerable like the integers. The set of rationals, the set of integers, the set of algebraic numbers—all have α_0 for their transfinite number.

CANTOR PROPOSED A HIERARCHY OF TRANSFINITES

Cantorians are now prepared to show that there is a transfinite number higher than α_0. This number is c, the number of the continuum, and it may be thought of as the number of points on a continuous line of any length. It includes not only algebraic numbers but transcendental ones. It thus extends to all real numbers. But the primary property that is of interest here is that c is not denumerable.

It is this non-denumerable character of the continuum which shows it to be in a higher order of infinity than the denumerable domain of algebraic numbers. So, at least, argue the Cantorians. That c is greater than α_0, "an infinite greater than the infinite," is a conclusion they draw from proving that c, unlike α_0, is non-denumerable.

On this point, there is an indirect proof of c's non-denumerable character that is considered classical. It consists in assuming that all the real numbers in the continuum, say between 1 and 2, have been enumerated and then proving that a new number can always be added, thus contradicting the initial assumption. In a more formal way, this proof is known as the diagonal process and can be illustrated by the following example:

Between 0 and 1, let us say that all enumerated numbers can be represented by the following scheme of decimal fractions in which each letter, large or small makes no difference, stands for a number between 0 and 9:

$$0.\ A_1 a_2 a_3 a_4 a_5 a_6 a_7 a_8 a_9 \quad \ldots \ a_n$$
$$0.\ b_1 B_2 b_3 b_4 b_5 b_6 b_7 b_8 b_9 \quad \ldots \ b_n$$
$$0.\ c_1 c_2 C_3 c_4 c_5 c_6 c_7 c_8 c_9 \quad \ldots \ c_n$$
$$0.\ d_1 d_2 d_3 D_4 d_5 d_6 d_7 d_8 d_9 \quad \ldots \ d_n$$
$$0.\ e_1 e_2 e_3 e_4 E_5 e_6 e_7 e_8 e_9 \quad \ldots \ e_n$$

Now the assumption is that all the real numbers can be enumerated in this fashion, where each of the above letters corresponds to a whole number and where each line thus represents a fraction between 0 and 1. But after this would-be enumeration is complete, it is then possible to show that a number can be constructed whose first digit differs from A_1, whose second digit differs from B_2, whose third digit differs from C_3, and so on down the diagonal which would result if a line were drawn to join all the capital letters in the above scheme.

The resulting number differs from every previous member of the series of fractions by at least one digit. Thus to the real numbers between 0 and 1, a new number can always be added. The same conclusions could be reached about the real numbers between 0 and 1/2, for instance, or between 0 and any fraction.

The real numbers which include all algebraic and transcendental numbers taken together are not denumerable.

Cantor's achievement consists in being able to deduce the existence of transcendental numbers which, before his time, had been generally viewed as discoveries of induction, like the discovery of π from relating the circumference of a circle to its diameter.

In addition to a_0 and c, there is yet a higher transfinite cardinal which may be illustrated in the following way:

In a finite class of objects, m, there are m^n subclasses where n denotes the number of the original entities which appear in each subclass. For instance, the class of three letters abc can be formed into 3^2 classes of two letters each: aa, bb, cc, ab, ac, ba, ca, bc, cb. A class of two letters ab can be arranged into eight subclasses where there are three letters to a class, $m^n = 2^3$: aaa, bbb, aba, baa, aab, abb, bab, bba. Thus it is with finites.

But what happens when this formula is borne to the level of the transfinites? In how many ways can the numbers of c be combined with each other? The answer is c^c, the transfinite analogue of m^n, and the number of correspondences thus established is called the functional transfinite f. It is even intuitively clear that $a_0 < c < f$.

There is a whole algebra of transfinite numbers, relating them to each other and showing how they react to finite and infinite exponents and coefficients. Such discussion can be by-passed along with the outline of Cantor's theory of ordinals which are really secondary in importance to transfinite cardinals. As a concluding remark, it can simply be pointed out that the hierarchy of transfinites, begun by a_0, c, and f can be carried on without limit. There is an infinity of infinities, according to the direction of Cantorian algebra. The number f can be transcended to a new order by use of a process similar to the diagonal procedure for determining the non-denumerable character of c.

Before putting Cantor's ideas under the lens of realistic philosophy, the three contemporary philosophies of mathematics and hence philosophies of mathematical infinity must be passed in review. They are the logicalism of Peano and Frege which reaches its climax in Bertrand Russell, the formalism of David Hilbert and his school, and the intuitionism of Brouwer, Weyl, and Poincaré.

RUSSELL REDUCES INFINITY TO A LOGICAL HIERARCHY

The name *logicalism* was coined by Rudolf Carnap and represents the inner nature of the Russell school, the reduction of mathematics to logic. Russell's avowed intention is to derive the whole science of number from merely logical constants. To do this, he gives a definition of number in terms of classes. Specifically and in Russell's techinal idiom of symbolic logic, number is "the class of similar classes."[1] This means, in concrete terms, for example, that all bipeds which are featherless form a class of similar objects called men. Another class of objects are, say, the particles found in a granite quarry after it has been dynamited, and these are called stones. Now the most general characteristic which these two classes, men and stones, have in common is their various numbers. Both can be set into correspondence with the integer series.

Number is hence the property of a class, because when things are numbered they form a class. The typewriter and the eraser are two objects, and their number is thus a member of the class 2. A pair of eyes, the hands of a man, the front wheels of an automobile—all have the same number which belongs to the class 2. They are all similar classes by their number which is the class uniting (classifying) all of them.

---

[1] *Principles of Mathematics,* 2d ed. (New York, 1938), p. 116.

This definition of number rests on the principle of correspondence which has threaded its way through the whole preceding discussion of mathematics and tests whether a collection is denumerable or not. It was remarked that Cantor, when he defined a_0, did not reach the transfinite by simply extending the finite. He went outside the series to define the number of a number. A similar hierarchical structure is hoisted by Russell. Where number is the class of all similar classes, the first application of the concept of class is on a different logical level from the classes of which it is the class. No *definitum*, the logician rightly holds, can occur in the definition of itself. Otherwise, he would chase his objects into the nonsense of a vicious circle. The class (C) of similar classes (c) involves a metaclass or a metalogic; for nothing can be taken as intrinsically evident to a logician in the purest air of his science. When he classifies, he does so in terms of genera that lie beyond the thing classified, mounting in the branches of the famous Porphyrian tree. (C) is at a higher Porphyrian altitude than the (c)s which it organizes.

As long as finite classes are considered, Russell's definition is in general accord with the discursive character of modern method. In the world of matter, the law of inertia dictates that things are determined by forces and factors beyond them. In empiriological physics, considered from the viewpoint of its method, one concept is defined in terms of what is outside it, with pure discursion, untempered by the intuitive, as an ideal. Discursion is to method in empiriological physics what inertia is to matter.

Russell's whole philosophy has for its target to make the modern method more discursive and, like matter, more controllable. To this end, he has suggested a metalanguage for talking about languages, and his followers have proposed a metalogic for the discussion of logic. A metalanguage can be in turn discussed by a metametalanguage and a metalogic by a metametalogic. To this hierarchy of languages and logics, Russell implies, there can be no limit. Though apparently he does not employ the term, it is perfectly in the spirit of his general outlook to call the class of all similar classes a metaclass and to call α_0 a metanumber.

But when discursion is applied to this metanumber and in general to the whole hierarchy of the transfinites, the skies are much more stormy than when the discursive method is applied to the area of finite quantities. This is clear from the very fact that a number which is truly infinite would have to include its own self as a member. The train of examining modern philosophies of mathematics has led to the so-called paradoxes of the infinite which Russell turns into one of the crucial depots of his philosophy.

A frequently cited example of a paradox is a statement by a Cretan that all Cretans are liars. If the statement is true it is false because a Cretan has uttered it. To rise above these contradictions, Russell proposes his famous theory of types, suggested by the work of Frege. A type is a rule which determines not the inner meaning of a statement but the extent of its application. All logical types, for instance, involve the principle that a statement cannot apply to its own self, putting the Cretan who speaks outside the Cretans spoken about.

In this way, the discursive temper of modern methods receives a new application, and intrinsic meaning is once again surrendered to the inertial view of things. In speaking of the number of an infinite number, which is to define α_0, the so-called transfinite is on a higher landing in the logical hierarchy than the finite numbers whose series it represents. It would appear, then, that Russell has polished Cantor's system by showing that there is no contradiction in an infinite number that does not include its own self as a member of the series which it represents.

One more facet of the many original principles which Russell develops in his mathematics and his mathematical logic is his conclusion that the infinite is intensional rather than extensional. What these terms mean can be made clear by reference to the meaning of comprehension (intension) and extension in classical Aristotelian logic with the former standing for content and the latter the field of individuals to which the content applies. Symbolic logic, and this naturally includes Russell's own views, is largely extensional. It is difficult to see with what right intension can come in at all since it involves something more than sheer logical form. But whatever inconsistency intension brings with it into an ambition to treat the world by logic alone, it is a matter of historical fact that Russell cloaks infinity in an intensional dress.

The reason for this can be suggested by the paradoxes which prompted Russell to his theory of types. The definition of infinity would have to be infinitely complex, since an infinity would be included in the definition. But this infinite complexity occurs neither in the thought of the mathematician nor in his symbolisms. There is a finite structure to the definition. It is *about* something else, *about* content. And content, to put it roughly, is in the intensional order. Thus a_0 is finite in the structure of its definition, but it represents something infinite, the series of all algebraic numbers. Even intension and extension are harnessed into a logical hierarchy.

FORMALISM MAKES INFINITY INTO A RULE

Russell is not optimistic enough to believe that the whole of reality, even mathematical reality, can be coerced into his logical conceits. Despite a discursive slope, Russell admits an empirical world yielding sense data for logic to organize. With David Hilbert, the logicalism of Russell secedes from his sensism, and in an island of pure logic, sets up a kingdom called formalism.

Formalism does not scruple over the origins of knowledge and over the data of intuition with which the mathematician has always been forced to begin his intellectual itinerary. Though it admits at least verbally that mathematics does not derive from logic but develops independently, it is pure logic that gets the priority. A system of mathematics need not have meaning and be configured to a real world; its only requirement is consistency. Logic is charged with manipulating the mathematical symbols, providing rules to derive and combine mathematical forms and thus acting as a "directive science." The chief aim of formalism is to hammer out a complete and consistent mathematical system from the fewest possible presuppositions. It is the purest kind of postulational mathematics. Content is sacrificed to form, inner meaning to mere rule. In the end, logic and mathematics must lose that difference between them to which formalists pay at least lip service. In both it is form, rule, system, or consistency that alone counts.

Hilbert's pretensions create a grave critical problem. Formalism forces mathematics and then its regulative logic to begin with undefined terms and principles that lie outside the system which they govern and can only be examined by a higher logic, a metalogic, on formalistic premises. This metalogic in turn must also begin with the undefined and undecided, if it is to be truly formalistic, and so the process goes on and on. Kurt Gödel showed that mathematical logic by which both Hilbert and Russell manipulate the foundations of mathematics must always contain at least a small number of undefined terms which cannot be treated in the system which they organize. These undefined entities are called "the undecidables," and their presence forbids both logicalism and formalism from ever saying the final word about reality or mathematics. The hierarchy of types, in which a higher applies to a lower but must in turn subject itself to a higher type to be meaningful, is likewise a case of "the undecidables." It is a pyramid without an apex.

Like the majority of modern logicians, Hilbert had to accede to Gödel's strictures. Mathematics need not be conformed to reality, Hilbert held. His school aims only to lay down rules to combine mathematical symbols, and when the rules fail, they must be scrapped for a better logic which is more consistent in itself and more adequate to the complete body of mathematical entities. Hilbert searches for a minimum of concepts, guided by the principle of economy, erroneously attributed to Ockham, that "entities are not to be multiplied without necessity."

In its search for mathematical consistency, formalism pushes into logic. It wants no traffic in objects endowed with content, as objects even in mathematics must always be. It is hard to see how mathematics and logic can be essentially distinct. Thus "A number is not an object in the proper sense but a property,"[2] Hilbert says. Mathematics, independent perhaps in its discovery, is here apparently crossing over into logic to ground itself. The individuals to which number applies cannot be numbered things because everyone is unique; so number is the property of a concept or a predicate, the property of a universal, remembering that a predicate designates something wider than the subject and is attributed to the subject as membership in a class is attributed to an individual. In the proposition, *John is a man, man* is wider than *John* considering *man* in itself. Number is thus the function of a predicate for formalism, or, reminiscent of Russell's definition, number is the predicate of a predicate.

The matter of human experience is always finite, and when the infinite comes in, says Hilbert, it does so in the manner of an idea. Infinity is thus discussed in an ideal proposition and designates an ideal object. In the so-called inductive side of mathematics, concrete objects are inspected and related to each other. One formula is conceived and derived from another. "When we generalize this situation," Hilbert writes,

> then mathematics arrives at a number of formulas, first those which correspond to the matter expressed in finite propositions, in essentially numbered equalities and inequalities, and second at broader formulae that in themselves have no meaning and form the ideal representations of our theory.[3]

Infinity thus exists in thought and thought alone. It is a creation of logic, working over a mathematical material. And it is an affair of formulae or rules. Such a notion of the infinite enables

---

[2] D. Hilbert and W. Ackermann, *Grundzüge der theoretischen Logik* (Berlin, 1928), p. 86.

[3] *Grundlagen der Geometrie* (Leipzig, 1930), p. 281.

the mathematician to withdraw from reality in the manipulations of transfinite numbers, and this retreat from content in favor of a system whose only requirement is freedom from contradiction is exactly what formalism wants. "The infinite divisibility of the continuum," Hilbert declares, "is an operation which exists in thought only, is just an idea, an idea which is refuted by our observations of nature, as well as by physical and chemical experiments."[4] Infinity here exists only logically.

INTUITIONISM DENIES HIERARCHY OF INFINITES

Another way of describing formalism is as a non-constructive mathematics. This means simply that the formalists seek release from the curves and tables, the pictures and the graspable quantities which the senses apprehend; formalism desiderates purity of form, without regard for the construction of an object in the imagination.

The directly opposite direction is trodden by the so-called intuitionists led by L. E. J. Brouwer and Hermann Weyl and suggested by the earlier doctrines of Leopold Kronecker and Henri Poincaré. Intuitionism in fact claims a descent from the Kantian notion of synthetic *a priori* judgments which attempted to validate Euclidian geometry because the space presented to man's senses is judged Euclidian. If formalism is non-constructive, intuitionism is constructive.

As a first approximation, intuitionism can be thought of as a swing from the vacuous forms of Hilbert into the direction of the empirical. It holds, as its name implies, that mathematics must begin with the intuitive, and that as a matter of fact, the mind is born with such intuitive richness which passing time forces it to use. The primary intuition, the bedrock of all mathematics, is the "intuitions of the bare two-oneness,"[5] Brouwer argues.

---

[4] Cited by T. Dantzig, *Number, The Language of Science* (New York, 1930), p. 238.

[5] "Intuitionism and Formalism," *Bulletin of the American Mathematical Society*, XX (1913), 85–86.

Though intuitionism is often claimed to have an affinity with western tradition, Brouwer's foregoing statement stands in contrast to the more orthodox notion of number in philosophy. There, number is prior to its properties, and one number is related to its successor mentally by the relating act of judgment. Objectively and subjectively, a thing is prior to its relations. *One* is what it is, first, and is then related to *two*, and the order of thought follows along with this arrangement of reality itself. In Brouwer's vision of things, however, one and two are drawn much more tightly together. They are intuited along with the link that relates them in this "basal intuition," and so in a single flash of insight there arise the concepts of one, two, and their relation. They are seen as succeeding each other; the relation of succession is welded into the very concept of two-oneness.

The intuitionists recognize the existence of only denumerable sets. To jump ahead to the region of the non-denumerable is unwarranted by the data of our intuitions. Intuitionism rejects the Cantorian hierarchy of the transfinites, and to that extent it is more allied to the traditional notion of mathematical infinity. Brouwer declares that the original two-oneness can be broken into elements, and one of these can be regarded as another "two-oneness." Indefinitely repeated, this process gives rise to the concept of "between." The notion of the infinite is precipitated from considering this idea of "between" which can be strewn indefinitely with repetitions of the "two-oneness."

This interval of the "between" is included in the basal intuition of "two-oneness," and it can never be exhausted by interpolating new units in it. It is therefore not a true collection. No infinity can be finited to a point of being compared with other infinities. Thus, Cantorians go far beyond the conclusions which intuition authorizes; α_0 is the only infinite which Brouwer admits as meaningful, and it is reached not by inductively extending a series or a set but intuitively and from the meaning of "between."

It may help to suggest Brouwer's meaning, which is highly debated in modern thought, if reference is made to the priority of mathematics over logic in intuitionism. Formalism, of course, emphasizes the regulative and the logical. The weight of intuitionism is more on matter or content and on the meaning of mathematical existents rather than on logical rules. Intuitionism is a constructive approach, holding that an entity to be mathematically real must be included in intuitive representation by the mind of man. This approach invalidates the Cantorian hierarchy of the infinities, which Russell and Hilbert refine by logic, since the differences among Cantorian infinities cannot be given a constructive, intuitive form in the world of "content" but only among the rules of logic. So intuitionism holds to one infinity only and refuses to submit mathematics to a domination by the logical order.

The unified whole of "two-oneness" must not be confused with Kronecker's finitism, where God made the integers and man everything else. To put it bluntly, what is involved in the notion of all the real numbers between 1 and 2? For Russell and for formalism, following the course which Cantor charted, this middle area is mapped out in terms of a series of infinite decimals, requiring an infinite number of operations. Not so for intuitionism. In this doctrine, the stretch from 1 to 2 is spanned by a law to construct the series of intervening decimals, a law that is involved by an analysis of "between"; there is thus a finite number of operations. There is no such thing as a non-denumerable set. There is no such thing as a more "between" or a less "between." To posit the non-denumerable, to heave up a hierarchy of infinities, to determine the indeterminate, is to range beyond the boundaries of intuition, which encloses numbers and their difference but refuses to give meaning to differences among infinities.

The mention of the indeterminate foists into the fore a peculiar tenet of intuitionism, the denial of the principle of excluded middle. For ancient as well as for modern mathematics in general, there is no medium between being and nothing, between being a triangle and not being one, between being congruous or not being so. A thing is either A or *not-A*, without the possibility of a middle ground.

Intuitionism on the contrary holds to a three-valued logic or three-valued mathematics. A collection of numbers can never be taken as A or *not-A*, until it has either been denumerated or yielded a law for denumeration. Barring such definite knowledge, the reality in question must be considered indeterminate. Thus, one should not say: either A or *not-A*, but rather: either A or *not-A* or indeterminate. Has Brouwer come upon the meaning of potency which Aristotle defined as the indeterminate and held to be a kind of middle between being and non-being?

The key vision of the intuitionists on the infinite is outlined succinctly in four steps by Hermann Weyl:

There first occurs in the mind of the mathematician a concrete individual judgment like $2 + 5 = 7$. In this matter, certain relations are intuited, which brings mathematics to a second or symbolic stage, where arithmetic graduates to algebra, so to speak. Here one can form the judgment: $m + n = n + m$. It is a judgment comprehended intuitively. At the third tier of the movement, the very concept of sum is seen to involve the possibility that to any given number another unity can always be added, forming a new number, and thus it is fourthly and finally seen that the series is open and infinite. The intuitionists allow us to transcend our experience but not our intuitions.

Such an analysis is quite close to the traditional view of mathematics. The difficulty reposes in the *a priori* and idealist character that is assigned to the intuition and in the confusion of content with relation.

WHAT IS ACTUAL IN MATHEMATICAL INFINITY IS A RULE

All this sometimes tenuous and technical array of data has been outlined with the sole view of achieving a summit from which the concept of infinity in modern thought could be viewed and evaluated according to realistic canons. It was seen first that at the root of the present-day concept of number is the notion of correspondence. It is this concept which, by analogy with the points on a line, propels the mathematician to define number in terms of an infinity of decimals, with infinity, according to Bolzano's pattern, taken to be any collection, or aggregate, or set, where any subset is equal to the whole.

Cantor's notion of the infinite results in the hierarchy of transfinite numbers where a_0, the smallest transfinite, is the set of denumerable sets, the number of natural numbers, indeed the number of all algebraic numbers since all of them, by proper rules, can be put into correspondence with the integers. The real numbers, by contrast, are not denumerable, and this non-denumerable character gives to c, the number of the continuum, a higher status in the hierarchy of the infinites than a_0 was seen to hold. Finally, a third transfinite cardinal was established as f, whose derivation was seen to be an affair of taking all the subclasses of c, which are greater than c, just as 8, the number of subclasses formed by the letters a and b, arranged in classes of three is greater than 2, the a and b of the original class.

Russell apparently made Cantor's notions more rigorous at the expense of locking mathematics into a logical skyscraper where the hierarchy of transfinites developed into a hierarchy of types. Formalism was shown not only to turn logic upon an inducted subject matter, as in Russell's approach, but to close mathematics off entirely from reality in the search after a system whose only law is consistency. To this retreat from reality, intuitionism raises a din of protest, claiming that formalism and logicalism alike dangle in a dream world, failing to keep their mathematical feet on the ground of construction. Intuitionism insists on construction and content rather than pure form and pure consistency, and it gives priority to mathematics over logic.

In evaluating the various theories and countertheories of the preceding sections, space will permit going only to the roots of the problem and letting the branches fall where they may after that. Furthermore, mathematics has only entered into this account of the philosophy of nature by the back door since it properly belongs in a higher order of abstraction than philosophical physics and ought here to be discussed only where mathematics is applied in the physical world. Yet it is a traditional principle that, putting it awkwardly, whatever does not involve an incompatibility in its internal structure has possible existence and the argument against an actual infinity in matter is not won until it is shown that such an infinity does involve incompatibilities and hence cannot ever be actualized in the quantified world.

There are two principles encrusted in the theory of finite number as the modern mathematician has jelled it. One is the principle that the whole is greater than its parts. The other is the notion of correspondence. But when these rules of thumb are applied in the domain of the infinite, they are found without credentials.

Bolzano's definition of the infinite says that the parts are equivalent to the whole and thus makes the classic whole-part picture invalid. Moreover, if Bolzano's idea holds, then correspondence likewise goes out since whole corresponds with whole and part corresponds with whole. An element no longer has one and only one correspondent.

It is certainly not legitimate, if one is talking about the real, to employ the notions of correspondence and of whole-part as premises for an argument that will deny both of them in its conclusion. If the premises were wrong, the conclusion is likewise false.

As a matter of fact, the notion of correspondence is the same broadly as equivalence or identity, and the principle of correspondence is nothing but the principle of identity, a positive way of stating the principle of non-contradiction. Now if quantity is the essence of things, as post-Cartesian empirical physics tends to say, and if the world is nothing but an infinite series of decimals, then it scrambles itself into the indeterminate chaos of the infinite regression. It becomes a Heraclitean continuum. It becomes a fluid universe where, it was seen, opposites edge into one another, and distinctions and identities are blanked out.

Thus, the principle of correspondence, if it has real application, forbids an infinity of particles in matter actually divided, and such an infinity would forbid the principle of correspondence. One or the other must go.

In another sense, correspondence involves defining equal number before defining number. It states the equivalence between the members of sets. Equivalence, self-identity, is opposed to non-equality, to more or less, and the whole traditional equipment of numbering is used before embarking on the definition of number in terms of infinite decimals. It is used as a premise and then ignored. It is used and then, purportedly, replaced by a more analytic definition like the notion of infinite fractions. You cannot replace a thing by using it to accomplish the replacement, just as the water in a puddle is not dried up by pouring more water into it.

How the traditional notion of number as discrete is used as the basis for modern number theory in terms of the continuum is borne in upon a critic not only by the principle of correspondence. The set of natural integers, inductively and abstractively known, is used as the pattern to which other sets are put into correspondence. The whole modern number theory rests thus upon a view of number as basically discrete, where each is self-identical.

The dissection which results in the definition of number by infinite decimals is something secondary; what is primary in reality and in knowledge are not infinities but unities, and it is only in terms of such unities that decimals and fractions can be constructed. Both rule and reality affirm the primacy of discrete number over infinity and the continuum—the rule which is the principle of correspondence or equality and the reality which is the integer system taken as a measure of all other numbers.

Before glancing at the legality of relating numbers to points in a continuum, Aristotle's notion of material or potential infinity may be fruitfully reconsidered. Such an infinity is, to use the language of Brouwer, the indeterminate, or in the style of Cantor, the continuum. What is actual about this infinite series is the rule for continuing the series, and the truly infinite matter to which the rule applies is an *ens rationis*. This corrals infinity into a logical class, quoting Russell's idiom or into an "ideal object," to cite the formalists. All these men have a great deal in common with realism, and a critique consists not so much in rejecting as in interpreting them. The number series is indeterminately long. A new integer may be progressively determined each time the mind adds unity to another integer, but the determination can go on and on because what is being molded is the potential, the indeterminate, the continuous, and what is actual is a determining rule; when physical determination stops it can be continued with tools of the logical or formal order.

There are thus logical constructs in modern mathematics which, while valid to the working mathematician who wants to control his matter and to derive it, are not in one-to-one correspondence with real quantity, and when actual, have only a logical actuality: that of rules or "regulative ideas." Hence such logical entities, designed to exploit their objects, cannot apply in philosophy which studies what is not exploited but only explored and what has its actuality not in the logical but in the real order.

A line, for instance, is not formed from points. For points are inextended quantities having only position. Much modern mathematics would agree with this ancient truth but would not be at all congenial as to the manner in which points are on a line. Realistically speaking, an infinity of points can be located on a line, even though they do not form the line. But the infinity is one of potency since a point is not determined, actualized, located, until another line has been drawn through the linear continuum. It takes two lines to locate a point, just as it takes two planes to locate a line and two solids to locate a plane. Thus the continuum is not actually infinite in its number of points but indeterminate. Each time it is divided, a new terminal point is determined, and the intervals caused by the continued division can continue to grow smaller and smaller without ever being exhausted. It is thus fallacious to say that there are just as many points on a long line as on a short one since the points on both are indeterminate and hence cannot be compared.

It is illicit, or at best equivocal, to compare the number series with points on a line. A line is not points but between points. If numbers are analogated to extensions, arithmetic to geometry, then as the size of decimals is decreased a new segment is determined on an original line representing, say, unity; the segment decreases with the decimal, and thus points that were potentially present on the original line are made the actual terms of the smaller segments. Segments, not points, resemble numbers. A point as the term of a segment does its job of terminating and by that very fact prevents the stretch between one and two from ever being an indeterminate continuum of actual numbers.

This makes even the series of rational fractions between one and two a discrete set as far as they are actual and a continuous set as far as they are potential. If the mind moves rigorously from one to two, it can never actually do so by traveling across intervening points. It takes abstraction to accomplish this task—abstraction that can bear upon the discrete because it alone can relate being to non-being, or in other words relate a thing to itself. It alone can bridge the gap between being 2 and not being 2. In brief, a point is a limit of a line, and where limits and terms are apprehended, intelligence is at work just as in the world of nature form as the term of generation cannot be counted but only understood.

Cantor's hierarchy of transfinite numbers may now be confronted face to face, and the discussion of it will shed further light on the remarks about determination, indeterminacy, and the infinite. The outline of his theory leading to α_0 etches out the fact that he has found a rule for determining or denumerating the rational and even the algebraic numbers. But rules for continuing a series do not authorize the conclusion that it can be completed in the sense of being assigned a number, in the sense that it is thinner than the series of real numbers which is called non-denumerable, in the sense that it can be compared with other types of real infinity.

Both reals and algebraics are equally infinite, in the sense that they can never be completely enumerated, and though comparative size has no real meaning here, there are just as many of the second type of numbers as there are of the first if infinity is what the word means. In the case of the algebraic numbers, the rules for enumeration are known; in the other they are not.

But knowing the rules for determination in one case and not knowing them in the other really has nothing to do with the fact that a sequence is indeterminately long or short or, to put it more concretely, that any continuum can be divided indefinitely. These directions of thought twine together into a conclusion that the semblance of act which the various transfinite numbers wear and which enable them to be compared are rules for dealing with the respective series and not the series themselves as accomplished facts. The act is logical and not real.

What is objective in all Cantor's cases is the indeterminate, and indeterminates cannot be compared with each other in the sense of more or less, lower or loftier in hierarchy, just as chaos cannot be compared with chaos. If there were degrees or determinations in the chaos enabling comparison, chaos would not be chaos. Different ways of determining the potential do not imply difference in the raw material, any more than the difference between a good bricklayer and a bad one is in the bricks rather than in the man. Men are still men if we arrange them in alphabetical order, in the order of height, or if we do not arrange them at all.

Modern mathematics has discovered rules for determining series and rules for showing that they cannot be determined, as in the case of transcendental numbers. Modern method tends to the logical order, that of rules, and Whitehead has aptly described it as a search after "rules of succession." The difficulty is that the rule is confounded with reality. For example, the sum system for denumerating fractions involves rules that as such lie outside the series. Cantor's a_0 is admittedly in this post-series area.

But when a rule lies outside the series it does not mean that it is a reality like a stone that can be represented no longer as a rule or logical entity but as a real number.

A number is not a rule, any more than Americans are the constitution which governs them. In one sense, it may well be the case that a rule is only the nature of a thing, defined regulatively by the mind and only logically distinct from the thing. Knowing that a number is made of unities, we have a rule for extending number, and knowing that man is a rational animal, we have a rule for identifying man whenever and wherever he may be found—in America or in Europe or upon visiting Alaska and seeing the Eskimos for the first time.

But in modern method, rules are stationed outside the realities that they govern so that the researcher, mathematician or empiriological physicist alike, may more effectively control his matter. The modern trend is to get outside the series in order to dominate it and, in the language of Kant and James, to make it. The modern approach likes to elevate method into the status of a thing so that it can be made more pliable. Getting a better hold on method means more control on the matter which the method measures. Modern method is like false teeth which can be taken out and inspected and cleaned and repaired. Man can get a more deliberate control on them. He can improve them. His natural teeth he can never even see, directly.

Admitting the right to use whatever working principles a scholar finds appropriate to carry out his mission, the philosopher assessing such a method must place such differences as Cantor makes, between his levels of infinity, in the logical order. They are different ways of dealing with what in reality is the potentially infinite, and when they are compared, as a_0 is compared with c and with f, it is rules that are interrelated, i.e., actualities that are logically different and not indeterminacies that are really the same. The rules for actualizing the potential do not mean that the potential is different as each rule applies to it or that it is any more exhaustible in one case than in another.

The hierarchy of transfinites thus corresponds to different ways of deriving number from the indeterminate, or different ways of dividing the continuum; but it leaves the reality of the raw material forever continuous and indeterminate, which is the Aristotelian definition of potential infinity. The philosopher quarrels with the modern method not when it makes its rules but when it mistakes these rules for reality. In line with the approaches suggested by Russell and Hilbert, the realist is driven to admit the differences between the infinities of modern mathematics, but he holds that they are logical and not real. Brouwer, when he flattens the Cantorian hierarchy into one infinity and calls it the indeterminate, is simply emphasizing what is real rather than logical about mathematical infinity, and the reason for his failure to capture the mind of present-day empiriological temper is that his views do not permit method to control matter; they do not recognize the status of empiriological method as that of an art, in the language of Dewey, or that of a logic, in the vocabulary of Russell. With Hilbert and Russell dedicated to logic and Brouwer to content, the difference between the two schools is more a matter of where emphasis is laid.

The denumerable or non-denumerable character of sets, as the Cantorians employ these terms, has nothing to do with whether a set is really infinite or not. In one case, a rule is known for actually denumerating, in the other the enumeration remains potential. The empiriological spirit is interested in formulas rather than forms. When we have actually enumerated the first trillion algebraic numbers, we are just as far removed from exhausting the infinity as when starting, rulelessly, at the potential. In fact, the continuum itself is a case of the confusion in mathematics between rules and realities. Thus c is the mathematician's rule for representing real numbers and more specifically a rule for illustrating their density. But the rule of the continuum must be kept distinct from the reality that it represents.

Such reasoning as this tends to hack away at the bottom of the Cantorian hierarchy which rests on the confusion of laws and the entities which they govern, on the confusion of denumeration and non-denumeration as dividing infinities among each other. The number of algebraic numbers is indeterminate, and so is the number of reals. Indeterminate cannot be compared with the indeterminate; the comparison is only in rules for determination which are different among themselves and leave in each case an infinite margin of further determinability. Mathematical infinity remains the potentially infinite; as act it is in the logical order.

There is no doubt that such schemes as Cantor constructs and as Russell and Hilbert adopt are powerful aids to the imagination. The empiriological method, to control, needs matter, composition, plurality. Its user cannot deal with the difference between being and non-being, and thus the discrete character of entities like numbers eludes his methods. So he fills up the gap between numbers by infinity, the continuum, the potential, thus feeding his imagination but starving his philosophy into a purely logical skeleton. This has its value, like a skeleton in a class of anatomy, but life and reality are something different.

In the top-heavy hierarchy that modern mathematical theory has become in defining number, it is easy to forget the foundations which are the series of natural integers that are taken as a pattern in the correspondence of sets and that test whether a set is denumerable. This series is best envisioned not by Cantor but in Aristotle who viewed number as a complex of unities, varied when a unit is added or subtracted. The fundamental thing about number theory then, when its bases are philosophically stressed and discovered to be the set of discrete numbers which is the pattern for correspondence, is not the continuum of potency but the unity of act. The continuum or the potential is something secondary. It is known, like all potency, with reference to act.

As Aquinas said, "the last thing we reach in knowledge is the material"—the continuum which even Whitehead recognized stands for potency while act or form appears in discreteness.

A distinction must be made here between determination outside the mind and inside of it. The quantity π and even $\sqrt{2}$ are determinate quantities; $\sqrt{2}$ multiplied by $\sqrt{2}$ yields 2, a very significant and determinate number; and the relation between the diameter and circumference of a circle is so determinate outside the mind that it is called a constant. Such quantities are determinate in themselves but indeterminate with regard to us when we interpret reality arithmetically. This determination in themselves shows that π and $\sqrt{2}$ are not merely infinite decimals pitching on a non-periodic sea, and the same conclusion could be drawn about the difference between two integers which must clearly be something more than an infinite line of fractions, since each integer can be subjected to very definite arithmetical operations and must therefore be something very definite in itself.

Now any unity that stands in nature, a man, a sulfur atom, or a sycamore tree is what it is as a formal unit, and the same is true of unities called numbers in the mathematical order. But men, atoms, and trees, standing undividedly, are yet divisible, and as an earlier section showed, they can be divided not just once but indefinitely as quantified things. The natural unities are determined in themselves by their form, the determining element in things; but they are indeterminate regarding their number of divisions because they bear inside them an indefinitely divisible material element.

Irrational numbers—transcendental and algebraic alike—thus bear out what Aristotle said of the continuum where a thing is undivided or determined in itself but always further divisible and determinable. As undivided or determinate entities, more densely sown in the field of number and more fundamental than rationals, Cantorians say, these irrationals show that the most ultimate of mathematical entities, even for modern theory, is not the continuum by which their series is purportedly represented.

Transcendentals and algebraics are thus units rather than affairs of continuity, acts and not sheer potency.

Intuitionism, logicalism, and formalism, as philosophies of mathematics, are all inadequate accounts, even when they are inspected internally. Intuitionism fails to account for form, formalism for matter, and logicalism tends at least to reduce one to the other. Intuitionism is too inductive, logicalism and formalism are too deductive. Neither radical induction nor radical deduction can afford a realistic account of things, even in mathematics. Moreover, there are inconsistencies involved in each of these schemes. Logicalism and formalism must use content, or they would be studying a vacuum. Intuitionism uses form or it would be studying a plenum. One extreme leads to the conclusion that there are only relations, the other tends to view things as irrelational. True science freezes away at either pole. Only a world of act and potency can own that temperate climate which avoids the errors of all extremes and makes a home for all truth.

Suggested Readings

Richard Courant and Herbert Robbins, *What is Mathematics?* (New York, 1941).

Bertrand Russell, *Principles of Mathematics,* 2d ed. (New York, 1938).

10

Place: The Measure of Motion

This is a restless universe on many counts, but nowhere is the traffic more apparent than in the passage of things from place to place, the fact of local motion. In infancy, man is attracted to things when they move, and as he matures to his status as a perennial questioner, he is still fascinated by the problem of motions in place. He is exploring the stars, improving means of transportation, or perhaps simply sitting by the fireside as the flames leap up through the chimney. *Where* is one of the proverbial five *w*'s that command the descriptive approaches to reality like history, journalism, and even the empiriological disciplines. In knowledge, things are often distinguished or united according to the place or places which they occupy; in action, for example in walking, man is always going someplace. As Aristotle remarked, a chimera is recognized as unreal because it is nowhere.

Local movement is one of the few realities whose acceptance escaped into the modern mind when the philosophical science of nature was surrounded by empiriological physics and left to die as a prisoner of the middle ages. The universe in Cartesian physics was one of quantity and local motion, and the twentieth-century intellectual is still insisting that he lives in it. When the quantum physicists sets out to picture the world entirely in terms of positions and velocities, or when the theorist of relativity reports that the universe is nothing but space and time, each in his own way is carrying out the terms of the Cartesian will. Both views are inadequate. But they at least bear their witness to the reality of local motion. The philosophical science of nature is pressed today not so much to establish the fact of local motion; it is more to establish that local motion is not everything.

Contemporary scholarship is much more focused on space than on place. This reverses the order of importance and degree of being which these two realities are assigned in philosophical physics. Indeed, the treatment of space belongs much more to mathematics than to the philosophical science of nature because it is an affair of dimensionality; it is a weak reality in the physical world, founded there truly enough but blown into the entity that we call space by the abstracting mind. An alien in the purely mathematical world, the philosopher of nature can consider such things as dimensions not in themselves but only as incarnated in the mobile universe whose career he follows. In the light of motion, he may, in fact he must, evaluate such challenges as the non-Euclidian world of relativity theory and the n-dimensional space of quantum mechanics. He must likewise face honestly up to the problem of the all-pervading ether of space which classical physics posited, the theory of special relativity rejects, and the theory of general relativity, under a new guise, reinstates. But before such vital contemporary problems are confronted, premises must be wrested from an inductive analysis of local motion.

The empiriological physicist classifies by measuring. He does not delve into what things are, and he measures reality by yardsticks, not by itself. Instead of getting down to the bedrock of motion by diving into the stream, he counts dead fishes on the bank. The philosophical science of nature, on the other hand, wants to know what place is. It is only in the light of motion that place can be studied in philosophical physics and only in this light also that the reaches of place in the physical, natural, mobile world can be scanned.

After a preliminary definition of place, its nature will be more fully probed. This requires a decision on whether place is relative, and if it is not, how it functions as a final cause which yields

a finer and more scientific definition of place. In connection wi
the problem of place appear the questions whether nature tol
ates a vacuum or is always a plenum, and if it is a plenur
whether it is infinite. The problem of infinity prompts the que
tion, whether the universe as a whole is in place.

Space can then be discussed, and here likewise there are ir
portant questions: Is space a full-blooded physical reality? (
is it an *a priori* mental form, as Kant held? If it is in some w
physical and real, is space non-Euclidian or Euclidian?

PLACE IS AN IMMOBILITY IN THE MOBILE WORLD

Place, (or position, in a language that is more mathematica
is the reality that answers to the question: *where?* This,
least, is what the ordinary man means when he uses the wor
The answer to the question might be the name of a city, or
street, the number of a hotel room, or a jewelry box on a che
of drawers. It might even be a planet, if the question is on tl
origin of light rays, or a continent, if we are discussing ge
politics. But the common factor in all such answers would be the
relation to the question: *where?*

The ordinary man thinks of place as a kind of vessel or co
tainer, and for a thing to be in its proper place is to be in i
proper surroundings. Moreover, at the level of common sens
place is considered as something stationary. Home is always c
the same street, and New York City is always at the same long
tude and latitude. But if place is stationary for the plain man, it
nevertheless known from motion. When he looks at the map
discover the whereabouts of the China sea, he imagines himse
as capable of going there. Without motion as joining two po\s
tions, place would be a meaningless thing. Even the mathem
tician discerns this fact, choosing for example to illustrate a li\n
as a trajectory of a moving point or a solid as the trajectory of
moving plane. It is good teaching technique because the ordina\r
mind hooks up position with motion and grasps one better by i
reference to the other.

But philosophy would be easy if it could be sublet to the views of common sense. Can the fact of place be more rigorously detailed? As a first approximation, it might be said again that this is not a Heraclitean universe. Though matter is always astir, there is a real immobile aspect to every motion, or the motion itself could never be and be discerned. There is a norm for measuring motion, not a numerical yardstick or a speedometer but simply an objective standard according to which a thing is said to move and indeed to move from this place to that. This norm is not anthropomorphic and subjective. If it is not real, neither is the motion. There must indeed be two immobilities to account for the origin of motion as different from its end. In other words, the standard is differentiated, as a foot rule that has two ends.

Such in general is the answer to whether place exists. It is an immobility in this rough definition, according to which motion occurs. More specifically, it is an immobility at which motion ends or, for our present purposes, where it begins. Unless this immobility is real in the outer order, the differences of origin and end would also be unreal and unknowable; if motion involves such differences, and they turn out to be unreal, motion likewise becomes impossible.

Aristotle likened place to a vase, and it is tempting to pursue the metaphor while forgetting along the way that it is only a convenient example. Water, gasoline, or orange juice can be poured into the vessel, and it can also be filled up with air. Obviously then, the place is distinct from the things that occupy it, called *locata*, if only because places remain the same while locata come and go. If place is not something distinct from matter or, what amounts to the same impasse, if a body as its own place, then a moving thing would have to cart its place along with it, and the movement from place to place that we define as local motion would become impossible. A similar absurdity would result if place itself were posited within another place, and so *ad infinitum*. There would thus be no immobility, and motion would be siphoned off again into the indeterminacy of the infinite flow. A body could not move from place to place if everything were fluid. There is an ultimate immobility involved in each new position that a body occupies; there are many immobilities because there are many places to which a body moves.

When water is poured into the Aristotelian vase, the vessel is a container. Thus the definition of place, unraveled as it is from the fact of local motion, may be extended to mean "surrounding immobility." Moreover, the outer portions of the vase, the handles, the ornaments, and even the exterior parts of the walls, do not touch the water. Only the interior surface of the container is in contact with the contents. This fact must likewise be legislated into the definition, so that place may be fully and formally defined as "the immediate, immoblie surface of a surrounding body."

The use of such terms as "immobility" and especially of "surface" lend, at first sight, a mathematical strand to the definition. But mathematical place, which empiriological physics borrows and applies, is something different from physical place. In geometry, quantities are located in terms of points, and since a point is a unity having position, there is no difference between a point and the position which it occupies. Changing the position means changing the point. In the proper sense of the word, there is no such thing as motion in mathematics, even the motion of points, lines, and planes. The physical definition, on the other hand, is drawn from the analysis of motion which is really all that matters in the science of nature. "Immobility" and "surface" are known with respect to motion, as its opposites, with local motion indeed etching out our concept of place in much the same way that changes of form thrust upon us the conclusion that there must be a primordial matter.

The physical definition may now be shown to involve five facts about place, all of which team up to carry its complete meaning. Place is immediate; it is immobile; it is a surface; it is something surrounding; it is of a surrounding body.

1. Place is an immediate or first surface since every body when at rest is immediately in place and not just suspended by its bootstraps. A book in a study is in the given room, but this is only its larger or general place. More properly, it is on a particular shelf, but most properly it is in the place dimensioned by the surfaces of the two books along side of it and of the air around the remaining portions. A body that is not immediately in place is in motion, like a toy balloon, floating freely in a room until it immediately touches a surface where it stops.
2. Place is immobile, since this is not a Heraclitean universe.
3. Place is a surface only; were it a body there would be a compenetration between a thing and its place.
4. Place is a surrounding reality since a thing moving locally changes with respect to its environing relations only and does not alter its inner constitution.
5. The surrounding thing must be a body. A spirit, having no parts like right or left, up or down, cannot bound anything, and a purely mathematical surface is an ideal, mentally detached from the physical country and incapable of containing its population.

RELATIVITY DOES NOT REFUTE ARISTOTLE'S PHILOSOPHY

Aristotle was much more minute in his account of place, but before he can be followed, the general contours of his universe must be outlined. His astronomy was a geocentric system, with the earth, at least at its center, pictured as immobile. Around this geocentric axis, the heavenly bodies circled in concentric spheres, and with the earth thus firmly anchored, *up* and *down,* owned something of an absolute significance. Indeed, once an immobile reference point was gained, it became possible at least in theory to specify the absolute positions of all other bodies.

Copernicus replaced geocentric astronomy by a heliocentric system, but despite this new astronomy, it did not seem necessary to scrap the notion of absolute place. The stationary reference point was simply shifted from the earth to the sun. Moreover, there arose the field physics of the nineteenth century, chiefly as the result of Maxwell's electromagnetic theory. Lorentz blackened the silhouette of the ether, an imponderable substance pervading all space and acting as a carrier of light. It was another vote for the absolute. The earth could move with respect to the sun, and the sun, as astronomy had shown, was swinging also by reference to the Milky Way. But this did not stop the music of classical physics. There was after all the ether to pipe it on—an immobile reality for tracing out absolute positions in the absolute.

Then came the Michelson-Morley experiment that stirred a revolution in empiriological physics as great as the noise of the Copernican victory over Ptolemy. A thoroughgoing classical physicist, standing atop the earth and measuring the velocity of sunlight—once when the earth was spinning away from the sun and again when it was spinning toward it—would have expected the composite velocities to be different. After all, was it not a simple matter to show that, in a railroad car moving forward at 20 miles per hour, a man walking toward the rear at the rate of 5 miles per hour would be moving forward at a combined velocity of 15 miles per hour? If he were walking toward the engine at 5 miles per hour, his combined forward motion would be at the rate of 25 miles per hour. A corresponding difference would have been expected on classical principles in the two measurements of Michelson and Morley, if the earth were really drifting through a stationary ether. But the difference was not observed. And the experiment, while rocking the leaning tower of classical physics was also rocking the cradle of the theory of relativity.

What Michelson and Morley showed, Einstein reasoned, was that the ether, this vast immobile receptacle of matter and energy, was not observable. If it were, then it would have been the norm to referee the composition of velocities in the Michelson-Morley experiment—just as motion, with respect to an earth considered immobile, justifies the classical conclusions about a man walking either forward or backward in the train. There is thus, Einstein went on, no detectable immobility, no absolute frame for comparing motions and measuring positions in the universe. It may well be said that the train is moving relative to the earth and the earth relative to the sun. But since there is no absolute arbiter of motion and place, it could also be said that the earth is moving relative to the train and the sun relative to the earth. Motion and place, lacking an absolute character, are always yoked to a relative frame of reference. This is the meaning of the theory of relativity.

Local movement thus becomes an affair of relation and gives primacy to neither of the terms. Ptolemy can arise from his tomb and live again with Copernicus. It can be said that the earth is moving relative to the sun or vice versa, depending on the observer's point of view or, more technically, his frame of reference.

Relativity will be more fully assessed in connection with the character of space and the reality of the ether. But for the moment, it is important to see if the weight of all these facts will break the Aristotelian scales. Place, it was said, involves the stationary, and since there are many places, there must be many immobilities in the mobile universe. But the failure to measure immobility does not argue to its non-existence.

Does this mean that the ether or some other such Atlas of the world must be reinstated? No, it simply means that measurement cannot touch any of the ultimates and hence cannot gain a hold on whatever might be involved by motion in the way of ultimate imobility. In quantum mechanics, the position and velocity of small particles cannot be exactly measured when considered simultaneously. But despite the pleas of scientism, this does not mean that particles have no position or have indeterminate ones. To affirm that a position cannot be exactly measured and to state that it does not exist is to say two very different things. Positionless particles on the level of atoms could no more give rise to positioned bodies like the rock of Gilbraltar than a house can be built by simply laying vacuums on top of each other.

Whether in the Aristotelian, Copernican, Einsteinian, or quantum systems, the two terms of motion are somehow immobile or the motion is an absurdity staggering from nowhere to nowhere, hence not motion at all.

The mathematics of Einstein show that he cannot adopt the Heraclitean viewpoint in practice. The relation of a thing to its specific frame of reference is, as a relation, absolute; and when one frame of reference is in motion with respect to another, definite equations exist for relating them. The theory of relativity seeks to relativize the absolute but ends by absolutizing the relative. From all this it may be concluded that with the ether or without it, in ancient or in modern astronomy, motion still involves the stationary which is not simply projected by man but is as real as the motion itself.

PLACE IS THE TERM OF LOCAL MOVEMENT

Burning paper does not mean burning the fireplace. The correcting of Aristotle "the empiriological physicist" does not necessarily mean the demise of Aristotle the philosopher, just as the decline of Newtonian physics does not mark the end of the broader methods that he used, especially the principle of inertia. The difficulty with Aristotle's notion of absolute place was that a geocentric immobility was unobservable. It was too mechanical in the first place, like the ether hypothesis, and stood at variance with the broader spirit of Aristotelian science of nature. Immobility is specified by motion. But what specifies the immobility? It cannot be said that a thing is immobile absolutely except by reference to an absolute, and how can the absolute be defined in the sensible universe except by reference to another motion. In Aristotle's doctrine of absolute place, there is too much of an appeal to the imagination which intelligence should have picketed. Place is always elusive to define because the imagination insists on legislating the definition. There is nothing absolute about a sensible picture, but there is something very definitely ultimate about the immobilities which local motion implies since a moving thing, far from carrying its place on its back, takes up a new position leaving the old one behind. Such immobilities can be understood but not imaged, discovered by abstraction to exist but not of the stuff for quantitative techniques to measure.

Does this mean that Einstein was right in turning local movement into a relationship rather than leaving it a truly dynamic event where one term is stationary and where motion takes place with respect to it? When *A*, apparently, moves to *B* can it just as legitimately be said that *B* moves toward *A*? From the viewpoint of quantitative measures, Einstein is certainly right since the empiriological physicist simply lays his rulers on the stretch which a motion covers, without the power to detect its principles and purposes. In deciding that a stone is 18 inches thick, it makes no difference whether one begins at 36 inches on a yardstick and counts downward to 18 or begins at 0 and counts upward. Origins and ends, causes and effects, objective order and cosmic purpose—all of these as such involve more light than empiriological physics can ever form by using shadows. *What* is not synonymous with the question *how much*, as any salesman knows.

Place is in fact a kind of end or purpose, and it is in this light that Aristotle, refusing like the modern physicist to forsake motion for quantity, defined place as "the term of local movement," since the water is certainly in the kettle before it boils out into space.

Psychologically speaking, a place is known more as a term than as an origin, and it is not until a thing starts moving that we know it was present in place beforehand. Prior to knowing where a thing came from in local movement, we know where it is going, and by reason alone, it cannot be established that movement had a beginning in time at all. Change is always christened by its term; there is a going or coming, rising or falling, analysis when compounds are broken down into elements, or synthesis when elements are built up into compounds. The term of local movement, at least psychologically, enjoys a primacy over the origin which is known, when known, more as an afterthought, as potency is known by reference to act.

This ascendency of term over origin in our knowledge of local motion holds true likewise in the physical order where local movement is the actualization of potencies in the order of place, and where the net result is a higher, nobler, and richer reality than the status of mere potency had provided. Final causality or purpose belongs to other chapters, but there is something of matter's eternal striving that enters into the philosophy of place. The actual local motion in the world and the tendency to be moved elsewhere that stamps a body when at rest are but an index of the searching by mobile realities for places that fulfill their destinies and are thus connatural.

A billiard ball, for instance, when struck by its neighbor moves to a different position on the table. Charged by the impact with a tension that demands response, movement to another position is the best expression of its nature. A ball of a different material, say rubber, would move differently, satisfying *its* nature, to borrow a phrase from Whitehead, and a ball of lead would perhaps not move at all. Movement toward an end, the end set by the nature of what is moved and different from one nature to another, is the only way in which local movement can be explained. Things tend to their natural places, to spots in the world of motion that most befit their stimulated natures. The empiriological ambition of replacing this finalizing role of place by the blind discharge of mere mechanical energy received wholly from the outside was confronted in Chapters 7 and 8.

The finalizing character of place might also be presented by taking Aristotle's suggestion that place has a conservative aspect. The arrow, shot from a bow, arches in time to rest in order to conserve its nature, its identity, and its being, which an infinite flight would wholly spend. The arrow could be envisioned, to use a homely metaphor, as trying to shake off its disturbances and come to equilibrium. By contrast to unending motion or to rest in the sky which would require potencies that the arrow does not own, the descent to the earth is the most connatural to this husbandry of resources.

If this sounds anthropomorphic, an analogy may be framed from empiriological physics which rests so heavily on two tenets from thermodynamics, the law of the conservation of matter and energy and the law of entropy, that energy is constantly degraded. Both laws apply to the same bodies, the one expressing conservation, the other a dynamism toward destruction. Place points up the first force and motion the second in this analogy. A thing moves toward a place, Aristotle said, by the tendency to conserve itself. Banished from one home, like a dime dropped accidentally on the floor, a thing seeks a place that is most connatural to it. It might have to buck opposing bodies like a plane in a storm or like the money when it meets up with the unyielding surface of the floor and bounces off into a corner. But it will choose the path of least resistance, to use an empiriological term; it will conserve itself, as Aristotle said, acquitting its nature, searching for ends that the nature sets, moved always by an outside agent but moved none the less on its own terms.

Such conservation is an expression of the nature in mobile realities and the tendency to the fulfillment of the nature's destiny. That is why it involves final causality. But no such mobile being fully attains its natural place since it always has further potencies and tends, as long as it exists, to move toward their fulfillment. If it ever attained a wholly connatural habitat, it would no longer tend to move and would have completed the mission of its existence. This is not to say that the places of things presently occupied are unnatural, any more than a man is not a man when he has not yet attained perfection. In this interacting network of the mobile universe, the places which things have attained are what their natures order under the circumstances. They are natural places in a very genuine sense. But there is a tendency to march onward toward that which is even more natural, as an apple partially red tends to ripen further. There is no equilibrium so long as this supremely natural summit remains unscaled. The arrow, at rest after its parabolic flight from the bow, still retains its natural tendency to be moved and will show it when another mover comes along to set it going. Matter, like man, is always restless.

Einstein, when he defined place as an affair of relation, and Aristotle, when he dubbed it "the term of local movement," were adverting to two different notions of place. The relativistic account is a snapshot of mathematical place (space) which is copied by empiriological physics. Aristotle, the philosophical scientist of nature, was loyal to his mobile subject. He spoke of natural place, as that which is in accordance with the nature of a thing and realizes its fullness. In more contemporary lingo, he defined the ideal case that makes other places natural to a thing as progressive approximations, like a tadpole stage which is natural in the development of a frog. A nature is most conservative when it attains its fullness because it has more act and inwardness to itself and less potency for an exterior agent to rule by actualizing.

Place, as the term of local movement, gives it directionality and does not permit it to be defined as a relation in which a car can be said to move with respect to the street, or the street with respect to the car. The purpose of local movement is the term, and direction is known not from yardsticks or frames of reference outside the moving natures but from their tendencies and goals. A meteor flying through space, water cascading down a mountain slope, or the molecules of oxygen dancing in the atmosphere of the earth have tendencies that motion is only fulfilling. Water is tending down the mountain and not the mountain up the water because the water by its motion attains a greater degree of perfection which is its end. It can drive ships, put out fires, and quench thirsts. It is the natural tendency of air in a punctured tire to escape through the aperture, and it is the natural tendency of dust, swirling in the wind, to settle down to earth again when the wind subsides. If the notion of nature is correct, things tend to conserve and fulfill their natures, before they embellish the universe as a whole. This statement would have to be qualified in order to distinguish in an individual thing its tendencies as a particular and as a member of the cosmic community. But for present purposes what has been said is accurate enough. For it is only as an aggregate of natures individualized that the universe has any being. It has no nature itself because it is not one substance.

Now Einstein starts with the cosmic dimensions of the universe in the attempt to anchor a frame of reference. Because Aristotle is concerned with individual natures, the seats of inner tendencies that are not simply the products of external relations, his philosophy parts company with empiriological ambitions and his doctrine of place with that of Einstein. It is these inner or natural tendencies that are accountable for local movement which, in turn, is their fulfillment. The discharge of this obligation to be moved is, in the order of place, local motion, and the purpose is to acquire new assets in nature's treasury which are more connatural places. An electron tends toward an atom that has become a negative ion because the electron is more potential and hence impoverished. The electron is the ontological starveling. Apart from other forces such as the random collisions of particles, it is not the ion that tends toward the electron. The falling snowflake tends toward the roof—rather than the roof toward the snow—because it is less stable and permanent, less independent and commanding than the tile. The water of the mountain spate, drawn perhaps from the sea into the clouds and then deposited in the winter snow, is more potential than its mountain bed which has been there for centuries and has channelled countless thaws that have preceded this. It is nature and not quantity, interiorities and not aggregates, principles and not mechanisms that the philosophy of nature is primarily after, and the directionality of natural motion, completely baffling to mathematics, will yield its secrets when the mind knows the combination of natures, tendencies, and terms which opens the lock.

This is all beyond images and beneath the mechanical aspect of matter on which one can lay a finger and focus the eye. Intelligence discerns that there are places in nature, and that far from being a mere matter of relations which relativity experts can juggle, local movement in nature expresses the tendencies in natural realities to move to places more connatural. Such a doctrine does not require that there be any such thing as a stationary body in the mechanical sense but only that there is a hierarchy in motion or, in the picturesque language of a Santayana "degrees of permanence." On such a premise, all things can still be in motion without giving the palm to Heraclitus. Immobility does not involve the stationary of a mechanical sort in the world of place any more than form is a fixed frame like that of a picture we see and feel. Philosophy is the child of intelligence, and if imagination can lay hold of its conclusions, it is a sure sign that philosophy is false to its promise of probing what is ultimate. Scientism is simply looking for final answers in the wrong places, like an explorer who would search for an orange grove in the arctic circle.

A VACUUM IS IMPOSSIBLE

No one who has gazed out at the starry heavens can help wondering about interstellar spaces. Is the universe a massive solid, or is it, as Sir Arthur Eddington declared, largely empty space? Is the universe a plenum, and if so, how can motion occur in it? If it is pocked by empty spaces, how can light, for instance, travel through them? The answers to such questions will try the case for the existence of a vacuum and later hear the supreme court of modern empiriological physics with its opinions about space.

The early Greek atomists, whose chief spokesman was Democritus, held that vacuums existed as the interstices between their atoms and that a vacuum surrounded the world. A vacuum can be defined as an empty place, a place without a body. As such, it was not only a fact for Democritus in explaining the separation of atoms and their motions from point to point, but it has also been the ambition of modern empiriological physics, especially in its prerelativity estate. Freshman empiriological physicists perform the experiment of pumping the air out of a bell jar, and they hear frequently of the velocity of light or the forces between electrodes, *in vacuo*. Electronics has transcribed the expression *vacuum tube* into common language.

It might sound like a verbalism to declare to the empiriological physicist that no matter how strong he makes his bell jar to resist the atmospheric pressure from without, if nothing separates the walls, they are not separated. This has sometimes led philosophers to distinguish a physical vacuum which the empiriological physicist tries to achieve and a so-called metaphysical vacuum which is said to be impossible. But if the philosophical physicist sticks to his last of nature, he can show from motion that even in the physical order a vacuum cannot exist.

On the premises of empiriological physics, electromagnetic energy, like light or electrons, would move with an infinite velocity through a so-called vacuum since there would be no resistance in their paths. Rate in a moving body—acceleration and retardation—is established for empiriological physics by the impact delivered to a thing and by the medium in which it moves. If a thing were traveling through a vacuum which is no medium, its own initial energies would propel it to its goal in an instant. Moreover, everything would move through a vacuum with an equal velocity.

Such would be an *ad hominem* argument against scientism, but philosophically speaking, this analysis is inadmissible. Everything moved is moved, at every moment of its motion, by something else. "Whatever is moved," the principle goes, "is moved by another." On such a premise, once the initial mover has ceased moving a body the medium does the rest, facilitating motion rather than simply impeding it. If this is true, no motion could occur in a vacuum since a vacuous medium is not a medium and hence not a mover. Motion would collapse in a vacuum.

Moreover, and in still a philosophical sense, local motion is the result of the fact that a body is first in a less natural place and tends toward its natural home. But a vacuum would not allow such a hierarchy. Far from attracting a thing as an end, it is totally indifferent, and having no parts, there is no reason why a thing should rest in one region of it rather than another nor why, if the thing continues on through, like a ray of light, it should have taken this or that path. A body at rest in a vacuum would be coterminous with it, a reality and a vacuum, something and nothing simultaneously. Leibniz was right in his famous maxim that nature shrinks from a vacuum. A vacuum would still motion and crush the nature that would enter it. It is thus not a place, nor can a body in place be said to occupy a vacuum. Place is the immediate, immobile surface of a surrounding body. It is something external, a fixed frame that a thing abandons in local motion to seek a station more fitting for its nature. Even granting that a thing should occupy a vacuum, as its place, and move to another vacuum or another part of one, local motion would produce no changes since the thing moved, at the end of its trajectory would be where it was before—in a vacuum.

But if it is easy to deny the existence of a vacuum, the denial does not explain the reality of a highly evacuated bell jar nor the more striking reality of apparent emptiness in the nocturnal sky. Classical empiriological physics pumped these areas full of all-pervading ether, and philosophy, to preserve the notion of place as an immediate surface, jumped at the idea also. But apart from the Michelson-Morley experiment, the ether ought to have signed only a very uneasy peace with the philosopher. If it permits a moving body to bite through it, it has to be elastic; if it holds things in their places, it has no "give" at all. In fact, it comes perilously close to a contradiction since it would have to be as resilient as rubber and as rigid as steel simultaneously. As an immobile reality, it was certainly contrary to Aquinas' idea that matter is ever tense with tendencies to motion and to his broader idea of finality in the universe. The ether idea seems dead now, and no one ought really to mourn it except those who wish to think with their imaginations.

In the wake of the Michelson-Morley experiment, the theory of special relativity which applies to uniform, translatory motion —say motion in a straight line—dispensed with the ether as unobservable. But in the theory of general relativity, which applies to non-uniform rotary motion, the ether comes vigorously back to blanket not only the interstices of matter but the whole corporeal universe.

This analysis, however, is not quite correct, since it is a mistake to give the same name to the classical ether which the theory of restricted relativity impugned and the new ether which the theory of general relativity introduces. Ether in this second sense is really the pseudonym for the whole universe which Einstein views as an all-embracing field of energy, thick where there is matter in the classical sense and thin where there is not. Matter and energy become equivalent in general relativity. The interstellar gravitational field which classical physics held to be produced by celestial bodies is found to be of the same massive stuff as the Newtonian stars. A field can be "weighed." It has "inertia." It can do work. It can guide even light rays like a river bed containing its water. The experiments confirming the theory in astronomy are too intricate to be discussed here. But though these experiments are few in number, every single one of them votes for Einstein. The release of atomic energy with corresponding changes in atomic mass has lowered the evidence of relativity from the stars into commercial laboratories and even into international diplomacy. This new ether of general relativity is indeed a powerful brush for the empiriological physicist in painting his world-picture.

In the generalized theory of gravitation, Einstein attempts, as others have done, to construct a more unified field theory that explains gravitation and electromagnetism in the same four-dimensional space-time continuum of non-Euclidian geometry. Einstein is again struggling toward what is potential in matter, what is beyond the differences of gravitation and electromagnetism and thus affords a richer field for man to exploit in his universe-building. The field of the generalized theory of gravitation, besides being more fundamental and more contentless than the field of the older relativity mechanics, is another argument for the universe as a plenum. Unfortunately, Einstein cannot suggest the physical analogues to his calculus that could put his new theory to crucial test; but if the future runs true to form, such tests are likely to be devised or some new field theory will be propounded that will transcend quantum and relativity physics toward a view of the world as more potential and continuous than our present empiriological picture makes it to be.

No realistic philosophical physicist need fear the advance of empiriological physics. He should be the first to encourage it since new data mean new insights, more facts, and subtler analogies the better to depict and also to deepen those timeless truths which are the life of philosophy and without which even empiriological physics in practice would be nothing but its own funeral. In the ether-field, where energy is but a diluted form of matter and where it is allowable to call an interstice of matter a material thing, mobile like other bodies, the traditional notion of place as an immediate surface is reinforced. There is no reason to posit the classical ether, out of apparently *a priori* gratuity, as an immobile backdrop for position and motion. The volume between the heavenly bodies and the volume in a highly evacuated vessel are material.

Relativity physics, philosophically interpreted, is a hint that the universe is a plenum, and Aristotelian physics on this point, rejected in Galileo and Newton, is retrieved in Einstein. It is true that there is danger, a grave one indeed, incurred by such reasoning as this. An empiriological theory can never graduate into the status of a fact. But if relativity is ever abandoned,—and its life expectancy may not be very great—its successor must contain an analogue to its ether and to its equation of matter and energy; and where the new theory carves out its successes, philosophy will fall heir to better analogues to express itself and will gain a better inventory of its own timeless riches.

The universe, as a plenum, might at first sight seem to clamp an embargo on all local motion. This was the reasoning of the early Greek atomists which led them to fill nature with holes so that a body would have a place to move. It is the reasoning also in the hidden cloakrooms where the law of inertia was prepared for adoption by empiriological physics. As especially clear from Galilean-Newtonian physics, motion is slowed down and then stopped by the resistances that it meets, so that its cause is really the removal of restraint. Motion on this view becomes more and more perfect as its environment becomes more and more evacuated. The ideal motion would be born of a vacuum.

But with the meaning of nature ever paving his path, the realist can show how the universe is full and yet permits, even demands, that constant local motion of its members which experience reveals. Motion is not the product of a physical vacuum, spreading out ahead of the thing moved, nor is it the mechanical sum of the outside agents that we call efficient causes. The moving thing, a nature, contributes something of its own. It is an original, spontaneous thing, endowed with inner tension, and it is this spontaneity that upsets the balance which a plenum would apparently be and moves firmly and smoothly to its goals. A nature is beset with inner tendencies to move; hence its motions are natural, and not simply mechanical like stresses and strains. Far from abetting a nature's movement, a vacuum would block it. A nature tends to a connatural place. Far from being a barrier to local movement, a plenum is its requirement.

THE UNIVERSE AS A WHOLE IS OF FINITE EXTENT

Let the case rest here that the parts of the universe, natures individualized, are in place. But what about the universe as a whole? The earth is moving relative to the sun, and the sun is moving relative to the Milky Way. Astronomy gives evidence that the Galaxy in turn is also swinging about a distant center. Is it possible that the entire universe, of which our solar system is only a small cross section, may be flying through space with a speed uncalculated and a destiny unknown? Such a question pivots on the problem of whether the universe is infinite in extent. If there is any issue that threads through all of these chapters, it is that of infinity. Gazing out into the vast expanses that astronomy explores, the mind cannot help asking if it ever comes to an end.

Sir James Jeans had a simple answer to this question. The heavens are not a solid canopy of stars, and the blank spaces show that there is nothing beyond them to shine through. But looks, especially in the philosophy of nature, are not the final court of appeal. Even if they were it could be asked if there were stars beyond the blanks whose light has not yet arrived upon the earth. George Gamow, another astrophysicist, writes that "our space seems to be infinite and rapidly expanding into infinity." An infinite that is becoming more infinite! Such an analysis shows again the dark and confusing clouds that hang over the modern meaning of infinity.

By using a principle which acoustics calls the Doppler effect and which, alongside a railroad track, is observed as the drop in pitch of a train whistle as the engine speeds by, astronomy showed that the distant stars are apparently receding to an even greater distance from the earth. The "pitch" in their radiation was observed to be dropping, shifting from the short-wave or violet end of the visible spectrum toward the longer waves in the red. The apparent fact of an "expanding universe" has been further investigated by Edwin Hubble. Indeed, it has become customary in astronomy to speak no longer of a single universe but of "island universes," of which our galactic system, where census figures estimate there are 40 billion stars, is only a single example. The neighboring islands appear as spiral nebulae, as curling clouds of flaming gas. It turns out, however, that the apparent nebulae of stardust are really extragalactic systems of stars. Hubble's telescope, clocking their motion, makes it seem that the so-called nebulae which are farthest away from us are flying outward not only at a constant speed but ever faster and faster as they go. There are many problems raised by Hubble's theory, especially in connection with the theory of relativity, and astronomers are asking their new 200-inch telescope at Palomar, California, to search the skies for the answers.

That the extent of the universe is finite can be wrung from premises in the foregoing chapters, and its unity can be better argued on the platform of final causality. This question of extensive infinity must be solved by reference not directly to quantity but primarily to motion, to natures. If monism is routed by the reasoning in Chapter 6, then it is already established that the universe is not a single substance, and the problem tapers down to deciding whether there is an infinite multitude of distinct material substances, stretching one after the other without end.

It should also be affirmed that if one body in the universe is finite in extension, then every other body must be finite. For supposing that another body outside the finite reality were infinite, it would overlap the smaller body by its very infinity and hence the finite body could not exist. In general, if there are natures in the world, terminated by form and thus finited, the universe is not infinite in extension since it would thus become an infinite series, actually existing.

In a more particular way, if Chapter 4 has established that there is no infinity in the direction of the small, where it is a question of division, neither can there be an infinity in the direction of the large, where it is a matter of a sum. It is by dividing matter that units are won for the addition, and there is no infinite multitude of bodies stretching out into space if division can still free new unities to be added to the sum. Infinity is truly infinite, that to which nothing new can be added. A proton, emancipated from an atom, would have no place to move in an infinitely populated world and would thus be immobile. For all the seats in the theatre of the world would be already taken by the all-embracing block of the infinite. If there is an infinite multitude of bodies in the universe, making for its infinite expanse, then the bodies themselves must be infinitely divisible and even divided in order to account for the infinite series.

A universe of infinite extent would abolish the reality of distinct places, and the mobile beings of our experience would forever be at a standstill. Places would perish in the infinite extent because there would be no immediacy of surface; all would be mediate. And local movement without place is unthinkable. Indeed, a finite nature, attempting to move on the premises of empiriological physics would have to dislodge infinity in order to realize its tendencies or, to put it in another way, an infinity would resist its movement. To say it simply but profoundly in Aristotle's words, if a thing is in place, it is somewhere; and if it is somewhere, then the universe is not infinite in its astronomical tent.

There is another avenue for the philosophy of nature to approach this problem. There are opposite tendencies in the world, for example the upward tendency of smoke and the downward tendency of a leaf shaken loose from a tree. There is a constant tension upward, or the universe would be crushed; and a constant downward directivity in nature or the universe would explode. The same fact of opposite tendencies in the order of local movement turns up in the other two dimensions, let us say longitude and latitude, showing that the universe is not simply unilinear and univalent in its tendencies but diversified and multidirectional. Far from setting off a fuze of infinity that would burn onward and outward in a boundless reality, motion is like a comeback ball or an echo bouncing backward after striking a cliff. Motion achieves something definite; it is not absorbed into an infinite sponge. Resistance does not tell the whole story of motion, but it is certainly a big chapter in its biography. Indeed, empiriological physics ought to be the last to deny it.

Extensive infinity, on the other hand, would be unidirectional and indeterminate. It could not be divided locally into up and down or sidewise since it admits of no centers, no definitions, no determinations, no immediacies and immobilities that we call places. Place is a term in local movement, but infinity is precisely that which is not terminated and is properly called the indeterminate. To put this argument concretely, if this is an expanding universe, there must be forces canceling the expansion, or the whole of material reality would be scattered in a single instant. The equilibrium in the order of place is a proof that the universe is finite.

It is tempting here to go on and to reflect on the equilibrium, the immobilities, and the identities which obtain in motion in the light of Aristotle's analysis of celestial movements as circular in character and thus wearing an aspect of constancy and rest. There is something of the Aristotelian circles left in motion and perhaps in the universe, and what we now call expansion may be only one of its arcs. But the further probing of this point is out of place here.

THE UNIVERSE AS A WHOLE IS NOT IN PLACE

The bounded character of our universe is a clinching proof that it is not in place. Wherever it ends, billions upon billions of miles from the earth, there is nothing beyond it by way of a surrounding body. If there were, the body would be part of the universe and could not be said to surround it. Admittedly this is another of those difficult trails that the philosopher proper must take, surrendering his imagination and moving by intelligence alone. Man tends to sow images of a something beyond the universe. He tends, like the ancients mentioned by Aristotle, to imagine that there is a body limiting the universe and another thing limiting the first limiting circuit, and so *ad infinitum*. The imagination plays many tricks that make philosophy at times rather unphilosophical. It strives, for instance, to rationalize the irrationals so that it can picture them. Destined to work only in the world of motion, it seeks to reduce immobility to a liquid state and when it fails, it calls immobility an "unobservable." Images fuel the emotions, and that is why empiriological physics, with its pictures and its power, has gained such priority with sensate man.

But a limited universe, not suspended in a vacuum as Democritus believed or in the absolute space of the Newtonians, cannot be grasped by the imagination. It is hemmed in not by a vacuum nor by space but by its own nature. Form terminates the potentialities of matter. A nature is thus terminated not by an outside nature but in itself. If the parts of the universe are thus self-terminating and the universe is nothing but an aggregate, it is clear to intelligence, but opaque to the imagination, that the mobile realities on the outer rim of a finite cosmos do not require a fence to contain them. Like the rest of natures, they are self-contained and self-terminated.

This outer shell of the material world, whatever and wherever it may be, is accidentally in place by reason of its parts. But as a whole, and in the proper sense of the term, it is not adjacent to another body and hence is not in place. Yet if there is nothing material beyond the universe, why do not the station keepers at the last frontier of matter rush off into the void, like air pouring into a vacuum tube when the surface is cracked? This calamity does not visit the universe for the same reason that a moving body does not tend into a vacuum. Motion owes its reality not to the absence of restraint but to the presence of inner tendencies whose principle we call nature. And these tendencies are pointed not to a void but to a place.

Written between the lines of this analysis is the answer to the problem of whether the universe as a whole is moving with respect to a point outside of it, flying off into so-called space like a gigantic earth of its own. The universe cannot be moving into something outside of it since there is nothing "there." There is no place that would terminate the local movement and no medium that would do the moving. Local movement on such premises would become a contradiction.

Einstein's theory, by failing to refer to this immobility, only did what would be expected of empiriological physics. This physics proceeds by correlating events with what lies outside them, and there is nothing beyond the universe with which to measure either its motion or its immobility. This is one of those ultimate questions which only the philosophical science of nature can answer, and that answer spells out the ultimate character of our universe as both finite and fixed. The fortunate failure of Michelson and Morley in their experiment and Einstein in his theory to detect the immobile is but a proof of the finite character of the universe. If they had laid their finger on the immobility, they would be standing outside the universe in order to measure it. Its limits would thereby have been transcended and they would be in infinity. The fact that no stationary ether has been filmed by experimental techniques is a clue that the universe is ultimately finite and ultimately immobile.

No mention has been made in this discussion of the differences between circumscriptive and non-circumscriptive, definitive and non-definitive presence in place. Nor has the scholastic controversy been raised about the type of modification which place gives to a body that is in it. Such refinements have been omitted in order to cope more fully with modern issues that must be studied and settled before sitting back to see the finished copy of the Aristotelian-Thomistic cosmos. These finer questions are no longer asked by the modern world, and the first task of the realistic philosopher of nature is to prompt it to ask them by confronting its larger difficulties.

SPACE IS LARGELY A MATHEMATICAL ENTITY

The failure of the modern mind to account for local movement is greatly the issue of its Cartesian parentage in philosophy and its Cartesian heirloom of empiriological physics as an ultimate view of reality. Local movement has survived in a world where location is repudiated, and the Cartesian view of a nature as "an extended thing" has been invited to fill the vacancy. This it has done in terms of space.

But space is something considerably different from place. The space of a body is really another name for its extension, and the space of the whole universe is the sum total of such extensions.

A mind, thinking mechanistically like Democritus when he placed his universe in a void, conceives of a body as occupying space and envisions a mobile reality as moving through it. Interpreting this, realists have rightly pointed out that space is a being of the reason, grounded in the real (*ens rationis cum fundamento in re*). Space thus becomes extension conceived in a mental light, considered in fact as a receptacle for a body or as an interval between it and some neighbor in the universe.

Empiriological physics has trained us to say such things as "portions of space," "movement through space," "the filling of space," "a body falling in free space." It has raised such problems as the non-Euclidian space of general relativity, which is not a hollow form but the very substance of things. This physical and even dynamic view, inspiring Einstein in empiriological physics, receives philosophical expression in Samuel Alexander. Kant, on the other hand, denied the objectivity of space, ranking it as an *a priori* form fitted by the mind on the data of sense. This dogma is still sounding from such otherwise distant cousins as Russell, the logician, and Heidegger, the existentialist. From many angles then, it is important to determine what space is, what status it has on the scale of being, and if all the things which scientism says about it are wholly and objectively true.

In a positive sense, space is what becomes of place when theoretical mathematics goes into action. At least in classical geometry, it is a vast, immobile, homogeneous locus for points, lines, planes, and solids. Empiriological physics has tended to become an applied mathematics, and it is only natural that the qualities of space should be transferred from their theoretical birthplace to the area where they are put to work. In empiriological physics, mathematical as it is, space wears the character of an interval, either between the extremities of a given extension or between the extremities of different things, leading to a distinction between internal space and external space. Internal space is the extension of a single body, viewed as its receptacle or as an interval occupied. External space is the extension intervening between a thing and a distant neighbor. On a cosmic scale, it is the totality of extension in the universe, and when the universe ends, imaginary or possible space can be multiplied outward indefinitely.

Space is primarily a mathematical entity, and its treatment is the business not so much of philosophical physics as of geometry which is competent to discuss such things as distance and dimension. The mathematical space of Euclidian geometry can be said to be infinite in the same sense as number. It is the potentially infinite. What is actual about it is the rule for continuing the extension, a rule that gives the mind the impression of dominating the infinite expanse and thus determining it into something actual. The rule here is sometimes confused with reality, as often happens in the case of number, and then applied to the world of nature.

Space belongs to mathematics because it has to do with the measuring of quantity and extension. Place is defined only through the lens of philosophical physics because it is an affair of nature, of motion, of finality. It is only when the geometry is applied to motion, as it is in empiriological physics, that the philosopher and mathematician can stand on a common platform. Space, as explored by the geometrician who inhabits the world of quantified being and considers matter as without motion and as purely extended, would be expected to plummet downward to applied mathematics, whether that of common sense or of empiriological physics. In this area, space presents a problem for the philosophical physicist. It is truly of moment to counter that space is something primarily mathematical, whereas place is something in nature. It is likewise important to keep repeating that space is simply extension viewed in a mathematical light and given a new name. But since the concept of space is applied so persistently by common sense and so successfully by empiriological physics, the philosopher of nature can underwrite his realistic analysis if he can show why the idea of space, somewhat barren in his own field, has been so fruitful in empiriology.

Pure empiriological physics is primarily an art for measuring matter. As in any art, beings of the reason (*entia rationis*) set the pace for matter to follow. Art diverges from nature where its principle is not in the matter moved but outside of it, more precisely in the mind of the artist. In art as such, form is not educed from matter but imposed by man. Maritain has remarked how richly empiriological physics is strewn with *entia rationis,* and perhaps the reason is direction of empiriological knowledge not to speculation but to art. Kant's doctrine of the *a priori* grounds of empiriological physics, Vaihinger's philosophy of fictions, Poincaré's notion of physical law as a mere convention, Mach's reference to it as an economy of thought—all of these references to mind projecting itself on matter in modern physics tend to sweep empiriological physics to the realm of art and thus to assume their proper places within a realistic philosophy of the empiriological method. For the philosophical physicist, the motions and places of experience are in nature. With nature, as an intrinsic principle, the empiriological physicist can have no traffic. So he ignores it, sustaining its motions and its places by the crutch of logical beings (*entia rationis*).

KANT WAS RIGHT, IN EMPIRIOLOGICAL PHYSICS

Space is in this category of empirical tools, be it the space of common sense which measures in a gross sort of way or be it the space from the refinery of modern physics. It is extension, placed in a new context by the mind in order to mechanize matter and carry on its task of mensuration. In the natures of things, the only reality of space is their extension, turned into a receptacle or interval by a maneuver of mind and thus made something other than the bodies within it (the other-ness being logical and not real). As a receptacle and hence exterior to its contents, space is not physically exterior to them like a separate realm of being. It is not a body collocated with its occupants or a liquid where a body swims from one place to another. Its exteriority to content is of art; interiority is of nature. The exteriority comes from the mind of the artist, from the *ens rationis*. It is in the logical order, and modern realists have been correct in their analysis of space as a being of the mind with a foundation in reality. But the probing of space is not the province of philosophical physics. For the philosopher of nature, the sole reality of space is that of extension, and what is of interest to him is not space so much as place, the term of local motion. Space becomes a problem for the philosopher of nature when empiriological physics mistakes its logical exteriority to content for real and independent existence, like the space of the Newtonians. Space is often turned from a logical device for measurement into an objective reality of being.

To repudiate the Kantian philosophy of space is the work of the metaphysics of knowledge, and it would certainly be out of order to raise the critical question here. But the apparent facts which led Kant to his decisions on space can be hastily inspected to show how long he was on insights into empiriological physics and how short as a philosopher of nature. Again, the problem is not to reject but to interpret and limit. It is to search out the partial truth which every great historical system of philosophy has laid hold of.

Measurement, the burden of pure empiriological physics, requires three things: the choosing of a standard, the measuring of the standard in terms of itself by a mental relation or *ens rationis,* and finally the measurement of other things in terms of it. It is the second step that saves the first from being completely arbitrary, and it is the third step that weaves an organization into the metrical results. Empiriological physics, unable to grasp things in themselves and fated forever, as pure empiriology, to view them as sums of outside forces, could never get beyond the second stair if it chose to limp through the universe alone. It thus relates an extended thing not to itself but to something else, creating the air of continuing to treat matter transeuntly. The outside thing to which extension is related is called space. It turns out to be an *ens rationis,* after the philosophical science of nature has worked it over, ranked in the same line as the measurement of a thing in terms of itself. The empiriological physicist, however, posits it outside the thing measured, to preserve his discursive method and to enable him to gain a hold on his matter from the outside, controlling it.

Now Kant, struggling to moor Newtonian physics, argued that space had to be an *a priori* form, prior to experience because presupposed by all sense knowledge. The first object that greets our senses is recognized, he argued in effect, as being in space; indeed, without this spatial reference it simply would not be noted, he added. Being prior to all experience, this notion of space can pour only from the mind, almost in the manner of innate ideas in the psychology of Plato. After noting the unanimity among empiriological researchers and the dissension among philosophers, Kant dogmatized that Newtonian space was absolute. But this absolute, he held, was not drawn from experience by way of abstraction; rather, experience was drawn from it, by way of projection.

If Kant, the philosopher of space almost as much as Descartes was the philosopher of quantity, had not started out with a prejudice that empiriological physics was philosophy, the western mind might have been spared the terrible disaster of his *Critique of Pure Reason*. As it was, he turned the working principle of an art into the pivot of his philosophy. He was right when he held that space, which comes into play only when we measure things, owed its principle to the mind. Formally, it is an *ens rationis*, since the real order shows it only as extension. The empiriological physicist sets it outside extension in order to facilitate his measurement, but he fails to set it back again when he finishes. What Kant did was to confuse the working principle of an art to measure the static with the speculative principles of a science for knowing the mobile. For Kant, empiriological physics, indeed Newtonian physics, was philosophy.

The empiriological physicist never carries out in all of his youthful fervor the ambition to measure all things in terms of what lies beyond them. For instance, in detecting the laws of thermodynamics he must use instruments that come under the very laws. As another example, he measures temperature in terms of length, say by the height of a column of mercury in a calibrated tube, and yet he needs the concept of temperature in order to define his measuring rods which are longer when warm and shorter in the cold. He could never get started if he did not recognize things (despite his method) as related to themselves or, in more technical language, as intrinsically evident. Everything that exists is original, and if it is known at all, it must be somehow known in itself since there is no common denominator for factoring the unique into a universal.

A nature is recognized in philosophical physics on the strength of its own intrinsic evidence, and extension, when known by the measurements of mathematics, must first be measured with respect to itself. Space is thus a convenient name to give to extension in its relation to the measuring mind, or what amounts to the same thing, it is a being of the reason for relating extension to itself. On such logic, at least Aristotle and Aquinas regarded phenomena like distance, dimension, and perspective as belonging to extension and requested mathematics to study them. If Kant had this tradition in mind, he was boxing his shadow when he said that space was not objective. Who said it was, before modern philosophy pitched its camp on the terrain of empiriological physics?

But what is not objective need not be *a priori,* any more than the two laws of thermodynamics are simply figments of mental forms. What is already knowable in itself does not exact an *a priori* apparatus from the mind to make it knowable. Kant gave a new twist to matter-form dualism. Matter, his philosophy holds, comes from experience, while form comes from the mind. This is how precisely traditional philosophy would define art.

Place, not space, is the concern of the philosophical science of nature. Space is handled by mathematics and mathematical physics. It may well be infinite as extension is infinite—potentially and not actually so. For it is extension which the mind thinks in the image of its own metrical purposes. It might be the extension of a body or the extension between bodies. Where place is an affair of motion and is treated in the philosophical science of nature, space is a creature of quantity and is properly discussed only in the science of quantified being which is mathematics. When a body is falling through free space or moving in space or filling a space, it is obviously not performing on the stage of an *ens rationis*. The physical side of the picture is extension which is the only thing real about space, and the descriptions of the empiriological physicist are in line with the points of view which his art requires. If space were something real, like a doorknob or the atmosphere, the same case could be made out against it that, in both a philosophical and empiriological sense, is argued against the classical ether.

RELATIVITY PROPOSES A NON-EUCLIDIAN SPACE

The linking of the ether and space opens the passage to the general theory of relativity and its so-called non-Euclidian space. This is a considerable departure from the classical Newtonian view which Kant had in mind and which, a century ago, in the non-Aristotelian world, passed for eternal truth. Einstein's ideas can be simply set down without preface or proof and then evaluated not to prove them wrong but to prove them limited. After all, philosophical physics is not concerned to dispute with the empiriological physicist over his facts but only to fit them back again into the common experience from which he departed and which must cross-check his findings to see how well they interpret it.

The restricted theory of relativity disqualified the ether as "an unobservable." In the general theory, it comes back to life not as a fluid between things or as the medium in which they move but as an all-engulfing field of truly cosmic proportions, the only reality of the universe. What is commonly called a physical body, the general theory says, is nothing but an acute configuration in this all embracing ether, even as an ordinary field, like the gravitational force around the earth, is the same thing in milder form.

Another name for relativity's ether is space, though this must be somewhat qualified since time also shares in its reality, as the next chapter will show. The point for the present is the new reality accorded to space, which is not the empty expanse of Newton nor the *a priori* form of Kant but the very stuff and substance of the universe. This continuum of field is even more strongly argued in Einstein's generalized theory of gravitation (1949).

In the principles sketched so far by relativity's crayon, there is a healthy emphasis on the universe as a plenum and especially on the real identity of space with extension. But the description of this new space makes it an even more difficult problem for philosophy than Kant's notion which it explodes. It is said, for instance, that space is anisotropic, meaning that it is not homogeneous but different from point to point. There is, it is said, a curvature in space, as shown among other things by the bent path of a ray of light. If one could see far enough through this curving continuum, relativity assures him, the lines that his sight actually follows as he looks straight away would enable him eventually to see the back of his head. To put the problem in pointed form, the space acclaimed by relativity is said to be non-Euclidian because Euclid's never-meeting parallel lines do not appear.

Einstein stands in the tradition of non-Euclidian geometry which developed in the nineteenth century and reached the decision that consistent systems could be constructed in which the parallel postulate is disregarded. Gauss, Bolyai, and Lobachevsky were among the leaders of this revolt from Euclid, but the system which Einstein adopted to chart his way through the cosmos was the so-called elliptic geometry which Riemann developed from the ideas of Gauss. Here a straight line is not the shortest Euclidian distance between two points. It is an arc, bending like the path of a ship which sinks beneath the horizon. It is a line not on a plane surface but on, say, a spherical one. Through a given point, Euclid postulated, only one line can be drawn parallel to a given line. On a sphere, however, all circumferences intersect, and it is impossible to draw circumferences that are parallel; every great circle intersects every other. The shortest distance between two points on the circumference is the smallest arc uniting them, thus not a Euclidian straight line but a geodesic.

Einstein discovered the analogues to Riemannian lines in the actual physical world and proceeded to describe all matter by these non-Euclidian curves. A geodesic was found to be not only an arc on a Riemannian ellipse but a good description of the actual lines in their field of ether space, of their contours, distribution, and direction—lines which are followed by the motions of the world and enable empiriological physics to forecast their futures. Curving and changing at every point, space is called anisotropic. Through these adapted Riemannian principles, Einstein was able to predict the bending of the light rays observed in the now famous solar eclipse of May 29, 1919. He was able to explain certain deviations in the trajectory of the planet Mercury which Newtonian principles could not handle. Such results are potent assets to the Einstein theory, though in its new and generalized form it may have to select a different non-Euclidian geometry to provide tests for itself, and Riemannian geometry like present relativity theory may revert to the status of a special case, true under certain conditions.

The issue here is not, however, about the merits of Einstein as against Newton nor even about the dynamic view of things which the general relativity takes. It is of immediate importance to pursue the statement that space is not Euclidian and, as Plato says, to follow reason wherever it may lead us. Poincaré also raises the problem as to whether Euclid is a good guide through the cosmos. Imagine, to paraphrase his example, that one walked from the ordinary earth where Euclidian geometry seems to hold and moved outward toward the farthest stars. Space could change its Euclidian clothes; time could run faster or slower. But with our bodies also subject to such changes, we would not notice that they occurred. Can we produce a passport to show that we are citizens of a Euclidian world?

THE EXTENSION OF THE WORLD IS EUCLIDIAN

Francis Bacon said that a problem well posed is half answered, and it is of capital moment to determine the precise sense of our question and what part, if any of it at all, is in the competence of the philosophical science of nature. Euclidian space belongs to mathematics, the science for measuring quantity. It is properly at home only in the world of pure extended being which is homogeneous and hence isotropic by the very purity of its estate. When Euclid is forced to trace out the arteries of cosmic motion, he is bound to fail since the problems of motion lie off his beaten highway. The question which relativity poses is not so much whether space is Euclidian or not, but whether extension is Euclidian. And that is not all. For relativity does not consider purely extended being but interjects the motion of light rays and planets, of matter and energy, of what it calls space and what it calls time. Einstein says in so many words that he takes geometry to be a physical science and rejects Euclid because his system is not physically observable.

Now it is a quite different thing to ask about the path of a moving thing, where the motion is plotted on a local frame of reference, and to ask about extension without reference to motion. A projectile shot from a battleship takes a parabolic path toward the earth when seen by an observer in a plane parallel to the trajectory. But this does not mean that extension, taken by itself, must necessarily be parabolic. The projectile passes through much more than pure extension, so to speak, and so does the light ray, or Mercury whirling about the sun. They are all matters of motion and are out of place in mathematics, the science of motionless, quantified being where alone the Euclidian or non-Euclidian character of space and extension has any sense. *Two* does not refer to motions of human feet but to their quantity.

Abstracting from motion, space retains its Euclidian character. It is only the extension of things, not their motion, that was ever deemed Euclidian. Euclidian geometry does not mean that mobile reality must always be a parallelepiped, and the ancient and medieval astronomers accepted it without scruple, even when they felt that the fundamental motion in the world was not rectilinear but circular. It is only with Descartes, who viewed matter as a system of Euclidian geometry and nothing else, and with Newton who made so much of motion in a straight line, that Euclid abdicated his traditional degree of abstraction and came down into the world of motion. It is more Descartes and Newton rather than Aristotle and Euclid that Einstein is against. It is only in matters of extension considered apart from motion that Euclid has any meaning. No genuine philosopher ever attempted to find the perfection of Euclidian circles, lines, angles, and points in the world of motion, and a physical test of the parallel postulate would involve the impossible task of carrying lines out to physical infinity. What relativity really shows is not the non-Euclidian character of extension, but that extension alone, pure and homogeneous, is not enough as an explanation of mobile reality.

The Euclidian character of extended being, as such, is independent of the path of physical motion and does not refer to it. Euclidian geometry is a general one, more general indeed than the philosophy of nature because it is at a higher level of abstraction. It shares the dignity of metaphysics as a science not of fact but of cause (*scientia propter quid*). Mathematical truths enjoy an absolute certitude, a degree removed from the motions that give a contingent tone to empiriological physics.

Now it is true that geometry cannot provide a direct proof of the parallel postulate, deducing it from the other axioms; all of these others are concerned about finite reality whereas the parallel postulate stands unique as a pronouncement about the infinite. But by using a proof which is called the *reductio ad absurdum,* and which consists in showing that the angles formed by a third line, that cuts across the parallels, forbid their actual meeting, the geometer discerns a rule, or forms what Kant called a regulative idea, about the Euclidian lines seen in their very nature.

Let us agree that the lines do not actually meet over a given finite extent. But do they meet at infinity? No, for the infinity of mathematics is only a potential one, and however far the lines are extended, the rule applies. If it did not, the lines would not have been parallel in the first place, and this is contrary to the definition, to the rule. It is the rule, not the infinite, which is actual; and since extension, pure and without motion, is homogeneous extension, the rule would apply no matter how far we travel out into space with Poincaré and Einstein. These empiriological physicists would be right if mathematics were a department of physics, and the example chosen by Poincaré to portray his principle shows that he rates mathematics as the science of sensible rather than intelligible matter, verified by the body of the observer rather than elaborated by his abstracting mind. Pure extension can be abstracted from a whirlpool as well as from a plain table top. Mathematics prescinds from what is of greatest interest in the physical order—hierarchical differences, cosmic motions, matter the root of contingency, and reference to time. Intelligible matter is pure form, and since form itself is invariant, it would betray itself if it were different from one stretch of extension to the next. If this form of extension were pure, there would be nothing to make it different from point to point except itself; as an invariant, it would also be variant.

The postulate of parallel lines corresponds to a rule for extending them, and if this rule did not force the parallelism no matter how far the lines are elongated, the rule would rebel against its own self and become a contradiction. It would be a rule for parallelism and not a rule simultaneously. In short, that parallels never meet is twined into the very definition of parallelism, considering not the motions of the world but its pure extension only, and if this Euclidian separation were not infinitely the case, the lines would be parallel and not parallel at the same time. No greater blow can be administered to a principle than to show it as violating the principle of contradiction. Thus, wherever pure extension may be, and it is found wherever there is matter, hence as coterminous with the universe, it will carry its Euclidian credentials which are nothing but a geometrical version of the principle of non-contradiction. Extensively then this is a Euclidian universe. Its fundamental motions may not be rectilinear, but this should not be surprising since curvilinear motion was even held by Aristotle as the highest of cosmic movements. The geometry of extension does not care whether rectilinear or curvilinear motion dominates our cosmos. It prescinds from motion.

A stretch of extension, measured in the Milky Way, provided pure extension without motion is considered, would fall under the rule just as man, taken anywhere in the world, is always a rational animal. Mathematics, it was said, is a science in which effects are deduced from their causes and vice versa. The rule here represents the formal cause. It is abstracted like a circle in mathematics, or a nature in philosophical physics. It is universal because pure extension prescinds from individual differences among the mobile objects; the rule is immutable because pure extension prescinds from motion (mutation); it is necessary because the matter to which it applies, being pure and undifferentiated, cannot impede it and thus produce exceptions to the rule; the rule is negatively eternal because pure extension makes no reference to time. (Einstein gives his curvatures a time character.) Thus the scientific character of Euclid and the certitude of his geometry are fully vindicated. Nothing more could be asked of a science than that its truths be universal, immutable, necessary, and negatively eternal.

Projective geometry has provided schemes for transforming the non-Euclidian systems into Euclidian ones, and in addition, it is a psychological fact that the Euclidian picture throws, if not its light, at least its shadows upon the non-Euclidian achievements. There is, at least in the wings of the non-Euclidian stages, the view of extension as general and as homogeneous; for only thus can continuity be achieved. Anisotropic space implies differences, hence breaks in the fabric, and it is only by reference to a deeper homogeneity of extension which is Euclidian and realistic that the geometer is able to achieve continuity in his figures and organization in his system, and that the applied mathematician is able to speak of a continuum and to construct a mechanics.

Mathematics is not simply a science of relations like logic. It has quantity for its object, and a critique of mathematics would be able to show that the non-Euclidian systems do not consider pure and general extension but qualify it.

This does not mean that relativity is to be rejected. It only means that it must keep its property in its own yard rather than throw it across the fences into philosophy of nature and the philosophy of mathematics. Its empiriological success is owed to the very factors which limit it as a philosophy. It has often been said in these pages that empiriological physics is primarily an art for dominating matter and that to move along toward this end, it must act as though matter were nothing but the potential and the controllable. In this light, it was the genius of Einstein to exploit the idea of a continuum where space, extension, motion, time, and even the differences between things and the relations between events and their observers are all lumped into a cosmic Heraclitean continuum which matter becomes when only its potencies or indeterminacies are attended. That is why Einstein has developed a purer empiriological physics than Newton, but that is also why he secedes from territory of philosophy. His latest theory attempts to include even electromagnetism in the continuous whole. Dewey and Alexander likewise have been logical in pushing empiriological method until the world becomes a continuum.

In the monism of method which relativity proposes, motion and extension, empiriological physics and mathematics, cannot be put asunder. The reason for Einstein's rejection of Euclid is that his parallel lines are not physically observable. Empiriological physics prefers the continuum or the potential. To pass from motion to extension, from empiriological physics to mathematics, involves a leap which only abstraction can bridge; and there is no continuity between the terms for empiriological physics to measure and maneuver. It is an abrupt break, corresponding to the difference between motion and non-motion, physics and non-physics, being and non-being. This gap is not controllable, capable of more or less, any more than non-being shades into being as Hegel imagined. In pure empiriological method, the hierarchy between motion and extension, experimental physics and mathematics, cannot be taken into account, and it is to the advantage of empiriological physics to try to get around it.

Now in the field of empiriological physics, as such, there can be no quarrel with Einstein. To a realist, his system, struggling forward to a purer empiriological form, has tremendously more to commend it than the Newtonian view. The difficulty is not with Einsteinian physics but with the tendency to transplant the working principles of an art into the certitudes of philosophy, thus equating our domination of matter to our knowledge of it, as pragmatism implies. It is good empiriological method to focus on the potential and to churn reality into a continuum where motion and extension are mixed into a community called the ether.

But good empiriological physics is not a science of nature any more than Raphael's art makes him a speculative genius or any more than Roman engineering can be equated to Greek philosophy. Einstein might predict and control better by his world picture of the ether, but in proportion as we control we move downward through the cellars of reality rather than skyward to its peaks. Empiriological physics succeeds so well because it is so shallow, like a man who might wade a brook but would drown if he tried to walk the floor of an ocean. It is only the potencies of things that empiriological physics considers, and by emphasizing the space-time continuum, greater attention is paid to what is potential and controllable.

Far less serious as a philosophical problem but still deserving of passing mention is the n-dimensional space of quantum mechanics (especially when the quantum system is treated by what is called matrix algebra). This is not really space, but a way of referring to number by analogy with the familiar relation between numbers and an ordinary graph, enabling high school students to plot the curve $x = y$. For instance, $x + y + z$ is a general equation for a straight line in three-dimensional space. When four or more factors enter into an equation, each (variable) term can be called a dimension, though no geometrical pictures of the "line" can be given. In this language, there are as many dimensions as there are (variable) terms. They might thus be called algebraic dimensions. They are not, at any rate, phenomena of extension, any more than arithmetic is geometry or number is a line. Discrete quantity and extension are different, but the story of their relation belongs to Chapter 12.

The present chapter has shown the reality and relations of place which is something natural in the real world and is necessary to explain motion. Place is the term of local motion. It was also seen that space is a being of the reason and that its only reality in the makeup of the universe is extension. Various views of space, inspired by modern philosophy and by modern empiriological physics, were weighed, to show not that they are wrong but that they are simply restricted. Place, as the term of local motion, was called a measure by Aristotle who used the word in the sense of specifying motion rather than quantifying it. In a sense, place is a measure of motion and space of extension.

The distinction between place and space, motion and extension, is a crucial one, especially today. The divergent approaches which are made to them by contemporary and by traditional thought require a constant reference to the distinction between art and nature. More and more in the relations between empiriological and philosophical physics that distinction looms up as the great divide.

Suggested Readings

Aristotle, *Physics*, Bk. 4, chs. 1–9.

Einstein, A., *Relativity* (New York, 1931).

Einstein, A., and Infeld, L., *The Evolution of Physics* (New York, 1938).

11

Time: The Measure of Motion

TIME MEASURES THE ORDER OF MOTION

In the Smithsonian Institution in Washington, D. C., there is a display of the various ways in which men have told time throughout the ages. The hourglass is of course a homely example; a modern version of it, sized to empty its upper chamber in three minutes, is still sold for cooks in boiling three-minute eggs. Other devices have included candles burning in a unit of time down through a unit of length calibrated on their sides. A rather unusual system which one locality employed was a pan punctured in the center and floating on water; when the pan filled and sank, a "clock-watcher" beat upon a huge drum to notify his community that a unit of time had elapsed. A sundial, recording time by the shadows of the sun, is preserved on the ruins of the famous monastery at Cluny, France.

Today, precision springs in watches and the crystal-controlled oscillations in the latest chronometers have replaced the shadows of the sun and the sand of the hourglass as our timekeepers. During the last war airplanes were shot down by timing mechanisms called radar which clock electromagnetic energy traveling to a target (and echoing back) with the speed of light.

But it is one thing to measure time and another to ask what time is. Minds have always been magnetized by the problem of time, but the magnetic field of force has rarely been directed into a clear and satisfying definition. Time has been a theme in ancient, medieval, and modern thought, and the concern of contemporary man with the sheerly material world makes the issue of time especially lively now. Kant drained time into a vacant mental form. Einstein, adopting the space-time continuum of Minkowski, depicts time as a dimension. Entropy, the law that the universe is running down, is a pronouncement about time, so much so that Eddington called it "time's arrow." A glance at the titles in the present-day literature of philosophy reflects a peculiar commerce with the problem of time. There is Alexander's *Space, Time, and Deity;* Bergson's *Time and Free Will;* Heidegger's *On Being and Time;* Bachelard's *The Dialectic of Duration;* Lavelle's *Of Time and Eternity;* Eddington's *Space, Time, and Gravitation.* Historical disciplines like geology, ethnology, and paleontology often favor the opinion that time is fertile and that a mere searching of the past yields a genuine science of origins and principles. Evolutionism, of course, inspires such a view. Confronted with the fact that no serious biological transformations have occurred within the memory of written history, evolutionists often answer that the theories need time and that by allowing the world more and more age there is more and more reason for its evolution. It is as though time were even a cause. A great many problems would automatically solve themselves with the proper definition of time.

The present chapter will begin naturally with a definition of time and then with a definition of the *now.* The terms implied by time will be probed, and the flow of time examined to see whether it is composed of indivisible *nows.* Time will be found to be neither a substance nor a cause but an "accident" of motion, which like motion itself is untractable to experimental techniques. The standard of time will open a discussion of the cyclical character of time.

The remainder of the chapter will discuss prominent contemporary views of time as found in Einstein's denial of the unity and irreversibility of time, Nietzsche's doctrine of the eternal return, the four-dimensional relativity continuum, the idealism of Kant and Leibniz, the crisis between relativity and quantum mechanics, and existentialism.

Time is not motion, and yet it is something so akin to motion that philosophers from Plato to Bergson have identified the two. Nor is time mere quantity like the shadow on a sundial, a line on a Cartesian graph, or the wave length in a ray of light. Yet there is so close a relation between time and quantity or number, that empiriological physics, as Bergson showed, tends to identify time with a line in space, and clocks tell time in numbers.

The sequence in motion is the factor that informs the mind of the passage of time. When a body moves, it is observed to be now in this place and now in that, since there is a certain order or sequence in which a moving body passes through various places. One place is in front of or behind another in the passage, and the mind is aware that time has elapsed. One place is before or after another, and the motion is numbered as now here and now there. Time is the number of motion according to a *before* and *after*.

As number time is a measure, and as a measure it has certain analogies with place. But the analogy does not go as far as analogies are sometimes pressed. Place is something permanent and fixed, as the last chapter argued; it is immediate and immobile. Time refers to a succession of *before* and *after*. It measures a thing with respect to antecedents and consequents. It does not compare motion with the immobile but motion with motion. And where things come to rest in place, they never do so in time. Time and tide wait for no one.

Time is a number or measure. Thus it provides a standard for organizing things into a system, as a mile is a scale for computing distance and a pound is a unit for reckoning weight. The *now* is a norm for organizing motions, for time is the measure of motion, numbering it according to its priority or posteriority with respect to a *now*.

Before and *after,* it should be emphasized, are primarily in the order of location, and in the last analysis, location involves place more than space. A moving body crosses a certain magnitude. It is first in one place and secondly in another. The priority and posteriority in motion refer to the successive places that a body traverses, and it is from this trajectory that the notions of *before* and *after* are born. With respect to a kind of reference point, called the *now*, a certain part of the trajectory and of the motion is prior and another part is posterior.

THE *Now* IS UNITIVE AND DIVISIVE

In grasping the character of time, the *now* forms a problem within a problem—the *now* that is always passing and yet is present, the *now* that flows and yet divides the past and the future, the *now* that seems ever the same and ever different? Where is it, what is it, and how does it exist? Time is a flow of *nows*. It is recognized because there is first one *now* and then another one. Is there a third *now* which divides them, and so on and on until an infinity of *nows* must be unreeled to relate the past and the future? If there were only one *now*, there could be no time; if there were only a passing, there would be no *now*. The *now* that is so forcefully evident to the mind is yet so elusive when the net is spread for its definition.

The *now* may be likened to the subject of motion, going from this place to that, and in one sense, a thing owns the same *now* as long as it exists. The ivy climbing the wall is the same plant today that it was yesterday, and the gold of a ring is likewise the same gold. Things that move in time bear a certain fixity with them across the temporal passage. The flow is never a pure flow. If it were, it would be indifferent in the order outside the mind, and the mind of course could never grasp it.

But though the permanence must be mentioned, the flow must never be forgotten. The *now* of today, though not completely partitioned from the *now* of yesterday, is somehow different from it, just as a moving thing has a permanent and a novel character as it goes its way. Aristotle likened this relation of sameness and difference to that of a point moving to generate a line. It is the same point that moves, and it moves through different positions, and it is by different positions that motion is measured. The line corresponds to time and the point to the indivisible and moving *now*.

The analogy to a line has more to offer, before it weakens to remind us that it is, after all, an analogy. The moving point is always the term of segment behind it and the principle of the segment just beginning. In the chain of time, the *now* is a similar link. But a point really terminates a line, and a *now* never simply terminates anything in the actual order since it is always a-flow. Here the point and the *now* part company, though inside a line, not at the ends of it, the *now* is truly like a mobile point, with segments *before* and *after* it that are not actually cut off into separate lines but, on the contrary, ever change character with their common mobile term. The *now*, like a mobile point, is unitive and divisive, a principle and a term, and this dualistic character of the *now* which accounts for its fluency explains also how time, under different aspects, can be continuous and discrete.

In the foregoing analogy, where the *now* was envisioned in the role of a moving point, with a portion of the line behind it (the past) and a portion ahead (the future), the two segments have a common term since they are not actually separated into two lines. Outside the mind, this pointlike *now*, dividing the past and the future, is one. However, the mind can consider it under a twofold aspect, as the end of the past and the beginning of the future, where there are two *nows* of reason corresponding to the one real *now* outside of reason.

In this strict sense of the word, the *now* is not a synonym for the present. The present is a very much wider term, including something of the past and of the future. In 1950, one may speak of the present century, which includes the time from 1901 through 1999. There is a present day, a present hour, a present second. There is, of course, only one real *now*, but there can be many *nows* of reason, yielding many meanings to the expression "present time." As a line is bounded by points, so a stretch of time like a second or a century is bounded by two *nows* which the mind sets up in order to slice out the portion of the temporal flow which it wishes to consider. The terminal *nows* of reason, which bound the flowing *now* of reality in, for example, a minute, are not parts of the time they mark off, and when the flowing real *now* is stopped again by reason as a new terminal to section off a subdivision of the larger time interval, like a second within a minute, the new *now* is again not part of the subsection. The *now*, again like a point, is not a part of the linelike flow of time. The *nows* of reason are also limits or terms, principles or beginnings, hewing out the portion of time that the mind chooses to consider.

But the real *now* as opposed to the *nows* of reason is the factor in the philosophical physics of time that must receive the heaviest accent. In this real and precise sense, the *now* is a moving boundary, like a point originating or terminating a portion of a line, and when taken in this terminal sense as a limit, the *now* is not a part of time because it is indivisible.

Time does not stop for man to measure it. It is a flowing continuum. A moving thing is now here and now there. One *now* comes after another, permitting the number which is called time. But the succeeding *nows* do not come like raindrops tumbling down at intervals; they are like points on the edge of a continuous ruler, indivisible because they are points but abstracted out of the temporal flow which is not a string of points but a continuum of motion.

Implying a changeless element just as motion does and isolated only when man stops the clock in order to consider it, the *now* flows continuously. Time is no more a string of *nows* than a line is a series of points. Two *nows* of reason bound a motion as two points limit a line. Between them is the flow that is time and that is, in turn, generated by the flowing *now*.

The view of the real *now* as a boundary between the past and future, where reason forms two *nows* from the single *now* that is real, does not of course breach the continuity of time. The real *now* can unite the past and the future and still divide them, just as a point may join one portion of a line to another and yet differentiate the two. Reason, considering the flow of time, can inject its own *nows* to divide the continuum, just as the spatial continuum, say a line, is potentially divided by points. In reverse fashion, when time is actually divided by reason which forms two *nows* where there is only one in reality, the portion of time considered by *reason* apart from the whole and called a second, a day, a year, a century, is *really* united with the prior and posterior time, thus continuing any unit period of time with the whole of it. For time is not a series of segments merely juxtaposed outside the mind. Such fragmentation of time is the work of the considering intellect. Outside the mind, there is a continuous flow. Reason cuts into it by considering the one real *now* as two and thus making a mental segmentation of what is actually continuous. For a point, unlike the real *now,* can be the beginning of a line without being the end of another, and vice versa. But the *now* is always both a beginning and an end in the real world, and where the beginning of the future is actually marked off from the end of the past, this is the work of the mind which actually segments for its consideration what is really and physically unsegmented and continuous.

TIME IS NOT MATHEMATICALLY DEFINED

When Aristotle defines time as the number of motion according to a *before* and *after,* he merely points out that the mind measures motion by the portion of its trajectory which is prior to the *now* and the portion which is posterior. But number is something mathematical, and Aristotle must be defended from the appearance of allowing mathematics to dictate to his philosophical physics.

Actually, there are two ways in which number can be taken. One is number applied to things (*numerus numeratus*), like ten men or two electrons or a dozen eggs. The other is number taken absolutely (*numerus numerans*), like ten or two or twelve. It is in the former sense that number is applied to time, the measure of motion, whereas in pure mathematics there can be no reference to time because there is no attention to movement.

Number in the definition of time is applied in the world of nature and hence invites the philosophical science of nature to consider it. If a shopper is buying two pounds of apples, he does not ask a mathematician to do a purely paper computation of the weight. He puts the quantity on a physical scale and relies on the motion of physical springs. In a similar way, number is applied to time.

But there is an even greater difficulty than this. Time involves a continuous flow, as the facts of nature indicate and as the continuity of the motion to be measured even demands. Since number is an affair of discrete quantity and is wrongly applied to a continuum, how can the stream of time be reckoned by number?

The closing thought in Aristotle's definition suggests the solution. The *now* divides time into the past and the future, and motion is measured according to this *before* and *after*. The so-called successive continuum which time involves is hence not an unqualified continuum, pure and homogeneous and undifferentiated in its contents. It is precisely a successive continuum. It is heterogeneous. It has the aspect of discreteness since there is a past and a future. This discrete character of time makes it a field for number.

But it might still seem that a numbered continuum is just as grave a problem as a discrete one, and if time is considered alone, this is true. It looks as though the philosophical physicist would have to choose between the discrete and the continuous and that he cannot have both in the same reality. Here matter-form dualism again comes to the rescue. Explaining motion, it also directs its light upon the measure of motion as would be expected. Matter is that out of which something is moved or made, and form is the term of the movement or the making. Matter corresponds to the unity underlying change and form to the element of diversity or discreteness which motion manifests and time measures by numbering. Time measures the order or succession of movement with respect to a *now*. It refers to the *before* and *after* in motion, with a heed for the unity of motion by reducing the *before* and *after* to an order.

Aristotle's definition must thus be taken not part by part but globally. Time is not number, for number is of mathematics and is reversible, at least in the sense that what is added to number can always be subtracted again to restore the original number; time is not motion, for if it were baldly motion and the measure of motion it would involve a vicious circle; time is not simply priority and posteriority, for such concepts are distinct in themselves and do not involve a flow. Because of the *before* and *after,* number in the definition of time is not reversible; because of motion, time is physical; because of number, it is the measure of motion rather than motion itself; because it is according to *before* and *after,* time has the aspect of discreteness; because of motion, it is continuous; because of number, it unites prior and posterior, as 8 and 10 are related in the same number system.

TIME IS NOT FORMED FROM INDIVISIBLES

The moving *now* is always one in its real status and is turned into two *nows* of reason to end the past and open the future which the mind wishes to consider. Thus, for instance, today, January 1 is compartmented off by the mind from yesterday, December 31, and if a year is to be considered as the present time, the mind operates similarly to terminate next December 31, dividing the real *now* into two *nows* of reason, one to close the present twelve-month period and another to open the next one. Between the *now* of the mind that marks off the beginning of January 1 and the *now* projected by the mind to terminate next December 31 is a time that could be called the present year. It includes some of the past and some of the future. Apart from man's mind, the only actually existing thing about time is the indivisible *now*. And this real now, as a boundary, is not a part of time any more than a point is the part of a line. The past and the future, the *before* and *after* with respect to this indivisible *now,* are envisioned by the mind and numbered.

From the foregoing discussion of the *now* there arises naturally the question of how far time can be divided by indivisible *nows* and where, if at all, a dividing line can be drawn between the past and the future. No special reference is planned here to so-called psychological time, like that treated by Plotinus and by Augustine, both of whom refer more or less to so-called lived time (*le temps veçu*). When Aristotle called time a measure, he left copious room for this psychological approach. Really it does not differ from the more general view of time in philosophical physics, except that the measure and the measured are united with the peculiar intensity made possible by the spirituality in man and the higher identity and self-possession and synthetic power which his soul bestows on him. Philosophers, as varied in views as Bergson and Heidegger and Alexander, are in accord that the human mind has a remarkable synthetic power, capable of unifying the past with the future, clasping them into what is commonly called the "specious present." In this discussion, of course, psychology and the nature of knowledge are not at issue, but if psychology goes its way realistically, it ought to rejoin the main thoroughfare of philosophical physics which these pages are attempting to map.

Motion and magnitude and time are all allied concepts. Local motion goes through a magnitude and is continuous because the magnitude is continuous, and time, if it be truly a measure of motion, must be continuous also. In dividing the trajectory of a moving thing, it is no more possible to come upon an indivisible element of motion than an indivisible quantity can be attained by dividing continuous magnitude. Always and always the division can go on and on, because the continuum is indefinitely divisible and hence potentially infinite. When physical division must halt, mental division can begin. Time, the measure of motion, follows the footsteps of motion, and motion is continuous because of magnitude.

The continuum of magnitude through which a body travels does not allow of an indivisible element in motion, and the continuum of motion requires the continuum of time. No matter how small a time may be, it is always further divisible into smaller times. The microsecond (10^{-6} sec) is a common word in the empiriological vocabulary, but there is no reason why it should not be split into millionths and billionths of itself and still be susceptible of indefinite further division. There is no smallest unit of time, just as there is no smallest unit of matter.

It is true that the *now*, by its analogy to a point, is indivisible. But the *now*, taken in its strict sense as a boundary, is not a part of time, as a point is no part of a line. Just as a line can be shortened by setting its terminal point nearer the origin, so a time like a day or a microsecond can be made smaller and smaller by dwarfing the interval between the *nows* which limit it. But the two points forming a line can never be superimposed or tangent, and neither can the *nows* which are their analogues in time. There is no minimum magnitude. There is no minimum motion. There is no minimum time.

Time can boast the nature of a true continuum. But the mind can cut into the continuum, chopping it into segments by indivisible pointlike *nows*, where the one *now* of reality is converted into two *nows* of reason and today is sharply divided from yesterday and from tomorrow. It is the lines, not the points, which resemble time, just as in Chapter 9 points were not said to resemble number, but the lines which the points terminated were said to do so. These analogies between time and a line and between a line and number reinforce the definition of time as a number of motion.

Time is broken down into the past and the future, which might be represented as two parts of a line. If the "specious present" is included, there is a triad like this morning (past), this afternoon (present), and this evening (future). But at what precise moment does the past give way to the present and the present to the future? Or, in stricter terms, when exactly does the future cease to be future and become the past? In a sense, the present owns the strongest claim to existence, since the past has already been and the future is not yet. This is where the analogy with a spatial line fails again since the temporal continuum, unlike a line, does not exist all at once. That is why it is called the successive continuum. The only really existing thing about it is the point-like *now* which is not a part of time but an ever-moving boundary between the future and the past.

As a continuum, the past and the future flow into one another, and they do so in the indivisible *now* which is always an end and a beginning. They are never actually divided because the *now* is never a beginning without being an end, and vice versa. In continuous motion, the limits of one part join those of the succeeding part so that there is no break between the elements of the trajectory. Two parts of a continuum have a common boundary. Thus likewise with time, the measure of motion. In its ceaseless flow, there are no minimum units. It is impossible to put the finger on a stretch of time and say, for instance, this is the past, completely isolated from the future. In fingering an oak leaf on a tree, an area of it might be more or less localized, but it is impossible to state that this or that area is precisely where one part begins and another ends, no matter how fine the eyepiece may be. In reflecting on an electron, with its radius of the order of 10^{-13} centimeter, it can certainly be said that the portion near the periphery is different from that nearer the center. But it would not be possible to draw a physical line through the precise point of separation. The parts of a quantitative continuum soften and shade into one another when we attempt to line them off precisely. So it is with the continuum of time. The past which has already been and the future which has not yet been are certainly different like the sections of a leaf. But their frontiers cannot be lined off, dividing time into two islands, inhabited respectively by the past and the future.

Two *nows* limit a stretch of time, but the interval so enclosed can ever be shortened, and in the smaller subinterval, say the microsecond, it is still possible to fractionate the past and the future into smaller units. One cannot say exactly where the past ends and the future begins. There is continuity and flow. Mathematics cannot cope adequately with the situation. There is something dynamic because it is motion that is being measured and something continuous because it is magnitude that is being traversed. Time changes when motion changes, begins where motion begins, and ends when motion itself comes to a standstill. There is no smallest part of it because there is no smallest part of motion, and there is no minimum in motion because there is no minimum in the magnitude through which the motion occurs. The continuum is always divisible into further divisibles. This is one of the definitions of it which Aristotle gave.

TIME IS NOT A SUBSTANCE OR A CAUSE

Before diving deeper into the problems which the foregoing analysis will help to solve, it would be well to pause anew upon the question: what is time? Objections and errors, doubts and difficulties, always open a truth to the answering mind, and in a subtle question like that of time the mind is especially in need of assistance. Some writers look upon time in their philosophical physics as "successive duration"; Bergson and Alexander give time an ultrareal existence and tend, like Plato of old, to confound it with motion itself; the theory of relativity weaves time into the so-called fourth dimension; Kant makes it an *a priori* form; existentialists, especially Heidegger and Sartre, are dutiful to Kant by degrading time into a projection of man; Kierkegaard calls the instant "an atom of eternity," and this sentiment is echoed in Lavelle. If Aristotle's definition is realistic, it ought to be able to absorb the truth in any or all of these doctrines and trim off their fallacies.

At present, the concern is with the first pair of opinions which, when discussed, can whet Aristotle's definition and the realistic appreciation of what time is. To call time "successive duration" is a begging of the question since duration itself ought to be defined in philosophical physics rather than presumed. It does not clarify time to call it duration.

Duration, in the authors who use it to define time, is called "continuous existence" or "persistence." But time is primarily concerned with motion rather than existence which is properly examined in the third order of abstraction. Besides, "persistence" is hardly more clarifying than duration. Time is the measure of motion, and this fact must be kept constantly in mind, especially in the light of empiriological developments to be outlined below.

The whole problem of the reality to be assigned to time can be better pointed by reference to the Platonic opinions of Bergson and Alexander, that time is motion or at any rate a kind of absolute existing outside the mind, invested apparently with the power of causation. Whatever time may be, it is not mere change or motion. It is the number or measure of motion. To identify motion and time is to go against experience and to engage in circular reasoning.

It is common experience that men grow old in time, and their growth and decline is an index of their age. But physiological and anatomical changes are not caused by time except in a metaphorical sense. They are produced by external causes such as illness or hard work or by interior causes which are but the natural movements of the human body (interiority is a synonym for nature). Time simply measures such changes; it does not produce them. The consciousness of the changes involves time. But the changes are factors which time simply measures without changing and discerns without altering. Time wears the nature of a cause in Bergson and Alexander. For Bergson, it is a vital elan coursing through the world; for Alexander, "Time is the mind of Space." For Aristotle, time is neither motion nor the cause of motion; it is motion's measure.

Duration, the metaphysician explains, is the being of the thing enduring. Thus, in God Who is eternal, eternity is the very Being itself; and in angels, who change accidentally but not substantially and are called aeviternal, duration is their imperishable substance. But time is primarily a measure of motion, rather than of being. The being of mobile things is measured only with respect to motion. Rest is timed because motion is timed. The *now,* as a boundary, is likewise not the primary datum that time measures. The motions which happen to things are in time, and their continuous existence, abiding and perennial, is measured by the parade of motions across it. It is only measured by what may happen to it and by what happens around it, by the ways in which it changes or resists, by its possible transformation of substance which is, in the case of living things, death.

Time thus measures so-called "continuous existence" as far as it is not "continuous" but changing, or subject to change, as far as it is not existing but dying or liable to death. Much of the real meaning of time is lost by calling it "successive duration."

We are different now from what we were in our youth, not primarily because time has passed but because changes have taken place in us and around us, changes that time measures without producing. Hume confused this point, and Bergson and Alexander make time a substance.

TIME IS AN "ACCIDENT" OF MOTION

Time is not the being of the thing enduring, as one would have to aver in defining time as successive duration and duration as the being of a thing. Time is a measure. Against Bergson and Alexander, it must be argued that time is not productive. Do these two conclusions, however, rob time of objective existence?

Time is not a measure as mathematical number is a measure, for it was already seen that Aristotle's full definition qualifies number and must be taken wholly to be properly understood. In fashioning clocks, sundials, and hourglasses to tell time—even in the theory of relativity, to turn the velocity of light into a timepiece—presupposes that we know what time is. A clock, for instance, is manufactured to measure the time it takes for the earth to travel around the sun. Events are measured in relativity mechanics by the time required for a light ray to travel from one body to another. But to build instruments around the knowledge of "the time it takes . . ." for the sun or a light ray to move means that we already have a concept of what time is. This, of course, does not argue for Kant but only against the dream of defining time from sensistic premises. It argues against the ambitions of quantitative measurement and of turning empiriological physics into a philosophical science of nature.

Time relates the stages of motion according to their *before* and *after,* but the result is not an actually segmented line in the quantitative order. Time is motion considered with its order, and this order is not simply a mental relation. It is an external and as real and as objective as motion itself or that "part" of a motion which actually exists. Though space as such does not exist without man, there would be time if there were no human beings to reckon it, in the sense that there would still be an order of priority and posteriority in motion; motions related to each other and motions related in their parts would still be related without the mind. Time is as real as place.

Aquinas called time a kind of accident in motion, and accidents though weaker than substances, are not mental fancies. Time is number in things (*numerus numeratus*) and not sheer mathematical number (*numerus numerans*). The order is dynamic because motion is dynamic and continuous because of the continuum in motion. This dynamic order, however, cannot be tortured into the quantitative forms of mathematics and of empiriological physics. It is a flow, like motion, and the shore of time changes as rapidly as the stream of movement.

TIME IS A DYNAMIC MEASURE

It was the merit of Bergson to have shown that time for the mathematician and for the empiriological physicist is simply a line in space. It is a fact that all our measures of time, like clocks, sun dials, interferometers, and cathode ray tubes record their data geometrically. But a line in space, a plot on a coördinate system in empiriological physics or the circle traced by the second hand of a wrist watch, does not tell what time is. The mathematical line is homogeneous. It makes no distinctions between the past and future. It was in this light that Bergson pointed to mathematical time as not having to do with duration. One should also add that space is weaker than time in the objective order and thus emphasize the folly of defining time by spatializing it.

Time could be reversed, according to the empiriological way of looking at things, and pure measurements, Bergson went on, would never inform man of the shift. It may be countered of course that the law of entropy indicates directionality and points toward the ultimate irreversibility of cosmic processes. But this law is abstracted from the facts which it is supposed to regiment. It is not detected ahead of them, like a general leading an army. Mere measurement cannot yield the law of entropy but simply records a certain correlation among facts. Which is prior and which is posterior is known, if known at all, by some means other than measurements.

Strictly metrical physics, the kind conceived by positivism and embraced by Einstein, who will accept only the physically "observable," cannot establish priority and posteriority because it really ignores the motion that joins them in the flow of time. It appreciates time by taking as its point of departure not place but space. Mathematical measurement records only the static. The Bergsonian line, the time of the mathematician and the empiriological physicist, could begin at the term and be plotted back to the origin, just as well as beginning at the origin and working to the term. The change would make no difference to strictly empiriological physics. It does not measure motion but position, and its measures are not dynamic but static. Time is a flow, and its reality cannot be appraised in quantitative figures.

It is clear that when speaking of time as a measure and of a line or number as a measure, two quite different meanings attach to the nature of measure. The one is dynamic. It is an order of motion itself. The other is static, a measure of quantity and position and the points between which motion takes place but not the motion itself. This does not mean that quantitative measures have no meaning in the physical world but only that the dynamism of motion can be caught only by a truly dynamic measure.

SUN TIME IS A CONVENIENT STANDARD

Measuring time is the work of a clock, but time in turn is the measure of motion. The dial on a clock is an order in space; time is the order in movement. Speaking in Ptolemaic terms, it was, of course, not necessary to choose the movement of the sun as the standard for reckoning time. There is something arbitrary and conventional in any time standard, just as it is convention to weigh in terms of pounds rather than of some other unit. It is the relations of the unit chosen to the thing measured that are not arbitrary.

Time could be told by reference to the evaporation of a given quantity of water under constant temperature, the rusting of a fixed amount of iron under constant conditions, the coloring of litmus paper in acid of a certain kind and concentration, or the movement of a weather balloon through a fixed space. That time is usually told by the sun is due to the continuity, simplicity, permanence, uniformity, repetition, and public character of solar movement and to its effects, such as night and day and the changes of season, upon human life. Solar movement—really it is the movement of the earth around the sun in Copernican astronomy—is fast enough with respect to man to make for definite periods according to which he can regulate his life, and yet it is slow enough to permit convenient subdivisions into what we call hours.

Continuity is most apparent in local movement, and since time is continuous, local motion forms the best standard for measuring time. Besides, local movement is through extensive magnitude and permits a scale to be drawn for telling time in more or less precise terms whenever one wishes to know it. Finally, the motions in sun time are vast and inclusive enough to allow any other cosmic motion to be measured with respect to it.

But clocks do for man what mathematics does for the empiriological physicist. They tell time without telling what time is. The clocks are themselves mechanical and moving things when it is motion that is to be measured. What is important is the comparison of movement, between that of a clock and that of, say an ocean liner navigating the seas. The comparisons, the order, the measure, is time; so that the abstracting mind, rather than sheer sensation, must form the concept of time and be the final judge about it, even though dials and mathematical plots and "solar" movement are helpful in suggesting a standard and public viewpoint. Any of the movements in the world can be related to that of the sun, taken by the time-detecting mind as a standard.

Each unit in the solar trajectory, more properly each arc in the path of the earth around the sun, can serve as a norm for motions before and after it. Motions are comparable in their time just as quantities in their sizes, and a thing may be called fast or slow depending on how far it has traveled while the earth has circled a certain distance about the sun.

The rotation of the earth around its axis measures a day, and the orbital motion of the earth around the sun measures a year. But how do we know what year it is? And what century? Astronomically, this can be computed from the orbital motion of the sun which is known to move with respect to the Milky Way. But in a rougher sense, a new year begins each time the earth completes its orbit about the sun and begins a new one. Time runs in cycles, and the circular dial on a clock imitates this.

TIME IS CYCLICAL

From the viewpoint of entropy as well as from the emphasis of relativity astronomy, these cycles may not be perfect; but there is something cyclical and repetitive about our universe, as experience so forcefully shows. This leads again to the conclusion that the fundamental motion in the world must somehow be curvilinear rather than straight, and that there must be more than inertial forces in back of it. If time has this cyclical aspect, there is all the more reason why it escapes empiriological physics and is available only to the probing of the philosophical science of nature. Circular movement in time, like reflection where the mind bends back upon itself in thought, cannot be caught by experimental traps. There is an element of sameness and permanence and almost supratemporal identity in circular movement. Empiriological physics views a thing as determined by external forces in obedience to the law of inertia, but it cannot handle sameness and identity and nature.

When a circle or an ellipse starts through its swing the second time, this can only be established by a third thing since the same line is being traced out again. But if this third thing is also a circle or an ellipse, if there is a cyclical character to the fundamental movements in the cosmos, it is obvious that the empiriological physicist gets nowhere by appealing to other motions to define time as though time were only motion or jelled with space in an ultrareal continuum. When two figures coincide, how are we to know that there are two figures except by abstraction?

Einstein's theory holds that the elliptical movements of the heavenly bodies are never quite closed, and this would be expected on a finer probing of traditional principles. The universe is not a repetitive monologue but open and expansive and progressive under a final cause. Einstein has detected a fortunate analogy to the open universe that is Aristotelian in spirit, if not in word. Here, the emphasis is on the cycles or sameness, rather than differences in the movements of nature. The days, seasons, years, and even the larger repetitive movements cannot, in so far they are repetitive, be tucked into the categories of empiriological physics.

The cyclical character of time makes its unity and its order and its character as a measure of motion even more apparent. Time is the order of motion according to *before* and *after,* and order is more apparent the nearer it comes to being closed. Time measures motion not as motion but only in so far as it has priority and posteriority which the measure emphasizes. The return of the days, of the seasons, and the even vaster weather cycles which meteorology detects reinforce the truth that the priority and posteriority in motion are not simply mental but something real.

It is the changes, not the time, that are ordered. Time is the order itself, though the introspecting mind often confuses time with changes and assigns it the role of a cause rather than a measure or order. Changes make us aware that time has passed, and time informs us of the changes. Time is the order of the changes, not the motions themselves, and if the order is real, so is time. From this awareness of change, the mind moves up to the order of quantity, building clocks to synchronize with the flow of time and interpreting the readings not in themselves but by reference to this flow.

RELATIVITY DENIES TIME'S UNITY

A question that rivals in importance the problem of continuity in time is that of time's unity. Is there one time for the whole world or are there many times unrelated among themselves? This question which drew only a slight mention from Aristotle is of special moment in this day of astrophysics, and of relativity, which allows that there are as many times as there are observers.

A single motion can be numbered according to the *before* and *after* of its own trajectory. But because the universe is a plenum in extension, what occurs in one part of it can be correlated in time with what happens elsewhere. Light rays leaving the sun can be correlated according to priority and posteriority with events on earth, just as the starting of a car in California, by comparison with the stopping of a train in New York, happens before or after or in the "specious present." Two distant events can be compared with reference to a standard that includes both, because the standard can reach out everywhere in its relations if the universe, as the last chapter argued, is an extensive plenum.

There is one time for the universe precisely because it is a universe. Individuals within it are related to each other, causing each other's motions, occupying each other's places, moving in a common extensive plenum, and working toward common goals. Of all these communities the most important here is the magnitude of the universe enabling all parts to be temporally related. All the motions of the world can be compared to the rotation of the earth about the sun, and thus they can be compared to each other. The continuum of quantity conditions the continuum of motion, and the continuum of motion assures the continuum of time.

The theory of relativity would impugn or at least qualify this thesis. It affirms that the simultaneity between two events is unobservable and that, if this is the case, priority and posteriority must lapse into a similar fate. If two light flashes are emitted from different sources, an observer, standing at the midpoint of a line joining the sources, would assert that the flashes are simultaneous if they reach him at the same instant. But how does he know that he is at the midpoint since there is no absolute in space like a stationary ether in terms of which he can assume an absolute position? Position, relativity mechanics goes on, depends on the state of motion of the observer or of a frame of reference. Just as motion is described by relation to a frame of reference, so is simultaneity and, to be precise, so is time in general. As the gravediggers of Ophelia argued, does a drowning man go to the water or does the water come to the drowning man?

TIME IS ONE

It was Bergson's merit to have underlined the measurements of time as always bearing a spatial or geometrical form. If space in its geometrical properties is always relative, the same fortune befalls time which must be fitted into spatial forms for the empiriological physicist to detect it. Mathematically or spatially measured, time is obviously relative, and Einstein, the empiriological physicist, was boldly logical in denying an absolute character to time. On his premises, there is no such a thing as time. There are only times.

But the failure to measure a reality does not black it out of existence. The empiriological method would like to find a reference point "outside" the universe of bodies, with respect to which the universe endures. Such a procedure is the only one that empiriological physics can follow if it would be completely faithful to its nature. The failure to find such a pivot for both extension and time would be expected if the universe is finite. If a metacosmic frame of reference were actually attained, it would, as metacosmic, be beyond the limits of the universe and in infinity, and if the universe were infinite in expanse, no motion and not even being would be found in it, as the last chapter proposed.

This remark italicizes the danger of taking relativity too seriously in philosophical physics, though in its own field it has proved its worth. The temporal character of matter does not require that there be something beyond it with respect to which it endures. This internal cosmic time, taking the universe as a single whole and finding that it is not timed with respect to a thing outside of it, is the meaning of relativity, and of Ernst Mach, who inspired Einstein with the hint that empiriological physics should consider "the all." Since the universe is not related to a material thing outside of it, to a metacosmic space and time, why should its own space and time not appear as irrelational and hence as relative? It is sound logic to insist that time is wholly internal to the universe, for only matter is in motion and hence in time, the measure of motion. But Einstein makes it so internal that it becomes a part of things, in the space-time continuum.

However, there is something more to be said about time than empiriological language can translate.

First of all, the continuity of motion reposes on the continuity of magnitude, and because of this plenary character of the universe, the motions of the world can be related in time. But care must be taken regarding the meaning of magnitude or of quantity in Aristotle as opposed to Einstein. In philosophical physics, extension is isotropic; in relativity physics it is not, it is anisotropic and heterogeneous. This means that the classical line-like continuum of time could not stretch from New York to California to correlate events in both states within a unified time.

Relativity physics mixes its motion and its quantity, without acknowledging the abstraction by which the mind distinguishes them on the terrain of philosophy. But if there is such a thing as isotropic extension, as the last chapter argued in behalf of Euclidian geometry, then abstracting momentarily from motion, it is possible to draw a continuous line in the isotropic extension between any two points in the universe. In this way, there is seen to be a continuity or unity of magnitude, which shows the continuity or unity of motion and, because of motion, the continuity or unity of time. Einstein confines himself to anisotropic space, but the philosophical physicist, while acknowledging relativity in the empiriological domain, goes on to discern the isotropic character of extension or magnitude, considered apart from motion. On this distinction, the solution of the unity of time can be worked out.

TIME IS DIRECTIONAL

But such a logic does not solve the more subtle question about directionality: Which event is before and which is after in a given sequence, before and after in the absolute sense? How can we possibly determine the way in which time is flowing in the cosmos, such that the course is irreversible in its flow and directional in its nature?

A kindred problem met in the last chapter with respect to place required a reference to final causality in order to be solved. There it was argued that place is the term of local movement and that the question of whether *A* is moving with respect to *B,* or *B* with respect to *A,* is answered by the question: which is being perfected by fulfilling tendencies to a loftier natural place? Place (rather than space which Einstein used) is the best framework for specifying time since the temporal flow means that a moving thing is now in this place and now in that. There is a *before* and *after* in local motion. Indeed, priority and posteriority are primarily known from this fact and seen by the mind to be properties not only of places but of the measures of motion as well. Measuring time by space leaves man's march on reality wholly open to the shortcomings which Bergson pointed out; measuring time by place is something else.

Place owns the character of an end or purpose, and the perfection of a thing can be measured by its progress toward its natural place. It is this line of attack that sets the order of motion above the grasp of relativity equivalences and assures that the motion of the world is one-way. All things tend naturally toward their more natural places, and there is a *before* and *after* in their trajectories depending on their progressive approximations to their natural terms. Einstein erects his doctrine of time not from place but from space which, outside the mind, is indifferent extension and by its very indifference does not allow order to be objectively defined.

There is another approach to the theory of relativity which underwrites the unity and directionality of time that philosophical physics defends.

Contrary to relativity theory, time is not primarily an affair of simultaneities between events or between parallel series of events. It refers to a single motion and to the *before* and *after* within it. Motions are compared with each other in a secondary sense, and if the comparison is mathematical alone, attempting to find an indivisible physical unit in time so that the two sequences can be compared with absolute mathematical precision by the superposition of two such indivisible physical units, the effort will surely run aground. Philosophical physics insists that there is a *before* and *after* in a local motion, depending on the *places* which bodies occupy or traverse. Einstein does not think in terms of this march of a single body seeking its place but in terms of the whole cosmos, where individuals are not considered or at least are not considered primarily. Einstein wants to establish simultaneity in order to define *before* and *after*, and hence he requires at least two series of events. Philosophical physics first discovers *before* and *after,* and simultaneity comes in, when it comes at all, only in a secondary fashion. Directionality is here established not by measuring two motions in space but by discerning the finality, of one of them, in place.

Having established directionality in a single body which is now in this place and now in that, comparisons with other motions are possible in the isotropic plenum of extension that is our universe. But the discussion at this stage, where two chains of motions are involved, assumes a more mathematical rather than local and final and truly physical air. It is this second or mathematical stage that is alone emphasized in relativity theory, which, as empiriological, cannot enrich itself with the local, final, physical principles that philosophical science of nature studies at their own level and in the first order of abstraction.

This does not invalidate the mathematical and empiriological approach to time, it does not reject relativity physics. It only weakens empiriological physics as a philosophical study of the universe. Philosophical physics indeed admits this secondary and more mathematical development regarding time, where two motions or more are interrelated. But philosophical science also draws an important conclusion at this secondary level. For the universe is one in magnitude since it is a plenum, isotropic when its extension alone is considered; and just as there is a continuous trajectory in a single motion whose parts form the temporal sequence, so there is a Euclidian continuum of extension between trajectories that enables the comparison of motions and gives time a unified character.

There is a comparison of trajectories, and this is likewise of vast moment in the present context. Comparison of motion is not a comparison of points, as Aristotle would have argued against Zeno. It is a likening of lines. Time is analogous to a line, not a point. There is a continuity of a motion and hence a continuity in its time.

Now these unities that are linelike and not pointlike are comparable to each other in the continuum of time throughout the universe, just as the past and future form a continuum in an individual motion. The simultaneity of such lines is determined not by points but by planes, and the planes are tied together not by points but by solids. Thus the whole problem reverts to the solid bodies of experience, with the mind and not the senses comparing them. Time is not a question of midpoints or points of reference or punctual simultaneity but of experience in our physical world of motions and of places.

Before and *after* are known prior to simultaneity and prompt the relativity question about it. Because of their final character, they retain their objective one-way order even if absolute point-like simultaneity cannot be mathematically determined. When the modern mind pledged itself against finality in the universe, it forsook its best explanatory principle for a philosophical science of nature.

The unity of time can be guaranteed not by seeking an anchor outside the universe with respect to which the cosmos is moving but by seeking an end toward which the motions work. All moving bodies in the world have the same end, and time is a measure of their progress in attaining it. Time measures the advance of things to their goals; and if their ultimate end is somehow one, then time has a unified character on a cosmic scale. But finality has had to solve the problem again. The debate between empiriological and philosophical physics turns upon the distinction between finality and mathematical equivalences; quantity and motion; space and place; isotropy and anisotropy; measurements between several motions and the discernment of order in a single one of them.

Relativity is an empiriological theory. It aims to measure by mathematical equations what is not really equalitarian but progressive and hierarchical and finalized. As in the rest of empiriological physics, it tends to afford man control on matter. It measures time by space which has no final character and not by place which involves ends. Making no necessary distinction between *before* and *after*, it can consider time as reversible, just as a mathematical equation has two interchangeable sides. Relativity theory has to flatten the material world in order to pick it up by control; it is only the mathematically observable, the inert, the quantified that man can manipulate, and since relativity is interested in unloading itself of all that cannot be experimentally observed and mathematically computed for making man the master of matter, it ignores, for its purposes, whatever masters man, like natures and their natural places and their natural ends. But ignoring such realities for purposes of logic does not blank them out of ontology.

THERE IS NO ETERNAL RETURN

According to traditional thought, time is irreversible. Though some of the Greeks, especially Alcmaeon, denied this, a belief that the clock cannot be turned back has prevailed among all western thinkers with few exceptions. One of these exceptions, the most notable indeed, is Friedrich Nietzsche who revived the older Greek doctrine of the eternal return. His Superman who was believed to be emerging in the evolutionary process would not rest forever in his supernal state. He would crash to earth, Nietzsche predicted; then the cycle leading up to his appearance would commence all over again.

It has already been pointed out that Einstein's theory, allowing of no way to distinguish the *before* and *after,* opens the way to the doctrine of reversibility in time.

Nietzsche, like relativity theory when it becomes a philosophy, can also be refuted by the finality in motion, the tendency of all things to seek their higher natural places. Time measures their progress toward this end. If time moved in circles so that motion always returned to its point of origin, it would be different when it began its second time around the course than it was at first. Its history, during the second cycle, would be posterior to that of the first. It is because the wheels of a car make not simply the same but successive revolutions that an auto moves along the highway.

If the second circle of Nietzsche's eternity were not posterior to the first, hence different from it, it could never be recognized. Time measures the progress of things, and as far as this difference of stage does not appear, there is no time and no awareness of it.

Above all, motion would be impossible if it were reversible, and tended to the same place where it began. Such a universe would be not mobile but static. If a thing tended to the same place where it is, it would always remain there. Time is not reversible unless motion is reversible. Time is a one-way street.

TIME IS NOT A DIMENSION

The general theory of relativity—and this is retained in the generalized theory of gravitation—melts time into a fourth dimension of matter and views the cosmos as a four-dimensional space-time continuum. Changes in matter are not simply described as differences of a spatial nature but also by the fact that the same matter exists at different times. It is not strictly correct, according to Einstein's canons, to speak of an event as a phenomenon of space and time. This was presumably the infection of classical physics. In the theory of relativity, there are not two realities but one, space-time. Relativity considers the classical cut between space and time to be unobservable.

But a certain distinction is still authorized. Space and time are related by $\sqrt{-1}$, which is an imaginary number and seems to indicate already at first glance that the achievement of combining space and time has not been equal to the ambition. The identity of space and time may have been achieved at the cost of a mathematical trick that has no physical counterpart or, if it has, implies a distinction in the continuum. Physically speaking, there is another distinction. There are spacelike intervals between events and timelike intervals. Two events A and B, occurring on different bodies, have a spacelike reference if a light ray, emitted from the first body, when A occurs, reaches the second body before B occurs. They have a timelike reference if the light ray reaches the second body after B occurs. Is time a dimension like the three dimensions of space?

The general drift of empiriological physics must be borne in mind when this problem is broached. Empiriological physics will acknowledge only what is experimentally observable. Such a physics woos the most potential elements in things, and when potency alone is emphasized the world retires into an undifferentiated continuum, reversible because indifferent and a space-time monotone because continuous. Empiriological physics is on the trail of what is controllable in matter, and it will acknowledge as real only those things which it can detect with instruments and make with laboratory devices. In the last chapter, it was seen that empiriological physics does not admit the break between geometry and experiment. There is a leap between the mathematical and physical orders which is not just a question of more or less. And the same sort of gap occurs between space and time.

Space belongs to extension and time to motion. But relativity would not admit the hierarchy between extension and motion. It blends them into a continuum, and it does the same thing to space and time. The senses cannot detect and define hierarchy. They cannot jump the gap between extension and non-extension, space and non-space, time and non-time, being and non-being. Only intelligence can consort with problems of hierarchy, of difference, of being and non-being, of contraries and contradictories.

It is then entirely logical for relativity mechanics, in order to gain a domination over matter, to view its subject matter as a continuum. That is what the potential and the controllable become in the end. Because the difference between extension and motion yawns as a break between two orders of reality, it cannot be derived from experiment but only from experience. Relativistically, sensistically, experimentally, it is truly unobservable.

But the view of the world as sheer potency, which has fattened empiriological physics in its control of things, does not carry weight in the philosophical science of nature. Time may be just as important and coequal with space in merely describing the continuum that our senses touch, but there is as much difference between time and space as there is between extension and movement.

Space is static; time is dynamic. Space is a permanence; time is a passing. Space is indifferent; time is hierarchical. In brief, there is a duality about the world that intelligence can detect but that the senses and scientism must pass over in silence. Both place and time are measures of motion, the one performing its function in terms of extensions (surfaces) and the other in terms of that dynamic order in which a moving body occupies various places.

Aristotle said, against the sophists of his day, that the denial of the principle of non-contradiction results in a continuous universe where one thing tapers into another with no difference between them; he also argued, against Heraclitus, that his continuous and undifferentiated universe led to a denial of the principle of non-contradiction. Einstein is unable to distinguish between opposites because his empiriological system is, as experimental, unable to reach the notion of being versus nothingness in terms of which opposition is understood. He hammers out a continuous universe and is logical in pressing the sensistic approach to a rather natural conclusion.

But there is as much difficulty with a space-time continuum as with a static dynamism or a passing permanence or a square circle. The philosophical science of nature does not expect the empiriological physicist to use a philosophical approach in his measurements but only to remember that beyond measurement there is another view of reality which tells us what things are.

The continuous interval between space and time which relativity physics maps out is a mark of its shallowness, not depth. Time is in a different order from space; it measures a moving thing as now in this place and now in this, and to make it one with the place it measures would be to identify the measured and the measure, the static and the dynamic. Space would move as time moves, and the mind would be unaware of a passing.

The theory of relativity in a way is like the philosophy of Bergson who cloaked time as a real thing, and it is even closer to the philosophy of Alexander who speaks like Einstein of a space-time continuum.

Sharply at odds with this view is the *apriorism* of Kant and even Leibniz. For Kant, time, like space, is a mental form thrust by the mind upon an indifferent matter which the senses present. Kant argued to his conclusion by a logic similar to his discussion of space. Time, he said, is presented as a precondition of sensible experience; things could not be recognized as succeeding one another unless a concept of time were enjoyed beforehand. Experience presents things as occurring at various times, but the notions of simultaneity and succession, by which these times are united, are, Kant went on, in the *a priori* form of time.

Both the ultrarealists like Alexander, Bergson, even Einstein, and the idealists like Kant and Leibniz have not tumbled completely into error. Time is not a substance; it is an order. It is thus neither real like a copper atom nor wholly mental like purely logical being. The ultrarealists take the motion which time measures to be the whole of it; the idealists take measure without regard for the reality of motion and the priority and posteriority which make Aristotle's definition complete. Time is neither a substance nor a mental form. The truth lies somewhere in between these extremes, where time is as real as the order of motion and presupposes a material that it measures.

Kant failed to gain a proper grasp on the nature of abstraction by which the mind draws from sense experience certain general notions which make that sense experience intelligible. Kant, unfortunately, let his jutting to empiriological physics become a landslide over his philosophy. In empiriological physics, nothing is intelligible in itself; it is always known by reference to a yardstick, and Kant, in his doctrines of space and time, merely tried to find what the fundamental yardsticks are. In empiriological physics, things are measured by what is prior to them, and Kant simply drew the conclusion that consistently there must be something prior to the first sense experience in order to make even this cognizable.

Kant contorted abstraction and self-evidence and the whole nature of human intelligence. His view of time also plays into the hands of empiriological physics by voiding it of all dynamism and by turning it into a logical form without objective significance. The way is thus paved to eliminate all but quantity from the objective world and to view the rest of realities as mere projections of the human mind.

Kant played his part in the history of both empiriological and philosophical physics, but there is no use refuting him further in his blunders about time. Kant's doctrine on this point, from the empiriological view, is already dead; it is time as an objective fact that relativity physics has attempted to plead. The contemporary empiriological pattern is not that of Newton which Kant contrived his space-time system to explain. The new physics is that of Einstein and Planck, relativity and quantum mechanics.

REALISM UNITES QUANTUM AND RELATIVITY INSIGHTS

Relativity physics emphasizes the continuum in space and time. It is striking that the other modern approach to empiriological physics which is called quantum mechanics takes the exactly opposite view. Holding that velocity (a temporal phenomenon) and position (a spatial phenomenon) cannot be exactly measured together, quantum physics declares that there is an abrupt discontinuity between space and time. This is what philosophical physics would lead one to expect. The static and dynamic cannot be fitted together any more than a triangle can be superimposed on a quadrilateral figure.

The difference between quantum and relativity theories is deeply grooved, and one of the two systems is fated to be discarded, or both of them are likely to be transcended by the experimental insights of tomorrow. Suffice it to say here that the matter-form dualism explains how there can be continuity and discontinuity, the static and the mobile, the spatial and the temporal, in the same universe. It would agree with relativity physics that there is a unity between the dualistic elements, and would second the idea of quantum mechanics that form is not the same thing as matter.

Empiriological physics has the nature of an art, and the two leading contemporary systems but represent different slants on a subject matter that refuses to surrender itself wholly to either one.

An artist tries to get the most and best out of his medium, using now this chisel and now that, standing at one angle and then taking another. The current crisis in empiriological physics is nature gaining revenge, as it always will, for the attempt to erect a partial picture of reality into the whole stucture. Matter-form dualism can explain both the successes and failures of contemporary empiriological systems. It takes a binocular view of the real.

EXISTENTIALISM MAKES CAPITAL OF TIME

Existentialism, especially in the systems of Martin Heidegger and Jean-Paul Sartre, is Kant hounded to his very extremes. These two men set out to probe the question: What is *a priori* to the *a priori?* When one radically attempts to think about himself, it is argued, he moves backward to examine his preconscious state as though man, in true Kantian fashion, were to be examined apart from the external world that he thinks about. In this reduction of himself, man finds his existence shriveling up to a point. Reflecting on ourselves to discover our being in its purity, we come to see it as simply an existent, simply "there" without any content or relations. This may be put in another way by saying that an individual is always irrelational; he cannot know what he is, because he is an individual and knowledge is always of universals. Therefore man is seen in the existentialist reduction as a unique existent, not conceptualized and thus not known scientifically. He is also radically free because law is always in universal form and he is always an individual.

Heidegger and Sartre sum up this isolated character of the

individual by declaring that man is abandoned (*geworfen, délaissé*). He has been "thrown-into-the-world," Heidegger writes, and when he attempts to look backward to discover the preconscious state which would account for his conscious life, seeking so to speak what is *a priori* to the Kantian *a priori,* man finds that he cannot isolate that state of affairs in his being which set him going along lines of thought and will. For man must always be conscious in conducting the examination. He is always ahead of himself, Heidegger says; he does not discover his abandonment until he has already been abandoned and in the status of being "before himself" or ahead of himself, he can never really look back and see his past as it was before his conscious life caught fire.

This notion of "before-ness" singles out the dominant role of time in Heidegger and Sartre. Man is projected, abandoned, "thrown" ahead of himself. But who is the thrower? Since man is radically free and isolated and original, severed from outer agencies and guiding laws, it can only be himself that has done the throwing; he has no connections because he is an individual. This means that man projects himself. He thus produces time, or more exactly, he temporalizes himself. To understand himself, he projects himself. He throws himself forward. And forward means temporally so. Heidegger has written a book called *On Being and Time*.

It is easy to conclude from the foregoing remarks that time is the essence of man. Man creates time. The mystery of being is to be sought in time. Kantian to the last syllable, Heidegger and his disciple Sartre, see time as a projection of man, a network emerging from the ego. Their existentialism finds its chief argument for this in the note of abandonment which is discovered when man finds himself as a pure existent, without goal or guidance and cut off even from a continuity with a motor cause. The human reality is ever "before" itself since it can never return to the preconscious state, where it originated thought, and grasp the forces prompting that thought into being.

Heidegger has developed his existential themes from Soren Kierkegaard, a Danish anti-Hegelian who did not intend the conclusions reached by Heidegger and Sartre but whose principles open the way to such extremes. Kierkegaard laid great stress on the moment. He found that man was present to himself, aware of his individuality and concreteness, only in the instant, which provide the high point in man's experience. Insistent on this privilege of the moment, Kierkegaard called it an "atom of eternity"—a phrase which is also found in Lavelle, a contemporary theistic existentialist, who calls the instant "the intersection of time and eternity." Lavelle, even before Sartre, insisted on the Kantian method of examining the subject first, and his metaphysics is an analytic of man. But in Lavelle, time is a mark of finitude, while man also participates in the infinite. The instant is the locus of this participation.

EXISTENTIALISM IS INADEQUATE

Two questions surge up concerning the preceding remarks on existentialism: Is time a projection of man? Is the "now" of time the same thing as the "now" of eternity?

To solve the first question, it is important to dig down to the root error of existentialism which begins by analyzing man and things on the premise that man is aware of himself as an individual before being aware of a world. This is not true, as the opening chapter argued. Thinking does not begin with the individual and the unique but with the general and the universal. Reflecting on our subjectivity is a late experience in man's thinking curriculum. He first thinks about being in general and derives his principles of thought from this fact. He does not charge, unaided and unarmed, into a study of himself. He is bolstered beforehand with principles that make his self-analysis intelligible and not an isolated acrobatic. Such an attack throws out the whole existentialist procedure. It is not time that makes man intelligible to himself, but being. Man is aware of being before he discovers that he is in time; his notions of motion, priority, posteriority, and number all precede his awareness of time. Time is a measure of motion, and is no more the fancy of mind that is the motion which it measures.

The second question is more subtle. What do we mean by the *now*, by the instant or moment? It has already been pointed out that the *now* of things in one sense remains the same while time passes; it is the identity which abides across change. But in another sense, the *now* is different with each motion, since the temporalized reality, being dually principled, undergoes a change and in the present can no longer fully claim its previous *now*. In precise words the real *now* is a boundary, uniting and dividing, and time is no more a series of *nows* than a line is a series of points. Time is formed by the flowing *now*.

Because of its fluent and bifurcated character the *now* of time (*nunc fluens*) cannot correspond with the standing now (*nunc stans*) of eternity. The *now* of time is not an "atom" to quote Kierkegaard, since the temporal *now* is fluent and cannot partake of eternity which is not fluent; nor is the *now* an "intersection" with eternity since eternity is the mark of a being which is simultaneously whole, as Boethius said. Rather than being simultaneous, the *now* of time is successive, hence partially different with each progress of its flow. Rather than being whole, the *now* is flowing and changing.

Man has no natural experience of eternity. The closest he comes to it naturally is in contemplating eternal truths. The permanence of his being is, of course, an imitation of the permanence of God, as the metaphysician shows, and is measured by time as rest is related to motion. Time has primarily to do with motion. No part of it has to do with eternity which is the exact opposite of motion.

The existentialist approaches to time differ sharply from the temper of scientism mentioned earlier in this chapter. Scientism makes too much of man, the observer, removed from the experience he is surveying and counting it as an audience watching a motion picture. Existentialism accepts nothing but experience and will allow no room for observations drawn out of it.

Truth once again marches down the middle. A realistic science will build upon experience and thus be realistic. It will build by speculative principles imposed by that experience. It will thus be truly scientific.

Suggested Readings

Aristotle, *Physics*, Bk. 4, chs. 10–14.
Callahan, John F., *Four Views of Time in the Ancient World* (Chicago, 1948).

12

Motion and Quantity

QUANTITY IS AN ADMITTED REALITY

Philosophical physics, dealing today with quantity, is liberated from at least one of the burdens which so frequently delay its larger tasks. It does not have to linger over the proof that quantity exists. As in the case of local motion which Descartes wedded to quantity at the onset of modern philosophy, realism must labor now not to prove that quantity is real but more to trim down its value as an account of the world. The modern mind likes to think that mathematics or quantitative measures are alone able to process a world through the machinery of knowledge, and that quantity is all there is to matter. The problem of quantity looms as a major issue in the debate between empiriological and philosophical physics.

It was another homage of Aristotle to experience that he did not define quantity in the abstract. It is a concrete reality, especially as the philosophical science of nature comes upon it, and Aristotle defined it so. He spoke of quantified being (*ens quantum*), sinking his feet once again into experience and the real world.

Aristotle defined a quantified thing as that which can be divided into parts each of which is capable of an independence and an identity of its own upon the division. " 'Quantum' means," he said, "that which is divisible into two or more constituent parts of which each is by nature a 'one' and a 'this.' "[1] The quantified is therefore the divisible or the partitive.

[1] *Metaphysics,* Bk. V, ch. 13.

401

Now matter is actually composite in several ways. It has already been seen that prime matter and substantial form, the principles of motion, congeal in mobile beings. But neither of these principles can exist as a "one" or a "this" in independence, and their union is not properly in the order of quantity. Matter and form are often called entitative parts.

Quantitative parts are the results of dissecting continuous magnitude into separated units, like the slicing of a tomato or the felling of timber. The two halves of the tomato remain after the division, and both the trunk and the tree, united before they were sawed, are independent identities after the operation. Another example of quantitative division is the breaking of a piece of chalk into two parts, both of which are so independent of each other that two different people can now write on the blackboard where only one was able to write before.

Quantitative parts are sometimes called integral parts.

Certain difficulties about the structure of matter require that the foregoing examples be taken, at least for the present, as analogies to help form an idea of quantitative division and how matter-form composition differs from a quantitative one.

Having broadly identified quantity, this chapter will break its associated problems into four major families.

The first part states more precisely how quantity is studied in mathematics and in philosophical physics, and what quantity is in relation to mobile substance.

The second part deals with the problem of the continuum, first defining it and then showing that matter is neither infinitely divided nor indivisible, but bifurcated by act and potency. Zeno, in his ancient and modern setting, is evaluated, and the continuous character of motion is argued. But continuity does not imply homogeneity on the part of the continuous substance.

This opens the way to the third broad series of topics, which sounds out how quantity affects substance. After outlining the two types of quantitative division, it is shown that substance needs a minimum of quantity and that quantity is the closest, of the material accidents, to substance. Matter operates through quantity and quantity solves three important questions about the structure of mobile being. However, quantum mechanics, represented in the example of the Bohr theory, seems to challenge the whole philosophy of quantity as developed in philosophical physics; this theory will be briefly evaluated.

The chapter thus far will have emphasized the divisibility by which quantity is defined, and the final portion of the chapter will consider what can be called the formal effects of quantity: measurability and extension in place and impenetrability. There is a summary section, restating that quantity is not nature but has a unity that is called predicamental.

THE SCIENCE OF QUANTITY ABSTRACTS FROM MOTION

One of the urgent issues about quantity is deciding what aspects of it are treated in mathematics and what aspects belong to the philosophical science of nature. Mathematics abstracts from motion, and though it does not, as some authors have implied, concern itself with quantity divorced from being, it does consider being only as quantified. As Aquinas says,

> . . . the mind can consider sensible realities not *qua* mobile or material but *qua* substances and magnitudes; and this is the meaning of abstraction from matter and motion. However, the intellect does not so abstract that it understands magnitudes and species to be without matter and motion.[2]

What are the properties and principles of being or substance, the mathematician asks, when we take it barely as quantified and consider it to be without motion and the matter that motion involves?

There is no final, efficient, or material causality in the mathematical grade of abstraction. The triangle of the geometer and the number, say 2, in arithmetic, have no inner principle of motion and hence no nature. They do not tend in the order of

---

[2] *Commentary on Aristotle's Metaphysics*, Bk. III, ch. 7.

final causality, as though a triangle would incline to be a square or 2 would tend to be 3. It is also mathematically irrelevant what produced the triangle or number in the material things from which they are known. Mathematics is not concerned with the manner in which things came into existence nor with their native purposes. Finally, mathematics is unbusied about the material cause. It is mathematically unimportant whether the idea of a triangle is realized in wood or in glass or whether the 2 applies to dollars or electrons. As Chesteron wittily puts it, the multiplication table is not made of mahogany. Mathematics thinks away the material, efficient, and final causalities to consider being only under the formality of its quantity.

PHILOSOPHICAL PHYSICS STUDIES QUANTITY THROUGH MOTION

The philosophical science of nature, on the other hand, does not start with the fact of quantity, and of course it does not end with it. Its territory is that of motion, and it migrates to a discussion of quantity rather late in its career and even then considers quantity not in itself but by the light of motion which uncovers it to the seeking mind. Philosophical physics discovers quantity because the subject of motion and its pathway are divisible. It studies lines and surfaces not as simply quantities but as terminations of mobile beings.[3]

The world of motion is more than mere quantity or quantified being; it is charged by the three causalities that mathematics alone cannot trace. Mobile things are richer and fuller than sheer quantified being. A triangle has no power to stretch beyond itself. But moving things are fertile; nature means interiority and growth, and if not always reproduction, at least productivity.

Quantity is thus only one of the aspects of the mobile world, and its physical reality is forced upon us by the facts of motion. Quantity is never grasped in itself by the senses. Sight races toward the colored, touch attends to surfaces that are hard or soft; but quantity always appears secondarily, for instance, in the

---

[3] Aquinas, *Commentary on Aristotle's On the Heavens,* Bk. I, ch. 1.

size of the colored object or the expanse of the tangible surface. Mathematics studies, not sensible, but intelligible matter.

Quantity is nowhere perceived in nature as something subsistent in itself, and considerably more selective abstraction is required to isolate it for attention than to study motion which is more manifest and more universal and more sensible in the world of experience. Spaier was closer than scientism to the truth of things when he said that "quantity is nothing but measured quality."[4] It is only to be inductive and realistic to study the world in the light of motion before surging into the mathematical order of abstraction, where motion is ignored and where three of the four causes needed to probe the moving world must be locked out.

But the philosophical science of nature, even though unable to cope with quantified being in and for itself, nevertheless comes upon it in the physical world. When a body in local motion moves toward its term, it traverses a magnitude; its path is spread out and continuous; the trajectory can be divided into parts, so that an observer can mark off the halfway point or any other point of interest. The distance from term to term in a moving body can be broken down into any number of subintervals.

Quantity is not the whole tissue from which matter is made, but it is certainly something real in the real world. Without it, there would be no separation between the origin of motion and its term. All local motion would be stymied; a thing would have no distance in which to travel. Quantity, in its character as divisible into parts, appears immediately then as a factor of separation or partition in the moving world. If it does not cause, explain, finalize, or constitute motion, at least it conditions it.

But the conditions of motion do not reveal what motion is, what produced it, and why it occurs. Conditions of motion no more explain motion that the fact that conditions on Mars are favorable for life permit the deduction that life is actually present there.

---

[4] Spaier, A., *La pensée et la quantité* (Paris, 1927), p. 33.

Not how a thing looks but how it operates is the key to the secrets of nature. Both the magnitude which a body traverses and the term which it occupies on coming to rest show the body itself as quantified. Different parts of the trajectory are occupied by different parts of the moving body, and the body thus reveals itself to philosophical physics as quantified. In the proper sense, it is a body precisely because it is divisible. And quantity, where it enters the philosophical science of nature at all, comes into play only after other issues about motion have been settled.

The most characteristic thing about the material universe is the network of natures that exist in it, and the most characteristic things about the natures are their tendencies. If no other points could be conscripted, this would be sufficient to show that quantity, where it exists, is something subordinate in nature to deeper principles and higher purposes than mathematics can gaze upon. Quantity is embroiled in a larger reality, the nature which is conditioned by it, and in this physical mode of existence, it shares in motions and their causes, conspiring in the three-ply dynamism which mathematics overshoots and is all the more real because uncontrollable.

What is only quantified, like a sphere, does not tend to move because it is a sphere or to produce anything else because it is quantified. A sphere of iron will move not because it is a sphere but because it is iron, and the spherical shape, though a condition in the motion, is swept along in obedience to the nature of the iron rather than as the cause and explanation of the motion. The sphere does not cease following the laws of quantity, when it moves, but by the same token, it is not the cause or principle of the motion. The rejection of empiriological physics as a science of nature is not so much its failure to account for structure; it is more the natural dislocation of mathematics with motion and with the profile of matter that motion unmasks.

BY QUANTITY MOBILE BEING IS DISTENDED

Quantified being is defined in terms of its divisibility. But since division is a negation of unity and can be grasped only in terms of unity, Aristotle's definition needs further testing. As it stands, it would appear to tell what a quantified being is not, and when quantity is taken alone, without reference to its natural home in being, it is difficult to say anything more.

Actually, empiriological physics likes to take quantity alone and isolated from the rich world of motion. It was shown in Chapter 5 that the experimental spirit pictures reality in terms of its inertia. When a thing is explained by the sum of forces acting upon it, it is explained in terms of what it is not rather than in terms of what it is. The Cartesian reduction of matter to quantity netted the same result in the history of thought as Galileo's taste for inertia. Quantity, taken alone, just like inertia pure and simple, can be defined only by negatives.

But taking quantity in its natural setting enables the science of nature to go beyond the negative character of Aristotle's definition and the negative character which matter wears in a system like empiriological physics, which would like to create the world to the image and likeness of man. Quantity is a plurality of parts, but the parts are not simply geometrical units like cylinders and rectangles. Putting it coarsely, they have content. There are parts of atoms, parts of tomatoes, parts of a piece of chalk. There are not pure parts, and there is not sheer plurality.

Quantity is always a quantity of something and is hence not alone in populating the universe. Quantity must be defined in terms of substance to be properly understood, and that is why the positive meaning of Aristotle's definition surmounts the negative character of its form. Aristotle defined "quantified being."

By its quantity, the being which is quantified is spread out. As John of St. Thomas so well expresses it, "quantity is said to furnish integral parts to substance, not constituting them but ordering them among themselves."[5] Without quantity, a mobile being like a hydrogen or a calcium atom would be indivisible. Its *integral* parts, which are naturally fit for diffusion, would crumble into an inextended status, and such realities as distance and

---

[5] *Cursus philosophicus Thomisticus, Ars Log.,* Part II, Question XVI, article 1.

dimension would never be born. The calcium and the hydrogen would still have the natures which the parts scatter abroad, since mere quantity does not bring content into existence. But without quantity, the parts would not be stretched out in geometrical patterns; they would spiral inward toward collapse.

Quantity renders the parts distinct; without it, they would be compenetrated and indistinguishable. Quantity orders the parts outside one another in that extraposition that is called extension. Without quantity, the parts would be collocated and confused, With quantity, the parts are dispersed in an order of priority and posteriority. Without quantity, the parts would not be formally present; the being whose parts are distributed by quantity would only have the aptitude or exigency for parts. Quantity makes these parts actual. Though not the essence of matter, it distributes a mobile being into a priority and posteriority of position in a whole.

QUANTITY IS NEITHER A CAUSE NOR A SUBSTANCE

Quantity may be redefined as the order of integral parts in the being which it affects. And this definition is making a calculated reference, as all accidents must, to the something beyond quantity, namely the being or nature which is quantified.

To speak of order and spreading and dispersal might incline to confusion. It might be tempting to conclude that quantity orders like a final cause or operates like an efficient one. But quantity is not fueled for either line of causality, it has been noted, and it would be a most serious error to think of a substantial change as involving first the appearance of substance and later the arrival of quantity to disperse it. Nor, it was also shown, does quantity, as such, obey a final cause as though it were a nature, teeming with tendencies and capable by its own inner principle of spreading matter out in this way or that.

It should further be emphasized that quantity does not emanate from its subject, like a field around a magnet; for substance could then account for its own quantity and would be divisible.

There would be no difference between quantity and substance, and Descartes would be right. The foregoing discussions have actually proved him wrong.

As a matter of fact, when a new material substance is formed, the substantiality and the partitiveness appear together; the substance is responsible for what the parts are and the quantity for the fact that there are parts, one outside the other. Quantity does not explain the "content" that is in the parts; it is only their distribution into an estate of distinctness, dimensionality, and distance. Substance does not account for quantity as its product, for then it would be quantity itself. Quantity, as an accident, is never without substance in the nature of things, and a substance in nature is never without quantity, as a sequel will show. But it is not logical to say that when things appear together they are the same thing. Quantity answers not the question *what* but *how much*. It is not a cause but a disposition, something incidental to causality and to the natures which move in the universe. No answer to the question *how much* can ever say *what* a thing is. Quantity is the arrangement of parts outside one another and has nothing to say about the matter which the parts extend. Quantity then is neither a cause nor a substance.

This is where mathematics and mathematical physics part company with the philosophical science of nature. Looking at an envelope is not the same as reading the letter inside. In the same way, quantity, as the extraposition of parts, cannot pour out an intimate knowledge of the reality which the parts disperse. Not being a cause or a substance, the order of parts which defines quantity is order taken as a disposition in the static sense, the sense of geometry, where priority and posteriority are not in causal sequence, one producing the other, but in a countable series, one coming after the other.

In a country of quantity where it has chosen to be naturalized, modern thought has been consistent in its friendship for both Descartes and Hume. Taking Cartesian quantity as the essence of matter, the modern mind has abandoned the traditional notion of causes and has adopted Hume's account which sees in the world only countable series, studied not as natures in causal ferment but as numbers in temporal succession.

QUANTITY MAY BE DISCRETE OR CONTINUOUS

This reference to extension and counting provides a convenient break to recall the distinction between the two species of quantity: the discrete and the continuous. Discrete quantity is quantity separated into units; it is the domain of number and arithmetic. Continuous quantity is an extended stretch, like a line in one dimension, a surface in two, a solid in three dimensions.

Continuous quantity is studied in geometry and may be defined as any quantity where the boundaries of the parts are not actually but merely potentially present. Thus, in a continuous line six inches long, there are not six segments, an inch in length, laid end to end. There is an unbrokenness of parts whose limits or boundaries are not actually bitten off. Two parts of a continuum have a common term.

Continuity may be contrasted with contiguity where the parts are only tangent or adjacent to each other without having a common border. Contiguity belongs to discrete quantity.

Discrete quantity is of considerable moment in an account of matter, especially when the philosophical physicist probes such questions as the plurality of mobile beings and how they are individuated from one another. But in an introductory work of this sort, discrete quantity may be left to incidental treatment in order to cope with the problem of the continuum, one of the oldest and yet one of the liveliest issues in the philosophy of nature. It has already been mentioned in the chapter on infinity, but it deserves treatment for its own sake.

Empiriological physics explores matter by dividing it, distracted by quantity and neglecting the natures which are quantified. It has divided molecules into atoms, atoms into nuclei and orbital electrons, nuclei into neutrons and protons, plus other particles of lesser fame like neutrinos and mesons; apparently the neutron can be broken down into a proton and an electron. How long or how far can division go on?

MATTER IS NOT INFINITELY DIVIDED

There are, at first glance, two possible answers to this question; either matter is actually divided into infinity or somewhere the division must end in what is no longer capable of division but is indivisible. The dream of a matter divided into infinity is in the general drift of empiriological physics, which recognizes nothing but quantity and inertia; dynamists like Leibniz, Boscovich, and Whitehead have chosen the second alternative. In general, dynamism reduces the extended and divisible universe of experience into inextended and indivisible parts. It is as though a line, stretched out into space, would be nothing but a series of points which are without extension.

Neither of these alternatives agrees with experience that the philosophic science of nature ought to explain rather than expel in its realism.

If matter is viewed as actually divided, all the arguments developed in Chapter 4 can be called up again. The infinitism of the empiriological temper holds that its atom smashing does not break up things that are formally one in nature, but merely discovers the divisions as already and actually there. It tends to the opinion that matter is infinitely divided in this fashion and that its work is to count the divisions, pausing now and then to catalogue something like a proton but confident that the proton itself is actually plural. The infinitism that lurks in the empiriological bias would portray a universe scattered into sheer plurality, pure passivity, indeterminacy, disorder, chance, and chaos; it would lead to nihilism, making motion and even being impossible.

But though rejecting the infinitism which a rigidly experimental method implies, it is easy to see how scientism reaches its conclusions. By the character of its method, empiriological physics must ignore form. As experimental, it understands only what can be controlled in obedience to the law of inertia, and since the potential is the plural, an inertial universe is a plural one.

As mathematical, empiriological physics views matter in terms of quantity which, taken alone, is a sheer plurality of parts as Aristotle implies.

Hence, both the matter of empiriological physics and the logical superstructure of its method, both the inertialism of Galileo and Newton and the mathematical preferences of Descartes, join forces to stroke a plural picture of the world. It is easy to see how a physicomathematical approach to the real, using inertia as its only ontology should adopt mathematics as its only logic.

Taken in its proper context, that of art, such a procedure gives a control over nature but no certainty in our knowledge. Nature, however, is not art, and control is only one field of human endeavor, subordinated to ultimate truths and ultimate goals. The appraisal of empiriological method is not to deny it but to delimit it. It is easy and comforting to control things, and more difficult to explore them very deeply for the sake of knowledge alone. But modern man in general has been willing to sacrifice knowledge for the comfort and power of his empiriological disciplines.

In reality it is higher to know that an atom is a being than to know how to make an atom bomb.

MATTER IS NOWHERE INDIVISIBLE

The infinitism of the empiriological method is the fruit of exaggerating the inertial aspects of matter. It is an overplay on the active or non-inertial side of nature that has begotten dynamism. Leibniz, the greatest of the dynamists, was seeking a sufficient reason for that causal interaction of things which the Cartesian slant, so prominent in his time, was unable to explain. How can one thing affect another if there is no change save local movement? How can unity inhabit a universe that is nothing but quantity? Such questions inspired Leibniz to view the world in terms of monads, indivisible in themselves, sealed off from each other, almost vital and spiritual in their natures, and acting together not through causal interplay but by virtue of a harmony preëstablished in the universe by God. Whitehead, under the spell of Leibniz, fashioned a world of "actual entities" which are units of process and hence are essentially mobile and creative. Boscovich telescoped the extended world into inextended points.

Now it is obvious that there is something to the mobile universe besides quantity and inertia; otherwise it would not move. But dynamism is an unwarranted extreme, as illogical in many ways as the infinitism which it opposes. Philosophy should begin with experience underfoot and not pull a preconceived theory out of the hat. Experience discloses the extension of the mobile universe, and if matter is extended, it is always divisible.

For instance, an extended surface, an inch long, can be divided physically into fractions of inches and fractions of the fractions. Finally, the division would become so fine that even molecules would be divided from each other, but molecules are extended and hence divisible. A hydrogen molecule has a diameter of 2.7×10^{-8} centimeter. Mathematically, this extremely small body can be further divided; physical division would dissect it into atoms and the atoms into nuclear particles and orbital electrons. The electron has a radius of 1.4×10^{-13} centimeter; empiriological physics has "not yet" divided it, as Millikan says, but it is still divisible because extended.

Nowhere does extension trickle away to the inextended as the division proceeds. Nor can it ever do so. The indivisible and inextended could never yield extension as experience discloses it. Putting inextended things together still leaves the result inextended. Putting together points does not form a line. Since points are indivisible, where one touches another it does not do so by parts, with point A for instance touching point B on its left side and leaving the right side free to touch point C. A point has no division into right or left, up or down, front or back. It is indivisible, and hence if it touches another point, it does so wholly. The result is not an extended stretch but the superposition of points.

Tangent points would only coincide with each other. They would never stretch out. There would be no more extension in a million such points than in a single one.

Points do not sum up to extension since they are unities having position and are only reduced to the genus of extension as a privation. For indivisibles cannot yield the divisible and the extended, just as a million empty pockets could not produce a cent of cash.

POTENCY AND ACT EXPLAIN THE CONTINUUM

The Aristotelian distinction of act and potency can arbitrate the conflict between dynamism (finitism) and inertialism (infinitism), preserving what truth is to be found in each and avoiding their errors. It discerns the contrast of what is actually divided and potentially divided or simply between what is divided and divisible. A whole, say an atom, is something unitary and undivided if the arguments in Chapter 6 are sound. But being an extended thing in not only one but in three dimensions, it is divisible, and empiriological physics has actually realized the division in its atom smashing. The atom, stable and stubborn in its identity, may be characterized then as not actually divided in nature but only potentially so. The empiriological physicist does not simply discover divisions in the atom. He makes them.

The mobile world is the one place where there are two sides to every story because there are two sides to the material things.

Inertialism fails to see that things have natures which are principles of interiority and unity. To have form is to have feature. It is correct to say that an atom for instance has a unity of its nature and from within itself, rather than deriving its together-ness from pressures acting from outside it. What is held together and what holds it together are the same thing. But a material thing, unified and undivided, is still divisible, and when the division is made actual, the parts are likewise further divisible though they may not be actually divided.

Dynamism accepts the unitary character of natures. But it fails to alight upon their potential aspects. It stresses form more than matter, act more than potency. Alert that natures are undivided as they stand in the universe, dynamism confuses the undivided with the indivisible and must logically construct a self-moving universe like that of Whitehead's actual entities which are essentially "creative."

Realism would admit the infinity of matter but insist that the infinity is one of potency. Until the division occurs, ultimate particles like molecules and atoms, being substances, are not actually divided but potentially so. There is no limit to their divisibility.

Realism would insist with dynamism, on the other hand, that there is a finite character to matter. It is actually undivided because the division and the infinity are only potential. Empiriological physics, by dividing matter, can never get to what is ultimate. But by the same fact the possibilities of unlimited progress stretch out before it, if higher intellectual and moral agreements among men can be reached in time to save the deeper cultural forces that have favored the interest and methods in all scholarship.

If empiriological physics had paid more heed to philosophy in the nineteenth century, it would not have adopted the smug Victorian attitude that billiard-ball atoms were ultimate and indivisible bricks. Realism would likewise warn against some of the descriptions of atomic energy as the "basic energy of the universe." A century from now, perhaps sooner, experimental physics may have electron smashers and proton smashers, liberating an energy even more basic than that binding energies between presently known nuclear particles. There may even be meson physics and meson bombs. The philosophical physicist can assure the empiriological physicist that his protons, electrons, and other units are divisible. It is up to the experimentalist to devise means of doing the actual dividing. This is one of the many points where philosophical physics can be of service to empiriological physics, receiving in return a richer mine of data to illustrate its principles, born of experience and alive to truth wherever found.

ZENO'S ARGUMENTS ARE FALLACIOUS

Thus far, it has been assumed that matter is continuous and that it is not, as Eddington expresses it, but a sprinkling of microscopic dust through vast stretches of empty space. In the stick of chalk mentioned earlier and in the case of the extended surface of the foregoing sections, it may well be that there is not continuity but a very tight contiguity between molecules; the chalk may be something like a heap of sand where the particles are not interpenetrated but simply an aggregate. There is very good evidence for saying that this is the case. But there are likewise striking arguments from the theory of relativity to say the opposite and to hold for the continuity of an iron bar or even a raindrop.

The aim of this chapter does not require the solution of this question. But if molecules and atoms in isolation are substances, as Chapter 6 argued, then continuity certainly exists at this level and at the level of subatomic particles for the brief flash of their own isolation. Aristotle discusses the problem and principles of change before grappling with the issue of the continuum, and it is valid to bring to bear upon the present question whatever conclusions were reached in the foregoing chapters about motion. But before going any further into the discussion of where continuity certainly makes an important appearance to form true units of quantity, it would be luminous to go again to facts of motion by which the philosophical science of nature solves all of its problems, including the present one.

The philosopher who made the continuum such a live issue for Aristotle was Zeno, the Eleatic, who concocted arguments from quantity in the attempt to prove that motion is impossible. Some of Zeno's so-called paradoxes are rather tenuous to outline, but a knowledge of one of them is sufficient here since they all pivot about the same principle and reflect the same error. Zeno argued, for instance, that an arrow could never be shot toward a target by an archer because it would have to cross an infinite series of intervening points or places. Actually, it would not only fail to arrive at a target, but since the first fraction of its trajectory would be paved with an infinity of points—one point can be located between two others *ad infinitum*—the arrow would never move at all. Working like mathematical physics from quantity to motion, Zeno trusted his *a priori* reasoning more than the facts of experience. He declared the universe to be immobile.

Modern mathematics has rediscovered Zeno in the swirls of dust it has kicked up over the problem of infinity, and since mathematical discursion declines to accept the unities which realism discerns in nature, it aims to reconstruct the unity which motion demands from purely mathematical raw material. Zeno held that an infinite series intervened between the origin of motion and its term. Modern mathematics admits the series but holds that it converges toward a limit. Thus, a geometrical progression like 1/2, 1/4, 1/16, is one in which the terms grow smaller and smaller tending to zero while the sum tends to a unified and recognizable number. It is often believed that a convergent series can account for the unity of trajectory which Zeno denied and can thus permit motion to occur, Zeno to the contrary.

However, Chapters 4 and 9 showed that such convergences are a support for the imagination and that the difference between 1 and 2 is not a matter of infinity but is abrupt. The same reasoning applies here. The convergence braces the imagination but only approximates the differences which are sharp and absolute in reality, available not to images but only to ideas.

The infinity involved in a converging series is the potential one. Actually, nature is a meshwork of unities. There is the unity of a continuum wherever motion has a trajectory and hence wherever it occurs. Only form or act, only the unity or interiority of natures keep the infinity of mathematics from ever becoming actual and absolute, where it would throttle motion into a complete stop. Nothing could ever move if it had to cross the infinite series. The end could never invite it by attraction and the efficient cause could never span infinity to produce its motion.

Aristotle employed against Zeno the argument that Bergson

invoked against scientism; he was obsessed by the idea of what is multiple in motion, Aristotle charged. He overlooked the unity which motion involves. What is moved does not go along in steps, like a heap of snow melting flake by flake until the whole is gone. A moving thing moves as a unit, and in a world where there are forms and unities bound up with inertias and quantities the simplicity of motion, as blended with its plural character, can be explained.

MOTION REQUIRES A CONTINUOUS TRAJECTORY

Even more striking and more compelling, there is a unity of motion shown by the continuum of space that a body, in local motion, is observed to traverse. This pathway can be divided and divided, and nowhere does the indivisible appear. If it did, and if the distance between the origin and term of a moving thing were a discrete series of indivisible elements, the body would move by leaps and bounds. It would not really move but would appear now in this point, now in that, and in the interim would have to pass out of existence. In the "skip distance" between two points, nothing could move the thing since there is nothing there to do so. By the time the moving body has lurched to the second point, not to mention the last and terminal point, the influx from the initial cause and the originality which it bestows upon the moving subject would have been lost. A moving thing would be self-moved since it would be broken off from subjection to a cause, vanishing in the interval between points to appear anew, abruptly and causelessly, where the interval ends. Or if it is caused, then the cause must make it out of nothing, to which it has previously fled.

If the stretch between origin and term is not continuous but a series of indivisibles which is the only alternative to continuity, causality would be ruled out from another angle. A cause touching the indivisible would coincide with it, like the superposition of tangent points. Cause and effect would become the same thing. Motion would be impossible once more. In the efficient order, the cause must be divisible, hence continuous, and the same conclusion applies to the effect. Otherwise their contact would be superposition and coincidence, equivalence and indistinction, and the extrinsic cause would cease to be both extrinsic and causal. It may then be taken as a valid principle that cause and effect in the efficient order are divisible and continuous.

If a trajectory is pocked by indivisible subintervals, final causality would perish also. The initial tendencies of things would have no meaning if they had to be snapped out of existence to attain the goal of the nature which bears them. Besides, a reality at its term would be completely different from the initial reality which vanished in gaps along the trajectory, and hence the initial tendencies would never be fulfilled.

The intrinsic causes would, of course, evaporate in the gaps of the trajectory, giving way to a vacuum, which is another absurdity.

Hence, the lack of unity or the denial of the continuum in the stretch which a moving body covers would actually eliminate the four causes of motion and thus make motion impossible. A mere quantitative attack upon the moving world, like that attempted by Zeno and by modern mathematical physics, cannot make out a convincing case that there is or is not such a thing as a continuum in nature. But studying the continuum as a problem raised and solved by motion is only to treat it as philosophical physics should. Without the continuum motion would not only remain unexplained. It could not occur at all.

It may be concluded from the foregoing study that, in addition to the testimony of experience on the continuous trajectory of a moving body, reason can defend the reality of the continuum in the light of the fourfold causality in nature.

CONTINUITY DOES NOT IMPLY HOMOGENEITY

If the atom and the molecule are substances, as Chapter 6 argued, then they are capable of causing, because substances have natures and natures have tendencies, and tendencies are poised for action to a goal; a nature is defined as a *cause* and principle. The atom and molecule and other such unities must be divisible or continuous units, organized by their forms so that there are no gaps in their structure and having throughout their being the same nature whose parts are spread outside of each other by quantity. The form is indivisible since it exists wholly in the whole and wholly in all of the parts; it would not be indivisible if it were interrupted between the nucleus of an atom, say, and the orbital electrons. Form represents the indivisible or simple principle found in mobile being; primordial matter, or more properly quantity, is the source of divisibility and partition and extraposition.

The continuous character of atoms and molecules does not require that they be homogeneous or insure that they would appear as undifferentiated if microscopy could ever resolve itself to the point of seeing them. A differential structure should be expected in matter, and something analogous to the Rutherford planetary atom is surely to be found apart from experiment. At least, sound philosophy on the basis of sound empiriological physics would accord with the view that the positive particles of the atom are concentrated near its center as Rutherford reasoned.

But such differential texture within the atom does not mean that its parts are separated and discontinuous. If the positive charge is concentrated in the center, it could be pointed out that the brain of man is concentrated in his head. But in the human body, as physiology shows more clearly than anatomy, the head is not separated from the lower portions. It is motion of a thing, not looks, that grind the science of nature on to its conclusions. In a similar way, the atom can have a heterogeneity of appearance and even a heterogeneity of function without becoming a mere mechanical aggregate.

The form of mineral matter is much less dominant over the primordial substrate than in man's case, and it would be expected that it would be able to achieve less of a unity among the parts of atoms than the soul of man obtains over his material principle.

Matter is *almost* inert; the form is weak, and partition and plurality are strong. This has sparked empiriological physics to dazzling triumphs over mineral nature and led to the belief that the aspects studied by empirical methods are the only aspects that matter owns. But there is just enough form in the mineral world to make the empiriological approach inadequate even to touch what is highest in nature, its form, unity, finality, and motor character. The presence of this form, which constantly steels matter to resist the empiriological physicist when he attempts to treat it as purely passive, forever challenges the existing empiriological techniques and forces them to be revised in time to push on their control and their conquest.

MATHEMATICAL AND PHYSICAL DIVISION DIFFER

If what has been said is correct about atoms and molecules, it is also clear that a neutron, proton, or any other subatomic entity is not quite the same inside the atom as out of it; as food is not the same after digestion that it was before, so if the atom has a formal unity, its parts which are virtually present in it share the nature of the whole and no longer have the independence in being and in motion which they enjoyed when isolated. But care must be taken lest the elemental parts, like the subatomic units in the case of an atom, be confused with quantitative parts. Quantitative parts do not say *what* is extended but only *that* there is an extension.

This suggests the distinction between physical and mathematical division: After a mathematical division, the parts may still be of the same character as the whole. When a rectangle is bisected across its length, the two parts are still rectangles, and they are of homogeneous extension like the original. Division of a homogeneous continuum, where the parts are of the same kind of matter as the original, ought also to be thought out for its physical importance, as in the case of a hydrogen molecule divided into hydrogen atoms.

But the physical division might also result in a substantial change. If, for instance, the experimenter wielded a subatomic razor that could slice a helium atom into equal halves the two divided parts would not be helium. They would be hydrogen isotopes. Actually, the empiriological physicist achieves the same results with particle guns, dividing matter not into homogeneous parts or parts that resemble the original but inducing substanial changes by his division.

Mathematical division is the division of extension; physical division involves substantial change with new species of matter appearing in the residue. Both kinds of division can occur in the same motion, though there seems to be no reason why mathematical division could not occur without the physical one, so that a change of extension appears without a change in the type of substance under dissection. The case of hydrogen would seem to indicate that this actually happens.

SUBSTANCES NEED MINIMUM QUANTITIES

Aristotle argued that material substances have minimum quantities and that when they are divided beyond these requisite dimensions a substantial change is produced. This idea finds a warm confirmation in empiriological physics.

For example, if carbon is completely divided into units of about 10^{-13} centimeter, the resulting particles will not be carbon but subatomic particles. An outer orbital electron or even several of them can be chipped from the carbon and the remainder is still carbon, even if the original atom now has a different electrical quality. A neutron could also be dislodged from the carbon nucleus, and no change of substance would be noted.

But divided far enough and beyond a certain minimal value, carbon would cease to be carbon. Smashed so that all of its units were of the order of magnitude of 10^{-13} centimeter or smaller, the carbon atom would decline to be an atom at all. Chisel out a proton instead of a neutron from the carbon nucleus, and a considerable change takes place. The element no longer has six for its atomic number but five. It is no longer carbon but a boron isotope. Removing a neutron and removing a proton, particles of about the same "quantity" have two quite different effects upon the carbon.

But when Aristotle insisted that every substance, in order to preserve its identity and existence, required a minimum quantity specific to the substance, he was taking quantity in its strict sense, the extraposition of parts. What these parts are, quantity alone does not say; it merely says that there are parts. A probing of the kinship of quantity and substance with attention to modern atomic physics will break upon the truth that each kind of substance has its own threshold quantity beyond which it changes character. Unfortunately a long build-up will be needed before this problem of minimal parts can be resumed.

QUANTITY IS CLOSE TO SUBSTANCE

In a sense, quantity comes closer to being a substance than any of the other accidents. Its definition as a plurality of parts suggests its affinity to prime matter, the most characteristic principle of the mobile world, dividing it off from the world of spirit. Quantity, however, is still far from matter. It is an accident. It is not in the substantial order nor a principle of substantial motion. Matter is sheer plurality because it is pure potency; form is the term of generation, conferring on matter a substantial identity and thus making it complete.

But form does not invest the integral parts with an actual status. As act, form is indivisible. The spreading of the integral parts can be the work neither of the matter which is not actual nor the form which is not divisible. It is the office of quantity which is always a quantity of an informed nature.

Quantity is thus not matter. It presumes both matter and form, dispersing the substantial identity which results from their union. But though following the logic against the identity of quantity and substance, the fact remains that the plural character of quantity does make it a close analogy to matter.

Quantity is called the first accident of material being and the proximate subject in which the qualities inhere. This kinship of quantity and prime matter is already an argument that quantity is the first accident of mobile being. But there is another and more illuminating insight that comes from form.

MATTER OPERATES THROUGH QUANTITY

Material form is not capable of subsisting by itself (except of course in man's case where special reservations must be made to account for his spiritual soul). The material form is not great enough of its nature to claim that simplicity of being and operation, characteristic of realities from man upward. Just as a great mind can see at a glance certain truths that lesser intellects must take time and effort to reach, so higher realities operate more simply than lower ones, and with greater independence of outside instruments. What loftier beings do undividedly, lower ones can only achieve with a division of labor. The more eminent and intense a being is, the less transeunt is its mode of operation.

Giving the words a real and not merely logical flavor, it could be said that intensity is the converse of extensity in a striking way here. The more intense a form, the fewer steps are needed to reach a goal that a less intensified thing must approach pace by pace, part by part, doing by a kind of extraposition, and hence extension, what a simpler form does more simply.

Now in the mineral world, the form, with its destiny to exist and operate only in matter, cannot do its work unless it is spread out. Where an intellect can operate indivisibly, not like a point but completely above reference to quantity, matter has no such concentration and interiority and loftiness of nature. The material nature must be scattered to achieve by number and size what a higher being can do with fewer facilities. A mineral needs parts so that its form can operate; a plant begins to show the rise of an intensity in being over its extensity; an animal is even more striking in the unity which it clamps upon its parts; and in the mind and will of man there is a simplicity of operation which shows a complete lack of parts in the principle by which he exists and lives and senses and thinks.

In order to operate and hence to own a nature and be a substance, a material thing needs quantity before all other attributes. Quantity spreads out the matter-form union, disposing it into an extraposition of parts which, being distinct from one another, enable the form to divide its labor and to express its power of motion some of it here and some of it there. It cannot exercise this power either in a punctual way or in the supraquantitative manner of a spirit.

Quantity is naturally necessary when matter is contrasted with spirit, when transeunce is opposed to immanence, and when the foothills in the hierarchy of matter are set off against the peaks. The weaker a form the more it depends on quantity to spread it out, in some way reclaiming through number what it lacks in nature.

It is easy to see how Descartes was lured into taking quantity for the essence of matter; and it is likewise apparent why empiriological physics has scored so impressively on the Galileo-Newtonian stage of inertia, which holds the exteriority or extraposition of all matter's determinants. But quantity and inertia, however close they lie to the core of matter, are not close enough. There is always a minimum form in all matter, however inert, and form is in a different order from both matter which is an incomplete substance of pure potentiality and from quantity which is not a substance at all.

Aquinas pointed out the fact, witnessed in empiriological physics, that the figures of mineral things were rich in revealing their inner substances and their differences from one another. This would follow if quantity is as close to matter as the foregoing paragraphs set it and if quantity is the first subject of inherence for all the other material properties.

QUANTITY SOLVES QUESTIONS ABOUT SUBSTANCE

On the basis of the foregoing analysis which etched out the need for quantity by the very nature of matter and material form, three allied subjects can be explored: why quantity is the proximate subject of inherence for all the other material accidents, how elements are virtually present in compounds, and finally why substances require a minimum amount of quantity beyond which division introduces substantial changes.

1. Quantity is the proximate subject of inherence for all the other attributes of matter, its qualities like color and sound, rarity and density, and the operations like local motion, with its actions and passions that modify subjects. The truth of all this can be ground out by using the conclusion of the previous development where quantity was seen to spread matter out, meeting the requirements of its form for doing in an extensive and scattered way what the higher forms can do more intensively and with greater concentration.

The definition and discussion of quality and its divergence from the quantitative must be withheld until the following chapter. But quality could never do its work unless it were spread out, as mineral form requires. Bergson was more or less in stride with Aristotle when he called quantity "a distention of quality," for quality, like any other material reality, has to be dispersed in order to vindicate itself.

It is a commonplace observation that material quality has to do with extended surfaces, for the inextended could never be colored, and it certainly does not emit sound. Qualities in matter, being *of* it and *from* it, could not operate at a point or in a supra-quantitative and spiritual way. They must be extraposed, and this distention is quantity. Matter must be distributed in order to receive qualities, just as matter must be distributed before it can operate in any other way.

2. The genuine notion of quantity also enables a further probing of the virtual presence of elements in compounds. (Cf. Chapter 6.) Though there is one form for the composite and hence an overall substantial unity in its being, one part is distinct from another. The being is dispersed so that each part has different virtualities and potencies.

Matter cannot operate pointally or spiritually, and the form sublets its work to the various parts. Each part operates with different powers or virtues for the good of the whole, enabling matter to achieve in a divisible way what higher beings accomplish indivisibly. Matter is too poor to deploy its manifold of motions in a simple way. It requires a heterogeneity of parts, each one having a more or less specific function within a whole that is informed. The plurality of function in an atom, for instance, requires a plurality of different kinds of parts which are virtually present in the form of the totality. The more virtual parts there are in a material substance the loftier are its motions.

Philosophical physics would tend to anticipate the differentiation within the atom that empiriological physics has spaded up through the work of Rutherford. It would be an ally of Einstein in his stress of the anisotropic character of space. It would join in certain part-whole statements of quantum mechanics.

3. Lastly, the form's need of quantity in order to move explains the meaning of minimal parts in substances, beyond which they cannot be divided. Quantity extraposes the content of their virtualities. Too little quantity means that the form does not have what it takes to operate, and what cannot operate in nature cannot exist. Removing a proton from carbon removes a virtuality that the carbon needs in order to be carbon, and boron results.

Cutting up any atom by restricting the volume which it can occupy will eventually destroy the virtualities which the substance needs and a new substance will result. The smaller volume eventually becomes so small that it does not afford the extended facility for the present form to express itself, and the form vanishes in favor of another one which is more at home in the extension available.

The genuine notion of quantity would lead to a suspicion that further division of matter, especially the neutron or neutral meson, may bring further liberation of its virtualities. For matter requires a divisible and heterogeneous and differential field in order to operate and to compensate by expanse of quantity for what it lacks in strength of form.

THE BOHR THEORY HARMONIZES WITH PHILOSOPHY

The infinitely divisible was one of the ways in which Aristotle defined the continuum. His philosophy, as it has so far been defended, has forced the conclusion that a substance, like an atom or a molecule, is certainly a continuous unit.

But there seems to be a serious challenge to this whole idea in the quantum theory, as founded by Planck and ornamented by Bohr. Planck discovered that energy is emitted in discrete packets, and Bohr applied this novel notion to the atom. According to the Bohr theory, an electron in an outer atomic orbit can be excited into even more remote orbits by suitable means. When it falls back toward its native orbit, the theory continues, it does not do so continuously. It moves by a leap, and a quantum of light is emitted in the process.

The important and somewhat revolutionary turn of the Bohr atom is its discrete character. The quantum is not protruded little by little, beginning with zero and reaching a maximum of energy. It is emitted all at once, and the electron which obtains its release is therefore thought to move discontinuously. Such a phenomenon would seem to oppose the Aristotelian idea of continuity. (There is a similar discontinuity suggested by the photoelectric effect, as explained by Einstein, a contributor to quantum theory as well as the author of relativity.)

However, in the quantum atom there is more of an obscurity than a pointed difficulty. It should be remarked in the first place that the Bohr idea is hazy with theory and on purely logical grounds cannot compete with the Aristotelian notion of matter's continuity, as hardened by experience. In the second place, the reason for matter's apparent discontinuity may well be the interference of man's instruments, creating the uncertainty enunciated by the Heisenberg principle. In the third place, the apparent discontinuity might owe itself to any number of factors: the break between cause and effect, between matter and form, between the inert and the dynamic.

The Aristotelian doctrine does not affirm but on the contrary stoutly denies the entitative continuity between a thing and its environment, between datum and instrument, between matter and form which cannot be included in the same concept any more than position and velocity can be congealed into a single category.

This is not a fluid universe but a universe of discrete natures, and the apparently discrete character of energies measured on a refined scale might simply be the result of these gaps that make the airplane different from the air.

There is not enough data to interpret the Planck and Bohr hypotheses in detail. But there is copious evidence, on other grounds, to weight the scales against matter's discontinuity. This evidence was marshaled against Zeno's pointillism. It should also be reaffirmed that form is indivisible and that the same form cannot inform parts that are separated by a gap. The same facts of efficient and final causality that were invoked earlier break down the Bohr picture, when taken as an exact account of the way things are in nature instead of as mere analogy that must be interpreted in a larger context.

MEASURE NUMBERS THE CONTINUUM

Continuous quantity is measurable. It is known by measurement, which may in turn be defined as the correlation of the continuum with number. In the proper sense of the word, only the continuum can be measured. The whole or the parts or both are compared with some standard, and the ratio between the datum and the standard is expressed by number.

Defining the standard is as subtle as it is common. According to strict empiriological method where discursion is the rule and inertia the reality, the standard ought to be determined by another one outside it, and so *ad infinitum*. This infinite regression, however, is not only illogical in theory. Practice must always circumvent it. The empiriological physicist measures a yardstick first with respect to itself by making a merely logical distinction between the yardstick as a thing of continuous length and the yardstick as a standard to measure other continua. The empiriological physicist is required to accept the self-evident or the self-intelligible in choosing his norms, and he brings something more than his strictly empiriological method to the task. That something is human intelligence which is able to relate a thing to itself, understanding it as it is and hence not driven through the dark corridor of infinity.

Measurement provides no glimpses of the absolute. It simply compares beings of the same order with each other, moving neither up nor down a hierarchy but sidewise. A meter rod is not an absolute thing. It is scaled by lines that have thickness and are not the widthless lines of pure geometry, which would be invisible.

Both the approximate character of actual measurements and their failure to climb above the order where they begin bar the empiriological method, even in its logical instruments, from ever being able to probe content and study the true and real causalities of motion which are graduated into hierarchy.

No matter how gross or how fine, measurement can never bare the kind of being that it is measuring. It comes close, to the extent of the proximity between quantity and matter and to the extent that quantity distends the virtualities of substance. But measuring things is *toto coelo* different from telling what they are. Measurements record quantity. They register whether it is great or small, with respect to a norm. It is only by measurement that quantity is known and compared.

In many respects, mathematics is the most human of the sciences. It deals with quantified being, and the mind is quite at home among the quantified. As Maritain says, in metaphysics there is too much intelligibility, and in the physical order too little. Mathematics is facile, and this may account for its perennial appeal and its special prominence in the present.

In mathematics even more than in empiriological physics, the controlling power of man is front and center. The mind can construct in mathematics, as if creative, and the highest science, that in God which man analogates as a constructive mathematician, is one that not only thinks things as they are but, thinking, makes them so. There is no possibility of error in God's knowledge, and constructive mathematics imitates this. But quantity is not nature, and mathematics is not philosophy.

Finally, mathematics proceeds on the surface of the real, equating things of the same order with each other. Its horizon is the world of man's own power to conceptualize. Philosophy begins in the world about us and rises to a higher one. Empiriological physics begins in the world and descends to a lower one. But mathematics takes the world before man and compares its mutual regularities and relations on the same plane. Measurement is a human task, but the big and important task is to find what man is.

MATTER IS IMPENETRABLE

It is primarily by its quantity that matter is in place and is impenetrable.

Place, according to the classic definition, is the first surface of a surrounding body. The measure here is a quasi-geometrical one in terms of extension, but extension in its natural rather than a separate mathematical setting. It is by quantity that a thing fills a place, spreads throughout its dimensioning volume. But with this deference to quantity, it must be reaffirmed that motion is prior in the recognition of place, in propelling a body to it, and in explaining why the body is there.

Experience witnesses that two (or more) bodies no not occupy the same place. Each has dimensions, and each is commensurate with the place that it occupies. When one body moves into the place of another, the second body is dislodged.

If two bodies were in the same place, they would have more than a common location. They would have the same quantity. That would mean that two bodies were using the same extension as a field to deploy their powers, and the limits of matter do not permit such fertility. Two bodies with the same localized field of operation would have to be the same body, having the same virtualities and the same instruments. Quantity and material virtuality would be called upon to do more than they could if they had to channel two different forms into their natural operation. Matter is heterogeneous and rich in virtuality, where one part has one job to do; it cannot double up in the way that penetrability would require.

QUANTITY YIELDS A PREDICAMENTAL UNITY

In the mineral world, there is no motion attached to quantity as such. Growth, which the classical vocabulary called augmentation, is an increase in the quantity of the growing thing; but vital action, such as growth, does not appear in the mineral world, where there are no changes of quantity in the proper sense. Knocking an electron from an atom's edge is a qualitative change. Smashing the atom changes its substance. Piling a heap of substances together, like laying bricks, does not change the substances but only their position. There is more local motion than a change of quantity.

Quantity in the mineral world does not change.

This remark is easily grasped in the light of what quantity is. It does not have interiority or nature. It is not a cause or principle of motion. It does not tend to change. It has no final cause, and as a plurality of parts, spread out rather than concentrated and compenetrated, it does not of its nature move other things, like an efficient agent. A newspaper will burn not because it is rectangular but because it is paper. A box will rot in the weather not because it is one box and not two, but because it is wooden.

A cause acting in the cosmos must be a unit freighted with tendencies. Quantity is more scattered than determined when taken in itself.

The unity ascribed to quantity is usually called predicamental unity in contrast to transcendental unity which is a synonym for being and is studied in metaphysics. Predicamental unity is the principle of number. Such a unity added to another unity, for instance, is the number 2. Predicamental unity in the order of extension is number transferred to extended quantity and used as a *unit* to measure it. Predicamental unity is a yardstick; it is the principle for a sum. A number is specified by its last unity, and when this is subtracted, the next smaller integer results. The new number can be applied to measure extension.

But predicamental unity, the principle of number and of measured continuity, does not have a nature. It is not a principle of motion. It is entirely in the order of quantity, a factor of successive more than causal order and a means of organizing things rather than explaining their inner character.

The unity of a nature is not of this type. Two natures cannot be added together to get something new. Only an aggregate results from the addition. But quantity has no interiority that forbids its union with other quantities. It can be added and subtracted. The unity which it claims is of a different type from that of natures. A unit can lose itself in a higher number because it has no tendencies that would repel another unit or a series of them. Number is not the unity of nature but a unity of order, whose species or size is determined by the last unity added which terminates the rest, as matter is terminated by form.

Mobile realities have more than sheer quantity. They are always of a determinate quantity, as required by the being in which they inhere. The thing which quantity serves as an instrument to disseminate power and virtuality is determinate, and the quantity is determinate likewise. This is another way of stating that the quantity of any material being cannot be actually infinite. Quantity is terminated essentially not by outside forces but by the nature which bears it. There is an intrinsic termination of quantity because of the intrinsic principle in which it inheres, which is the unity not of quantity but of nature.

The shape and figure of a mobile thing is not the fruit of quantity. Quantity is the extraposition of parts. It is pluralizing and it says nothing about the organization of objects into round, oblong, or irregular figures. Shape and figure are something beyond quantity. They belong to the genus of quality, and they bridge over to the subject of the next chapter.

Suggested Readings

Aristotle, *Physics,* Bk. VI, chs. 1–10.
Nagel, Ernest, *On the Logic of Measurement* (New York, 1930).

13

Alteration: The Motion of Quality

Because quantity in the drama of modern thought has so popular a part, the last chapter was exempted from proof that quantity exists and headed almost at once to what quantity does in the mobile world and what it is. Here, at the doorway to a study of quality, just the opposite problem looms up. Since the time of Galileo and Descartes, and especially under the patronage of John Locke, philosophers have inclined to think that such accessories of matter as color and sound are coupled to reality by the mind. Extremists, like Berkeley, go even further to hold that all attributes of matter such as extension, and movement which Locke wrongly termed a quality, are only ideas. Though idealism is in retreat, there is a strong bias in modern thought to deny the existence of quality as such and to reduce to quantity and local movement what the ordinary man calls sound, color, and heat.

From the task of passing sentence on Locke and Berkeley, philosophical physics can of course be saved. Such work belongs to metaphysics since the problem of knowledge's value is not one of motion. This critical discussion, of course, should come after philosophical physics has had its say. For contrary to the Kantian dream, the critical issue must follow after the rest of philosophy has evolved, since knowledge is its subject matter or its content. Going before knowledge which it reflects upon and justifies, it would begin with nothing to study.

The philosophical science of nature must regard the problem of quality as it looks at everything else, through the keyhole fitted by motion. By alterations are meant those changes which result in new attributes or properties in a subject without the destruction of the subject itself. They are changes which are neither of substance nor of place.

Water is the same substance whether it is snow, ice, or steam. Moving the water from place to place does not alter its color. The changes in the appearance of water in going from one state to another are likewise unaccountable by sheer quantity, which is a simple extraposition of parts and does not imply that the parts are white, blue, or that they are colored at all.

Bodies not only change color. They also change in sound.

Moreover, the changes need not be directed from one species of color or sound to another, like the shift from yellow to orange or from middle to high C in a musical note. There may be changes in brilliance or loudness, an intensification or remission of the same type of color or sound. All such changes are what is meant by alteration, which occurs, Aristotle says, "when the *substratum* is perceptible and persists, but changes in its own properties, the properties in question being opposed to one another either as contraries or as intermediaries."[1]

Alteration, according to this description, requires three things: (1) there must be a *substratum* or a subject which does not change but loses one quality to acquire another as the result of the movement; (2) the changes are therefore of properties or *attributes* which inhere in the subject; (3) the old and the new attributes must be *opposites* like hot or cold or some intermediate temperature; the point is that one property is replaced by another of the same genus, by a different color, sound, temperature, or the like.

There are three different kinds of alteration. Simple alteration is a change from one species of property to another in the same genus, like changes of color or of pitch. Intensification or intension is the change from a lesser to a greater possession of a prop-

---

[1] *On Generation and Corruption,* Bk. 1, ch. 4.

erty, to a brighter color or louder sound. Remission is the opposite to intension.

With this preface of definitions and divisions in alteration, the next question will be the nature and divisions of quality itself. Examples throughout this chapter will be confined to color and sound for the sake of simplicity, and the empiriological view of these two fields will be sketched before showing that quality is not inertial but that the determinate must always be formal. Quality is therefore formal but only in the accidental order. Quality is, furthermore, bound up with quantity and so close to substance that any alteration tends to substantial change. Intension and remission and condensation and rarefaction will be discussed where they involve true alterations. Having defined and defended the various types of alteration, the chapter will then discuss the continuity of alteration as proposed by Aristotle and challenged by Bohr. Finally, realistic dualism will be reaffirmed as accounting for both quantity and quality in the real world.

QUALITY IS A PROXIMATE FORM

The region of the mobile world in which alteration occurs is that of quality which like substance, quantity, place, and time, is one of the ultimate categories of material being and hence has no higher genus which permits it to be defined. Quality, Aristotle declares, is what makes a substance qualified, a description that says very little except to give a concrete stiffening to an abstraction. Aquinas is clearer when he calls quality a mode or disposition of substance, which does not just extend its subject like quantity but determines it in the line of form. It informs the subject in a way analogous to the function of substantial form with respect to prime matter. Unlike quantity, it perfects and actuates the subject by adding something new to its potencies rather than simply distending parts without bringing anything new in the line of form to what is so dispersed.

Another way of gaining a hold on quality is as a proximate principle of operations. It is, in the order of properties, what a nature is, in the order of subjects. A substance acts through its qualities as through its instruments, affecting thus the realities surrounding it and revealing itself to man. Mineral substance, it has been argued, is impoverished; it needs tools to achieve what higher things can do in simpler fashion. Projects that matter itself is not great and nimble enough to accomplish, it calls on qualities to facilitate.

But mere mathematical division of labor is not enough to account for variety. There are deep differences of form among qualities, revealing even deeper cleavages among their substances; so much so that chemists can identify things often by their color, taste, or smell; so much so that geophysics can map the mineral structures deep beneath the soil by a study of the electrical, magnetic, or acoustic qualities which echo on the surface.

Moreover, it is through quality that the plural character of a nature which quantity prepares is made full and formal, and through quality too that the same substance can have different powers or virtues which quantity extraposes to enable the substance to realize its destiny.

It is, in short, through quality that a nature, fundamentally one, owns a diversity of more proximate principles which further its motions and reveal its character.

QUALITY IS FOURFOLD

Quality is a more elastic term than alteration, and a quick glance at its various divisions will narrow down the scope of this chapter and beam its issues into brighter focus. There are four species of quality; habit and disposition; potency and impotency, passion and sensible qualities (*patibiles qualitates*); and form and figure.

The psychological inclinations of man are called *dispositions,* if easily affected, and *habits,* when they are difficult to change. But the probing of these qualities does not belong to the study of inanimate nature and may be elided here with mere mention.

Potency and impotency are the proximate principles of operation in a given substance and are synonymous with its tendencies. Potency is a strong tendency like that of lead to fall. Impotency is a weak one, like that of an electron to budge a mountain. Such tendencies are not natures but stem from natures. Though the philosophical science of nature is concerned with them, they need not be considered in this chapter because they do not involve alteration. They are not altered in the proper sense because they change only with the nature changes and appear in the nature when it is realized anew. It is more correct to treat them under generation and corruption.

Passion and sensible quality (*patibilis qualitas*) form the third species of quality. Passion is a transient quality, like the redness of a blushing cheek. Sensible quality is more permanent and is, in the proper meaning of the word, alterable quality, changed without changing the subject. Examples of it are color, sound, taste, smell, hardness or softness of surface, heat, electricity, and magnetism.

Form and figure, the fourth and last species of quality, apply to quantity, though they terminate it in this way or that and hence involve more than the sheer extraposition of parts which is all that quantity can explain in matter. Figure is shape and form is proportion. The figure of a thing might be irregular, unsymmetrical, and unique, to a point of being unnameable to a mathematician. Form adds proportion to shape, and the example usually given of it is a work of art, like a statue which adds a new and proportioned arrangement to the figured matter of its medium. Form and figure can likewise be omitted in a discussion of alteration since they are not changed by continuous movement which a later section will prove essential to alteration. Form and figure vary abruptly like number. The difference between a polygon and a circle is not a matter of more or less polygon but is a sharp, discrete affair like the difference between 1 and 2 in arithmetic.

Ruling out some qualities because they do not pertain to philo-

sophical physics and others because they do not involve alteration, this chapter can be narrowed down to sensible qualities,
their reality, their relations, and their motion. "Narrowing down"
is a rather optimistic way of putting it. The subject of alteration
is almost as contested and certainly as complicated on the modern
scene as the discussion of substance and its changes. Hence to
simplify an otherwise colossal task, the following account of alterable qualities will be further localized to a discussion of color
and sound. On the basis of the principles developed and applied
in the study of color and sound, the philosophical physics of the
other qualities can be easily suggested.

EXPERIMENTALLY, COLOR AND SOUND ARE MECHANICAL

It will be fruitful to outline at the very outset what the empiriological physicist says about color and sound to align this view
with that of Aristotle, leaving experience to decide the issue.

The classical physicist regarded the color of a body as a play of
reflections, and with certain improvements, that view still holds.
Objects appear colored only in light, the most common and natural light being that of the sun.

Sunlight or white light, as it is often called, is in reality a composite of about seven distinct colors: red, orange, yellow, green,
blue, indigo, and violet. Most objects in nature absorb some components of sunlight and reflect the rest. It is the reflected light
which is actually seen and called the color of the given object.
For instance, grass absorbs all the rays except the green; sulfur
reflects only the light near the yellow band of the spectrum. Coal
absorbs nearly all the light, and snow reflects practically all of it.

Though satisfied with its grosser picture, classical physics,
when it got down to detail, ran into difficulties. It viewed light in
terms of electromagnetic waves, and concluding that the source
of reflected waves had to be electrical in nature, it came to say, at
last, that the color of a substance must somehow be determined
by atomic electrons. Yet how the electron could fill such requirements was a source of difficulty, some empiriological physicists

holding that the reflected light was a factor of the orbital motion of the electron about the nucleus, others saying that the electron emitted light determined by its vibratory motion. Either view left large problems unsolved.

About the time of this crisis and in the first decade of the present century, a whole new view of empiriological physics emerged out of the study of radiation. By assuming that light was not emitted in continuous electromagnetic waves but in discrete energy packets, called quanta, Planck was able to work out an equation for one of the facts of radiation (the black-body problem), unexplained by the classical system. Planck's idea on this point was developed especially by the work of Einstein (photoelectric effect), and the corpuscular or particle theory of light caught up with the wave theory that had full command of the classical highways. As a result, empiriological physics, without completely discarding the wave theory, came to hold that there was a particle aspect to light and to other forms of energy.

One of the pioneers of quantum theory was Bohr, who recast the prevailing picture of the atom to fit it into the quantum theory and especially to equip the atom with a quantum apparatus for the emission of light. According to the Bohr theory, the orbital electrons have certain stationary orbits in which they revolve without emitting light. Excited by suitable means, sunlight or otherwise, an outer electron will move further outward to more distant orbits, where it may be unstable. Falling back from an unstable to a stationary orbit, the electron emits a quantum of light whose frequency is determined by the energy differences between the two orbits. If the electron has gone to an orbit more removed from the nuclear center, the frequency will naturally be higher when it falls back because the quantum of energy is bigger. A higher frequency means a different light since color is determined by frequency (or wave length).

Hydrogen is the simplest element, and the Bohr theory has scored its most notable successes in explaining the different colors (spectral lines) which can be produced by apparently forcing its electrons out to remote orbits, where they snap back again toward the center. On more complicated atoms, the mathematical complexities make the Bohr theory difficult to verify, and there is evidence indeed that it is not even verifiable in principle. But the simple outline of an atom which it sketches, though modified by succeeding developments in empiriological physics, has been more or less retained as a qualitative working model of the atomic profile.

The color of an object is determined by the emission of energy when the electrons in the given atoms fall inward toward stationary states from orbits to which they have been driven by suitable excitation. And modern philosophy would have it that the quanta, peeling off from the atoms in question, impinge on the retina to create the psychological impression of color, much as electrons spray on a television screen to form a picture.

The study of sound, on the other hand, has not been nearly so fascinating to recent empiriological physics as the probing of light. This is easy to understand since visual data, compared to those of sound, seem much more important in nature, more measurable by instruments, more stimulating to the emotions, and often more convincing to the mind. It is as though modern man accepted the maxim that seeing is believing, and had no other credo. Recent engineering problems in ultrasonics have revived interest in acoustical problems, though most of the great minds in empiriological physics remain rooted to the study of matter and light energy, so greatly fertilized by the quantum and relativity innovations.

Sound is considered to be a phenomenon of waves. Its students were never prompted to posit an ether in order to account for the nature of what is waving. The classical idea goes more or less unquestioned that the sound waves are those of particles, like the molecules in the air. Light waves are called transverse because they move at right angles to the direction of propagation. Putting it crudely, they dance up and down from the line of energy flow, like the waves of the sea rising and falling. But sound waves are different. They are called longitudinal waves because their crests and troughs are not at right angles to the direction of energy transfer but in the same line. This wave motion, apparently taken by sound, can be grasped as a condensation and rarefaction of a mass of molecules, its expansion and contraction; this is a vibratory motion, so that sound waves may also be described as a series of longitudinal vibrations.

For a color to appear, sunlight or some other exciting source is of course a necessary agent, so that the color of an object is a kind of reaction or, in the literal sense of the word, a reflection. The same stimulus is necessary if a body is to emit sound, and the same preference for reflecting certain frequencies, while absorbing others, is shown in acoustics as in the reradiation phenomena in atoms. A tuning fork set in motion by a hammer will emit a musical note, depending on the material from which it is made. Some materials absorb well at one frequency and vibrate at others. Wood absorbs better than concrete, and glass better than marble. All such facts indicate the importance of the identities that are receiving and emitting sound. That importance will be later underscored.

The kind of sound which a body emits depends on the frequency of its vibrations, just as the color of an object was found to be determined by the frequency of the reflected light. Intensity —brilliance in the case of light and loudness in the case of sound —is proportionate to the height of the waves or the wave amplitudes. Hence, the notes on a piano scale differ from one another by frequency alone, but the same note can be pedaled into a louder or softer "volume."

From the viewpoint of empiriological physics, vibrations or wave motions are all there is to sound. Psychologists and epistemologists have on the whole come to look upon the sensation of sound as a mental state, generated by the longitudinal waves striking the tympanum.

QUALITY CANNOT BE WHOLLY INERTIAL

From what has been said thus far, several principles can be crystallized which will sum up the typical modern accounts of color and sound and make the transition to their philosophical appraisal:

1. Color and sound have been shriveled to the two factors of modern mechanism, quantity or mass, and local motion. Quality has been reduced to quantity, moving from place to place. In nature it is nothing more.

2. Quality has been boiled down to inertia. All its principles reside mechanically outside the impression of quality, which is created in the human sensorium by the machinery of particles and waves. Besides this, the quantity and the motion which are responsible for a given color or a given sound are determined by agencies external to them in nature, by the nuclei of atoms in the case of color and by mass factors in the case of sound; and such mechanical agents are in turn the inertial sum of forces beyond them.

3. There is no distinction outside the mind between subject and attribute. There are particles, there is motion, and there is nothing else. Sometimes quantity and motion are called primary qualities, but since the cleavage between subject and property or quality does not appear on modern premises, the term "primary quality" is hardly more than a name invented to make it easier to ignore ultimate issues.

Much has been written in these pages about the inertialism of the modern world picture, and a repetition of its failures will serve as a climax to a general theme in this book and at the same time assert the reality of quality in the formal, rather than mere mechanical, order.

A universe that was totally inert and that wholly yielded to the assault upon it through control and the equating of cause and effect would not be the universe that we know. It would be a continuous, indifferent, chance, potential, indeterminate, chaotic, and vacant reality. If there are differences at all in the things that exist, they owe themselves to factors beyond the inertia which is undifferentiated.

There are as many different non-inertial principles as there are differences. One difference of principle, combined with an inert subject, would make for one reality; two would make for two. So we could count through the whole universe. All differences must be non-inert; inert, they would be featureless—the same to each other and to the subject matter that they were invited to differentiate. Each differentiating principle must be different from other such principles and from the inertia which they all variously inform. If monism is wrong and a true plurality prevails in the universe, there is a manifold of form in the world bound up tightly with its inertias.

THE DETERMINATE IS ALWAYS FORMAL

This does not mean, of course, that nature and inertia, form and matter, exist side by side like a glove on a hand or a fence around the yard. Nothing that exists is inert. At least such existence is not actual. Inertia is compenetrated by form. The form is wholly throughout it and affects it from within. It would be better to say that a mobile being has formal and inertial aspects, since there is no frontier where form ends and matter begins. Their union is intrinsic, and they are separated not by something like fractional distillation but only by the abstracting mind.

In a universe run not by form and law but by power and inertia, action must be envisioned as a sheer brute triumph of a greater force over a lesser one. But to what does the greater force owe its greatness, the weaker one its surrender, and the action its directionality? If inertia is not tacked on a subject like a rug on a floor, the more powerful being moves the lesser one primarily by a superiority of form. It is form, the intrinsic principle of nature, that is the source of motion and it is form that the mover faces in the matter to be changed. Strength and weakness, the greater and the less, express differences, and differences, when fully probed, cannot originate in inertia.

There is no such a freak as merely mechanical action, the meeting of mere force with force, or a greater mass with a lesser one. Nothing is merely mechanical or merely inert or merely massive or merely force in the universe that moves about us. A hot skillet would be cooled by a pan of water; it would ignite a pan of gasoline. And the difference is due to the identities involved which differ by their form. When paper is sheared in the mills by mechanical cutters, again it is ultimately the non-inert which determines what happens or whether anything happens at all. Use the same volume of iron, instead of paper, and use glass of the same geometry as the knife, and this time the cutter, by shattering, is more affected than its would-be subject. It is form again, the identities which an action involves, that regulates the result.

But such reasoning is general. It does not establish that there are forms distinct from substance and united to a substance not as its principles but as its attributes. In the philosophical science of nature, where motion counts more than measurement, the discussion of qualitative form entails two proofs: first, that it is form which means that it is non-inert, and secondly, that it is qualitative, changed without changing its subject of inherence. The first proof rebukes mechanism in its quantitative references, and the second in its references to local motion.

QUALITY IS FORMAL

The account of color and sound showed in reality that the bodies emitting them are not mere inertias. In both cases, the body has definite, not indeterminate, characteristics, and when it is excited, it does not cede in unconditional surrender to the stimulus, but responds in its own way and on its own terms.

Color and sound thus reveal a selective action on the part of the mobile beings which originate them. But since quantity means only an extraposition of parts, without implying what the parts are, selectivity as such cannot come from quantity taken alone. Quantity, carved down to the bone, is a plurality, and plurality cannot of itself organize into the specific pattern of response which occurs in any body reflecting color or emitting sound.

Selectivity, specificness, patterned character, originality, discrimination that results in absorptions and reflections peculiar to the substance in question—these are the work of form, a principle of interiority and difference. Without the filtering by form, in both optical and acoustical phenomena, all the bodies of nature would look alike and sound alike. Originality does not arise from inertia or difference from indifference or order from chaos.

A discussion of sensible quality ought to distinguish between color in the copper and the color in the air where it is being transmitted to the eye. There is certainly a physical disturbance in the medium which instruments can detect and which seems to have particle and wave aspects in the case of color. There are vibrations in the air, associated with the transmission of sound from its source to its percipient.

All of this the philosophical physicist does not deny. In fact he insists on it. He only accentuates that such mechanical aspects as empiriological physics measures do not relate what color and sound really are. He points to the selective, hence formal, principle of color and sound within the emitting body and reiterates that sound and color stem not from quantity and its motion but from quality and its form.

A denial that color and sound are formal in their sources is an admission that they are only inertial, and what is inert does not actually exist, let alone operate upon the human sensorium.

If inertia is bolted out of the actual world, not by an *a priori* logic but because only the actual or determinate can own existence, the medium intervening between a colored or sounding body on the one hand and the percipient on the other is also something formal. But as a medium, it is transmissive or tool-like which means that without losing its own nature it somehow enables the form of the transmitted reality to pass through it.

Color, for instance, though it may have particle and wave aspects is not only these. For if it were changed by the medium and did not preserve its continuity with the object and hence be somehow unaltered by the medium, the mind would never know the source whence the color came.

There are two critical junctures in the history of the medium, the point where it receives the impression of the agent, say the object, and the point where it imparts this impression to the percipient. A medium always bears a likeness to both extremes since its precise function is to get the extremes together.

As a first approximation, one might suspect that for this reason alone, quality, and not merely waves and particles, is originated in its source as a form. There must be a series of likenesses running from the thing to the medium to the percipient, and the communication of likeness is in the order of form alone, and not of motor (or altering) causality in its strict sense. Since the purely quantitative and plural has no power to move and to select, no ability to formalize, it cannot act, and it cannot communicate likenesses which are communications of unity. What is communicated from the thing to the knower must therefore be a form.

Then too, quanta if they are ever isolated are not just "throbs of energy," to use a Whiteheadean phrase. They must be formal and qualified if they exist and operate.

A fuller probing of the role played by the medium in the transmission of quality and studied by empiriological physics only in its inertial aspects must be abandoned to a more advanced and detailed treatment of the subject than is here possible. But if any likeness is the result not of quantity and local motion but of form, substantial or qualitative, it can easily be deduced what directions a deeper display of the qualified rather than merely quantified character of the medium would take.

QUALITY IS NOT SUBSTANCE

Even if it is agreed that color and sound are forms, transmitted by forms, and received as forms, this outline has not yet established that they are qualities distinct from substances and hence not substances themselves, as isolated quanta of energy would be. An effective way of showing that a subject may be altered without being corrupted is to offer an example, and the following one is a classic from empiriological physics.

Before the advent of the quantum theory, it was a well-known fact that hydrogen, suitably excited, could be made to emit at least three different families of lines (spectral lines). The Balmer series of lines is visible; the Lyman series is in the ultraviolet region of the spectrum, invisible light of a very short wave length; the Paschen series is in the infrared, which is light of a long wave length and likewise invisible.

There were certain mathematical symmetries which all of these series seemed to follow. But it was not until Bohr developed the quantum hypothesis on atomic structure that the possible causes of these series and the reasons for the mathematical similarities took a definite shape.

Bohr, it has already been noted, posited two kinds of orbits in atoms. In a stationary orbit, the electron though moving about the nucleus does not radiate, the theory runs; but when it falls back to a stationary orbit from an unstable orbit to which it has been excited, it emits a quantum of light, where a quantum is a particle of energy whose magnitude is a function of frequency.

Bohr's theory gave a tidy background to the already established mathematics of the three series of hydrogen lines. He numbered the orbits out from the nuclear center and suggested that when an electron fell, for example, from the fifth orbit to the third the Paschen series was emitted; the Balmer series could come when the electron dropped from the fifth orbit to the second; when the electron moved from the fourth to the first orbit, Lyman lines were apparent.

Such a procedure sounds at first sight almost too simple to be true. But the Bohr orbital numbers as a matter of fact fitted neatly into mathematical equations for hydrogen lines, where there had hitherto been terms largely unattached to physical realities. Theory gave meaning to measurements, and that is all that is expected of it.

Bohr's theory was a far-reaching step in the world of empiriological physics, and it rings with familiar echoes in the philosophic science of nature, though as analogy and not proof. On the authority of measured fact, the "color" of hydrogen can be changed without changing the hydrogen, and this exactly is what is meant by alteration.

In mechanical terms, by forcing an electron in hydrogen to the first orbit and bringing it back to the third, the Paschen series of lines can be produced, and the other two series can be provoked in a kindred fashion. Hydrogen remains as the abiding subject through the changes of "color."

QUALITY REQUIRES QUANTITY

But thereby hangs a difficulty. At first sight it looks as if empiriological physics has found the whole secret of "color" change in atoms and that the secret is one of quantity and local motion, where electrons are simply displaced with respect to their nuclei.

It has already been seen, however, that color is a form. It involves selection and originality, and these spell out differences which are truly formal. Changes of color are not changes of position alone.

This factor of form, of course, does not forbid that parts of atoms might vary in situation because of qualitative change. It only says that the primary fact is form, leaving ample room for situational changes of particles as secondary phenomena.

In fact, since matter is so inert and since it is so close to quantity, it might be expected that any changes in a mobile reality, especially where virtualities are transformed, would have quantitative transpositions associated with it. But quantity and local motion have already been overruled as the full and final account of quality or any other natural phenomenon. The qualitative form, changing without a change of subject, is primarily responsible for color and sound in things.

If the report of the last chapter on the primacy of quantity in matter's incidental equipment is sustained, quality inheres in quantity as in its proximate subject. Qualitative changes do not require that the quantity remain the same but only that the substance abide uncorruptedly. If quantity is as close to the core of matter as the last chapter argued and if matter is so impoverished that it must be spread out to exist formally and to operate fully, then all changes in quality ought to affect the quantity of their subjects.

Quality could not express itself if it were shriveled up to a point. It needs an expanse if it is to be real and mobile. It needs such stretches at the distances of an electron from the center of an atom emitting color. Thus, the color of hydrogen in a given state could theoretically be computed from its cross section if the Bohr model is correct.

But quantity is the condition of quality. It is the proximate subject by which quality inheres in mobile being. Yet quantity is not quality despite the dependence of the second on the first. They differ as unity from plurality, parts from what the parts are. Quantity extraposes what quality modifies. Without quantity, quality would reduce to a point and even become something spiritual. It would not be a property of matter.

All this stress on quality as requiring a spread and hence requiring quantity can account for the empiriological victories under the flag of quantity alone. But quantity and inertia, though striking in the mobile world, are not everything, and empiriological physics never succeeds in reducing reality to these terms. If it did, the world would be vacuous, and ideas alone would be real. Huxley speaks of a "nothing-but" attitude. Flushed with its triumphs over matter, scientism likes to think that the world is "nothing but" the factors which wither into the empiriological method. In reality, pure inertia exists in the actual order only as an abstraction, and it is the forms and finalities and qualities of matter which make it real outside the mind. It is not philosophical physics that is anthropomorphic but the mechanists. Any art is anthropomorphic.

Here another caution must be inserted against the mechanical view of a subject with respect to its properties. An accident or attribute is not a parasite riding on a substance like a flea on an elephant. It is not only on the surface of the subject which it qualifies, but throughout it. The substance and its properties are compenetrated, intrinsically and immediately united, like a soul and the body which it animates. Spaier was approaching the truth when he wrote that quantity is "quality measured" and Bergson when he called quantity "a distention of quality." They are bound up together. The quality may have different virtualities in one part and in another, just as the arm of man is differentiated from his head though the two are parts of one substance. Despite the differences of a virtual character, making the quality more operative in one part than in another, it still remains one quality.

The Bohr idea of the atom hints a confirmation of all this. If the Bohr model of hydrogen is true or has some analogue in nature—which is more likely—it is obvious that the electron directly has much more to do with the emission of the various spectral lines than the atomic nucleus. And yet the whole atom is somehow involved in the lines which hydrogen emits. The same electron in another atom would behave differently under the same excitation. It takes its specific character from the atom in which it happens to be, a property of the whole atom but more operative in one part than in another.

A more deductive approach to this problem might be formulated thus: A substance is indivisible, and if a property qualifies it, it must qualify the whole of it. But quantity spreads out the substance, enabling it to be differentiated so that it can achieve by a variety of instruments the work that it cannot do more simply. Through the offices of quantity, quality is likewise distended, differing in the various parts while remaining the same quality. As a form, quality is likewise indivisible, so that what it modifies it modifies with all of itself.

ALTERATION TENDS TO SUBSTANTIAL CHANGE

Aristotle held that alteration disposes a substance to be corrupted, and he saw in this fact the final cause of qualitative change. At least substantial change is the ultimate goal to which alteration points. From the viewpoints of both philosophical and empiriological physics, it is easy to see that this is a well-grounded principle.

It has already been indicated, from the philosophical point of view, that material being is rather barren. It does not have enough richness to change in a partial way without tending to change altogether. Its investment is so small in the bank of nature that any withdrawal results in closing the whole account, or rather tends to do so.

Man, when he knows things, becomes them while remaining himself. But matter which is acted upon tends to surrender itself entirely rather than to remain itself and acquire the new. Matter is almost the inert thing that empiriological physics makes it out to be. When any part of a material thing changes, since the part is so close to the whole, the entire thing tends to change.

Alteration thus paves the way toward generation. It provides, as it were, a medium between the old form and the new, making their difference less abrupt than it would otherwise be, and helping the ingredient in the change to make the hurdle.

The footnotes to substantial change are extremely difficult to read in matter, though its general principles can be known with genuine certainty as Chapter 2 outlined. Delving into the details of the process, since the direction of substantial change is from being to non-being or vice versa, it is difficult to see how matter can bridge the chasm between the thing that changes and the thing that results.

That gap, alteration closes, or it at least tends to do so. Because it is continuous, it tends to compensate for the discreteness between the terms of substantial change by disposing the old substance to be destroyed and the new one to be generated. It brings distant terms close together.

All this reasoning modern empiriological physics tends to support. In the changes of the hydrogen atom, which yield the various spectral lines, there is a tendency not only to change quality but to change the substance. An atom, excited like hydrogen, when its electrons recede from the nucleus to those instabilities by which they emit "color," acquires more energy, as empiriological physics puts it. The atom as a whole tends in this way to become unstable.

If the electron is excited far enough from its nuclear center, the hydrogen will be destroyed and become a proton with the electron freed from its nuclear influence, and both proton and electron tend to sanctuary in some other atom. Changing the color of hydrogen too much will thus result in a substantial change; changing the color disposes the hydrogen to become something else. Like the rest of the elements, hydrogen has only a limited range of colors that it will take on. Going beyond this range means going beyond hydrogen itself.

INTENSION AND REMISSION ARE ALTERATIONS

If nothing is inert and if any change in the universe is thus something more than a puff of inertia, it can easily be decided that intension and remission are also alterations. Intension is the greater possession of a given quality by the subject; and remission is the lesser possession of it. A more intense quality is of the same type as the less intense, only it is more firmly rooted in the subject. Remission is the reverse. It is less of a radication in the subject.

On modern theories of color and sound, the first impulse is to assign the differences in intensity to quantity alone. In both color and sound, intensity is determined by wave amplitude while frequency makes for brightness or loudness. With such measurements only, it is tempting to make out a case that when a color is made more brilliant in an object more of its atoms have been illuminated to stack the waves, reaching the eye, into a greater amplitude. This would mean that a brighter color is owed only to a greater expanse illuminated in the colored object. Intension would thus be not a matter of quality and form but of quantity and extension.

Such an account is satisfactory as far as it goes. Two men on a scale weigh more than one of them, and two candles of the same size throw more light than either alone. But there is another and more elusive intension and remission which is possible in the single atom, the bearer of quality, and it is the increase or diminishing of quality within the single substance that is here of primary moment.

The constant mention of electrons and protons in these pages makes it unnecessary to point out that an atom has an electrical character. A moving charge is also a source of magnetism, and if for no other reason, empiriological physics holds that the atom also has magnetic properties.

By placing the source of radiation in an electric field (Stark effect) or in a magnetic field (Zeeman effect), at least one of the effects produced among the spectral lines emitted by the substance is a variation of intensity that depends on the strength of the magnetism or the electricity applied. This suggests that intensity of color may be varied by changes in the electrical or magnetic warp of the emitting body. It suggests that there is an intension and remission of quality which is not a matter of summing up the number of atoms possessing the property but comes from within the atom itself. As in simple alteration, there is a limit to the amount of intension and remission that can go on without changing the substance having the quality into a substance of a different type. Too strong an outer field would break an atom down.

A contemporary example of intension and remission within atoms might also be developed from the variation in spectral intensity produced by heating the emitting substances.

CONDENSATION AND RAREFACTION ARE ALTERATIONS

Quite similar to intension and remission, yet differing enough to deserve separate treatment, are the motions of condensation and rarefaction in matter. For Aristotle, these are qualitative changes, and it is enlightening to see whether such a verdict can be sustained in the modern intellectual court.

A substance is called dense when it possesses a great amount of matter under small dimensions, and rare when it possesses a small amount of matter under large dimensions. Density is a familiar concept in empiriological physics. It is defined as mass per unit volume and answers the question, for instance, Which is heavier, a cubic centimeter of water or a cubic centimeter of lead?

That condensation or contraction and rarefaction or expansion actually take place is readily accepted in both chemistry and empiriological physics. In fact, according to the kinetic molecular theory of matter, a substance is a solid when its molecules are densely thronged together, and it is a liquid and finally a gas as this crowding diminishes. Another way of putting it is to say with the chemist that in a gas there is considerable free space between the molecules, less space in liquids, and still less space in a volume of solid material. Compression is a matter of forcing the particles of a chemical substance into a tighter proximity. Rarefaction is a process of separating them.

Such a phenomenon as compression is easy to understand when dealing with aggregates of particles, like molecules. But this is not the type of condensation in which philosophical physics is primarily interested as it searches the ultimate recesses in things. The philosophical question is more about the fate of the individual substance. Can a single atom, for instance, be compressed or rarefied, and if so, is this a qualitative change?

From what has already been said, it is clear that there could easily be the compression and rarefaction of a single substance like the atom. Such changes produce different terminations of quantity. There is a rearrangement of quantitative parts with respect to each other, without an increase or decrease of their number which is potentially infinite. This potential infinity of parts would make a body pliable to such changes as condensation and rarefaction.

The change in extension and in situation which compression or expansion would have for a concomitant at the level of the atom is not the essence of condensation and rarefaction. Density and rarity concern the termination of quantity which is not the function of quantity itself but of quality. Qualitative changes result in such a disposition of the material in question that extensional and positional shifts are required.

Density or rarity does not add or subtract quantity but makes a new disposition of the quantity already present.

Apart from philosophical possibilities, there are strong arguments in the empiriological world that such compression and expansion among atoms actually takes place. The Bohr theory of the atom, expanding and contracting as the outer electrons move from one orbit to another is a case in point. In a change from one stationary state to another, there may be nothing else except compression or its reverse. But in the shift from an unstable state to a stable one, emissions appear, and hence condensation and rarefaction are involved in a larger context that is dominated by simple alteration.

Another slant on condensation and rarefaction is afforded by the theory of relativity. It argues that bodies are deformed by their motions, with mass increasing as velocity increases and vice versa, and the deformation is at least a suggestion of condensation and rarefaction.

Once more a warning is needed against taking empiriological data too literally. The difficulty with tracing out the analogues to philosophical principles in the empiriological world view is that empiriological physics has failed to provide certain knowledge in many cases and especially in regard to fundamental issues, like the behavior of individual atoms and their parts.

But here as elsewhere, it can certainly be pressed that there are analogues of some kind in nature to what the empiriological physicist says in his theories. Otherwise, the success of empiriological physics could not be explained. As analogies, well-founded data of empiriological physics can and do illustrate truths from philosophical physics.

Empiriological physics has locked its door to the genuine philosopher but left the windows open so that he can see in. There are no well-grounded data of experiment that do not illustrate,

when interpreted into speculative knowledge, the truly scientific
and certain principles which Aristotle kneaded out of experience
in the general parts of his *Physics*. What is scientific and certain
does not perish with the scientist, and certitude did not have to
delay its birth to the time of Descartes and Galileo.

This chapter has found empiriological physics fertile in analogy to illustrate what the philosophical science of nature says of
quality. It is true that many of the examples are blurred by their
cloudy theoretical status, but they must have some analogue, in
the real, at least remotely, to justify the prosperity of empiriological physics in using them. It is not the light of logical theory
but the weak shadow of reality at the fringes of the beam which
philosophical physics can salvage to help identify itself.

ALTERATIONS ARE CONTINUOUS

Alteration has unity and continuity. In this respect it resembles
local motion and differs greatly from substantial change. To affirm the continuity of alteration means that the old form is gradually converted into the new one rather than abruptly generated
as in substantial change.

There are instantaneous changes or so-called mutations only at
the beginning and end of the alteration, at the beginning because
a substance is not altered without a cause that disturbs its equilibrium and at the end because there is a termination or fixity of
the new form. To deny these terminal mutations would lead to
an eternal flow of quality, whereas it is a stable fixture of the being that owns it.

But the motion between the terms is not a series of leaps. It is a
movement that is continuous, preparing the way by a gradual
redisposition of the old substance for change into a new one.

Empiriological physics confirms this relation of the continuum
to quality. In fact, where empiriological physics speaks, the extreme view is taken that differences in qualities are not matters
so much of kind as of degree. Thus, two colors or two sounds
differ by being higher or lower frequencies in spectra that are

continuous, and brilliance or pitch can be continuously varied by varying continuously the wave amplitude. The Bohr theory accounts for differences in color as changes of an electron's situation within an atom, thus by that exemplar of continuous motion which is local movement. A change of situation, at least analogous to what Bohr envisions, can certainly be admitted, but there is more to alterations than this.

THE BOHR THEORY SUPPORTS ARISTOTLE

However, there is a problem raised by the Bohr theory. Does it not imply discontinuity in alteration since it involves the discrete leap of an electron from an excited to a stationary state and the liberation of a discrete parcel of energy called the quantum?

No, this Bohr idea is a vote more in favor of the philosophical science of nature than against it. An instantaneous change, which is mutation rather than motion in the technical vocabulary, does occur at the beginning and end of alteration if Aristotle is correct. A quality is not fluid but fixed, and it requires an extrinsic cause to start it changing and a stable term at which the alteration ends.

The Bohr idea of discontinuity may be simple adumbrating that sudden and instantaneous phenomenon which Aristotle saw at the beginning and end of alteration. In Bohr's idea, there is on the part of the electrons a local motion, which is the prototype of continuous motion; there is also discontinuity. These two aspects of alteration were seen by Aristotle. Once again scientism, which has deliberately spurned philosophical physics, may be entering it by the back door. There is an abruptness at the beginning and end of qualitative change, and Bohr's notion of discrete orbits may be a shadow of it.

REALISM IS DUALISTIC

The present chapter has shown that color and sound are not simply mechanisms of particles and waves but are ultimately accidental forms in the colored and sounding objects. It has not been denied that there are waves and particles, or something like them, in both optical and acoustical phenomena. On the contrary it has been stoutly affirmed that all material quality is radicated in quantity as its proximate subject of inherence. What has been said simply means that the waves and particles are the only aspects of color and sound that the empiriological physicist can grasp but that reality is a larger whole, where the parts when taken alone are sure to be distorted.

Quality is formal in the object, but it is more of a potency than act until light, if it is color, or an impact, if it is sound, makes the object actually emit what it is capable of emitting. Empiriological physics never gets beyond the potential or inertial side of quality, and without act, it can never be explained why anything at all is seen or heard.

It has frequently been said in this book that empiriological physics does not go far enough. In a sense, it goes too far, taking an aspect of the real and turning it into a substitute for reality.

The Cartesian stress on quantity and local motion and Galileo's preference for inertia and control have distorted the study of the universe as it is. Men are glorifying what they can make, without knowing what they should do. They are trying to coerce the world into their own image and likeness, and dismissing the principles which control man as "verbalisms," in the language of Bridgman, "meaningless questions" in the jargon of logical positivism, "supernaturalisms" as Dewey says, or as Communism puts it, "reactionary."

Aristotle's science explains why nature yields to art and yet resists it by the loyal opposition of its natural form. His thought leaves a tremendous scope to art, though exalting knowledge for knowledge's sake into the highest of human activities. In fact, Aristotle's logic is the first development of an art into systematic principles which it can assimilate as part of itself in practice.

Aristotle's view of things is a true dualism between nature and art, form and matter, cause and effect, motion and its goals, place and time, quantity and quality. Such a view of course does not set out to study things only in terms of the control which man can foist on them in his laboratory. It sets out not primarily to make man the master of nature but to discover the truths and the goals that master man, lighting his intellect and warming his will. It seeks to discover what things are rather than the aspects which man can make into something else.

Such a view of course does not aim principally to make men comfortable or emotionally at ease though it welcomes such ambitions when subordinated to higher ones. It does not aim chiefly at public hygiene and air-conditioned offices though it holds such things desirable in their place. But it makes something tremendously more important than machines. It makes sense.

Suggested Readings

Aristotle, *Physics*, Bk. VII, chs. 1–4.

John of St. Thomas, *Cursus philosophicus Thomisticus, Phil. Nat.,* P. III, QQ. III, IV, VII (Turin, 1933).

Millikan, Robert Andrews, *Electrons (+ and −), Protons, Photons, Neutrons, Mesotrons, and Cosmic Rays,* rev. ed. (Chicago, 1947).

Index